THE NEW NATURALIST

A SURVEY OF BRITISH NATURAL HISTORY

BRITISH GAME

The aim of this series is to interest the general reader in the wild life of Britain by recapturing the inquiring spirit of the old naturalist. The Editors believe that the natural pride of the British public in the native fauna and flora, to which must be added concern for their conservation, are best fostered by maintaining a high standard of accuracy combined with clarity of exposition in presenting the results of modern scientific research. The plants and animals are described in relation to their homes and habitats and are portrayed in the full beauty of their natural colours, by the latest methods of colour photography and reproduction.

THE NEW NATURALIST

BRITISH GAME

by

BRIAN VESEY-FITZGERALD

F.L.S.

FORMERLY EDITOR OF "THE FIELD"

WITH TWENTY-EIGHT

REPRODUCTIONS IN COLOUR

AND EIGHTY-ONE

BLACK AND WHITE PHOTOGRAPHS

COLLINS   ST. JAMES'S PLACE   LONDON

First published in 1946 by
Collins 14 St. James's Place London
Produced in conjunction with Adprint
and printed in Great Britain
by Collins Clear-Type Press
London and Glasgow

Reprinted, 1946

TO THE MEMORY OF MY TWO FRIENDS

ABEL CHAPMAN

AND

PATRICK CHALMERS

WHO WERE BOTH GREAT SPORTSMEN

AND GOOD NATURALISTS

AND GREATER MASTERS OF PROSE

THAN I SHALL EVER BE

CONTENTS

PART 5
THE DEER

PART 6
THE PRESERVATION OF GAME

LIST OF COLOUR PLATES

LIST OF COLOUR PLATES

LIST OF PLATES IN BLACK AND WHITE

LIST OF PLATES IN BLACK AND WHITE

Every care has been taken by the Editors to ensure the scientific accuracy of factual statements in these volumes, but the sole responsibility for the interpretation of facts rests with the Authors.

EDITORS' PREFACE

BRIAN VESEY-FITZGERALD is the editor of *The Field.* He is, also, a considerable naturalist in his own right. It will be a simple matter for the reader to determine this for himself for, at every page, he will discover the original observations and personal opinions of the writer.

The aim of the New Naturalist series is to present British Natural History from the scientific angle. But the series does not eschew contributions from those who are not primarily scientists. Mr. Vesey-FitzGerald is, as a matter of fact, extremely well read in the scientific sides of the natural history of the birds and mammals with which he deals, but he is also a countryman of wide experience, a wild-fowler, Vice-President of the Gamekeepers' Association, a friend of gipsies and, we suspect, of poachers. All of these things fit him well to describe the natural history of British Game and put it in a proper perspective.

British Game is a valuable possession which we must be at pains to manage properly. The future of game control and preservation is not going to be easy in a contracting British countryside ; it is our hope and belief that this book will be a useful contribution to the solution of some of the problems that lie ahead.

THE EDITORS

PLATE I

SIR RALPH SADLER AS A FAULKNER OF QUEEN ELIZABETH 1507-1587

Coloured etching after a painting on panel at Everleigh House, Wiltshire 1826

PLATE 2

RED GROUSE

Coloured engraving by Philip Reinagle 1808

INTRODUCTION

I HAVE called this book "British Game" and some explanation seems to be called for. Strictly speaking, the title is a misnomer, for the number of birds legally entitled to be known as game is very small, and there is only one mammal that may be so known ; whereas I have dealt with all those creatures which the sportsman pursues either for sport or because he thinks that they interfere with his sport.

The history of British Game is limited. If you are going to write a history of British Game you need not start before 1831, for the very simple reason that there was no legal game before that date. But very much the same creatures were pursued in Britain before then ; have been pursued, I imagine, for just about as long as man has been in Britain. I am not writing a history of the pursuit of wild animals in Britain, so I do not propose to touch upon the methods of those who slung stones from slings or shot arrows from bows. In any case, I do not think that the sling and the bow (for no man used the cross-bow, the bolt from which was propelled by pulling a trigger, for shooting birds, and the long-bow was a very different sort of weapon) can truly be regarded as substitutes for the gun. The earliest substitute for the gun was the hawk.

Hawking is of very ancient origin. The use of trained hawks seems to have developed first in early Thrace. They were certainly flown in England in Saxon times and probably earlier than that. I do not know that hawking had then become a science, and I should doubt if it had then advanced to the point at which you knew a man's social status by the hawk he owned. Time was when every man, according to his social rank, had a particular sort of hawk assigned to him. The more noble species, which were often imported at great cost from abroad, were reserved for kings and princes and noblemen : humble men had to be content with more lowly species. Thus the peregrine gentle, the gyr-falcon, and the goshawk were reserved for the gentry, the sparrow-hawk and the kestrel for those of humbler position, the sparrow-hawk coming by degrees to be identified with the Church (but not with bishops who were nobles), being the bird of the "holy water clerk ". The most popular (but by no means the most highly prized) bird was the goshawk. This was because both male and female goshawk are birds of very considerable bloodthirstiness when in pursuit of their quarry, but are remarkably mild and easy to handle. Moreover, goshawks were, and are, " birds of the hand ". That is to say, they were, and are, flown straight from the hand, from which they dash with the velocity of a shot from a gun. They had, and have, other advantages too. They do not have to be persuaded to return by the use of a lure. A goshawk is a bird that hits or misses, and if it is well trained (and if it is well trained it is also affectionate) it will immediately return to the hand after a miss (or maybe two misses) at its quarry. A good goshawk regards its master's hand as its home. The goshawk was the typical hawk of the English country gentleman, a bird to be carried about with one on one's walks abroad. (The falcon gentle, on the other hand, was more nearly allied to the chase and was usually carried by a mounted man, which, of course, made the whole thing, even in the days of the horse, more of a business.) And, of course, the goshawk was popular because in those days it bred in England and apparently in some numbers. Colonel Thomas Thornton, in his *Northern Tour*, which was published in 1804, states that he found the goshawk breeding in Rothiemurchus and Drumlochty, and from the former obtained his famous game-taking hawk which he christened Evelyn. I have seen doubt cast upon the gallant Colonel's statement (and it is true that it is a bit difficult to swallow some of his adventures), but I cannot see why this should be so. The goshawk attempted to nest in Lincolnshire in 1864, but the female was shot. It did nest in Yorkshire in 1893, for a nest with four eggs was found and the female was shot. No doubt in Thornton's time it was very uncommon, but that does not mean that at a much earlier date it may not have been common, or at any rate fairly common, as a nesting species. Indeed, I am sure that it must have been, for it was the practice of the falconers of old to let their hawks go back to a free life in the woodland when the season was over, and the time they chose for this was the end of March or early in April. And they would let their hawks return to the wild in order that they might breed under natural conditions. The custom is mentioned as early as A.D. 995, when Archbishop Aelfric refers to it in his *Colloquium*. You will also find it mentioned in *A Perfecte Booke for Kepinge Sparhawks*, which is a sixteenth-century publication, and again you will find it in the *Paston Letters*.

Hawking became so popular, and so fashionable, that the most stringent laws were passed to protect the eyries and nests, and a very heavy fine or imprisonment were the punishments meted out to those who stole another man's hawk. Henry VII passed such a law. Henry VIII made it a felony to take the King's nestling falcons or the eggs out of a nest, or to capture one of the King's hawks and not to hand it over to one of the royal falconers within ten days. James I was very keen on all field sports, and devoted a good deal of time to hunting the hare with beagles and hawks (the hare has only recently been regarded as an animal to shoot) and also to flying his hawks at birds. He also spent a vast amount of money every year on hawks. It is a mistake to think that hawking was a cheap amusement. You can pay a very tidy sum for a pair of guns from a first-class gunmaker to-day, but you will be a fool indeed if you pay the price a pair of good hawks used to cost. Sir Thomas Monson, in the reign of James I, paid £1000 for a pair of goshawks, and money was money in those days. But hawks were also at one time a King's ransom. One of the Crusader princes was ransomed from the Saracens for twelve Greenland Falcons. Twelve Greenland Falcons! Just think of what that means. It means, among other things, that there must have been a constant traffic between the continental mainland and Greenland and Iceland (for the ransom was paid in twelve months), and it also meant that falconry was pursued with zest and knowledge by the Saracen princes, and that they knew a Greenland falcon when they saw one. Our history books always leave out these interesting little details.

Falconry was popular, extremely so, throughout the Stuart period. Its decline commenced with the Restoration. It did not give way at once to the musket and the fowling-piece. That came later. It declined primarily because it went out of fashion at court. William III was indifferent, and the Hanoverian kings were not sportsmen. And then the improvement of firearms, the enclosure of waste-land, the gradual drainage of fens, the destruction of forests, and the introduction of shot finished it off. But it has never died out. There is to-day a Falconer's Club, and still to-day hawks are flown in the English countryside, though not as frequently as I, personally, would like to see. It will never regain its former widespread popularity, it can never now be more than the hobby of the few (the country is too enclosed and parcelled to permit it on any scale), but it would be a very great pity if it ever lost any of the ground it now holds. And it could, I think, be increased a little. It is not a difficult matter to take a hawk alive. It is not a difficult matter to train a hawk. I commend the hawk to gamekeepers. They would find one or two worth a good deal to them in the execution of their duties.

When were game birds first preserved for sport in Britain? I do not think that anyone can give the date. Colonel George Hanger, whose book was published in 1814, writes of gamekeepers. Hanger (who was afterwards Lord Coleraine) was born in 1760, and in his book he does not, quite evidently, regard gamekeepers as anything unusual. Lawrence Rawstorne, whose book *Gamonia or The Art of Preserving Game* was published in 1837, had evidently made a long and careful study of the art. And indeed for years before he wrote, pheasants' eggs, and probably partridge eggs also, were being put under hens, and young pheasants were being turned into coverts to be beaten out later, in something approximating the modern manner, to test the skill of the assembled guns. The " battue " was well established when Rawstorne wrote his book, and to hold a " battue " you must have known that there were plenty of pheasants in the coverts. They certainly were not wild pheasants. But one can arrive at an approximate date, according to one's opinion of the English Parliament's energy, through the Game Act. This measure was passed to protect people's game, and it was passed in 1831. Game preservation must have been very firmly and widely established before then.

And, of course, pheasants were reared for the table centuries earlier. They were almost certainly (personally I should regard it as beyond question) reared for the table in Roman Britain : not in the Britain visited by Julius Caesar, but in the Britain of the Roman occupation. We know that they could not have been so reared in Caesar's time, for Marcus Terentius Varro, the great Roman writer on matters agricultural, who collected the material for the third volume of his *Rerum Rusticarum* in 54 B.C., does not mention the pheasant at all. But by the time that Rutilius Taurus Aemilianus Palladius wrote his *De Re Rustica* (the date is uncertain but it was probably somewhere about A.D. 350) the pheasant was part of the stock of a well-to-do Roman villa. Palladius knows a great deal about the rearing of pheasants, and gives most detailed directions in his book as to the procedure to adopt. It is interesting to note that Rawstorne's directions do not differ so very much, and are identical in some respects. And the modern gamekeeper, quite unknowingly, follows to the letter some of the practices recommended from personal experience by Palladius.

The Game Act of 1831, since it legalised the status of the gamekeeper and gave him certain powers of arrest, put game and game-

Plate I

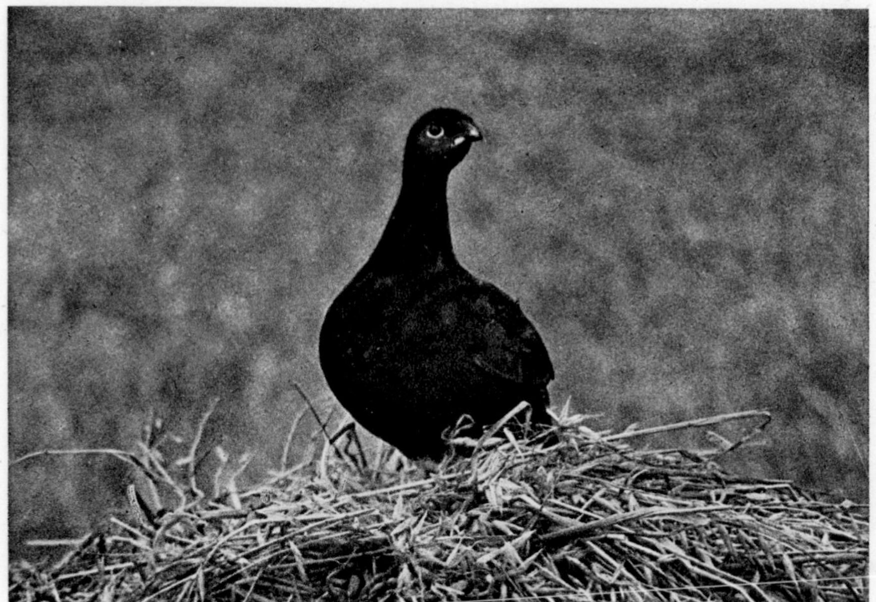

RED GROUSE HEN. Strath Spey. October 1943. G. B. KEAREY

RED GROUSE and family. Inverness-shire. 1939. ERIC HOSKING

Plate II

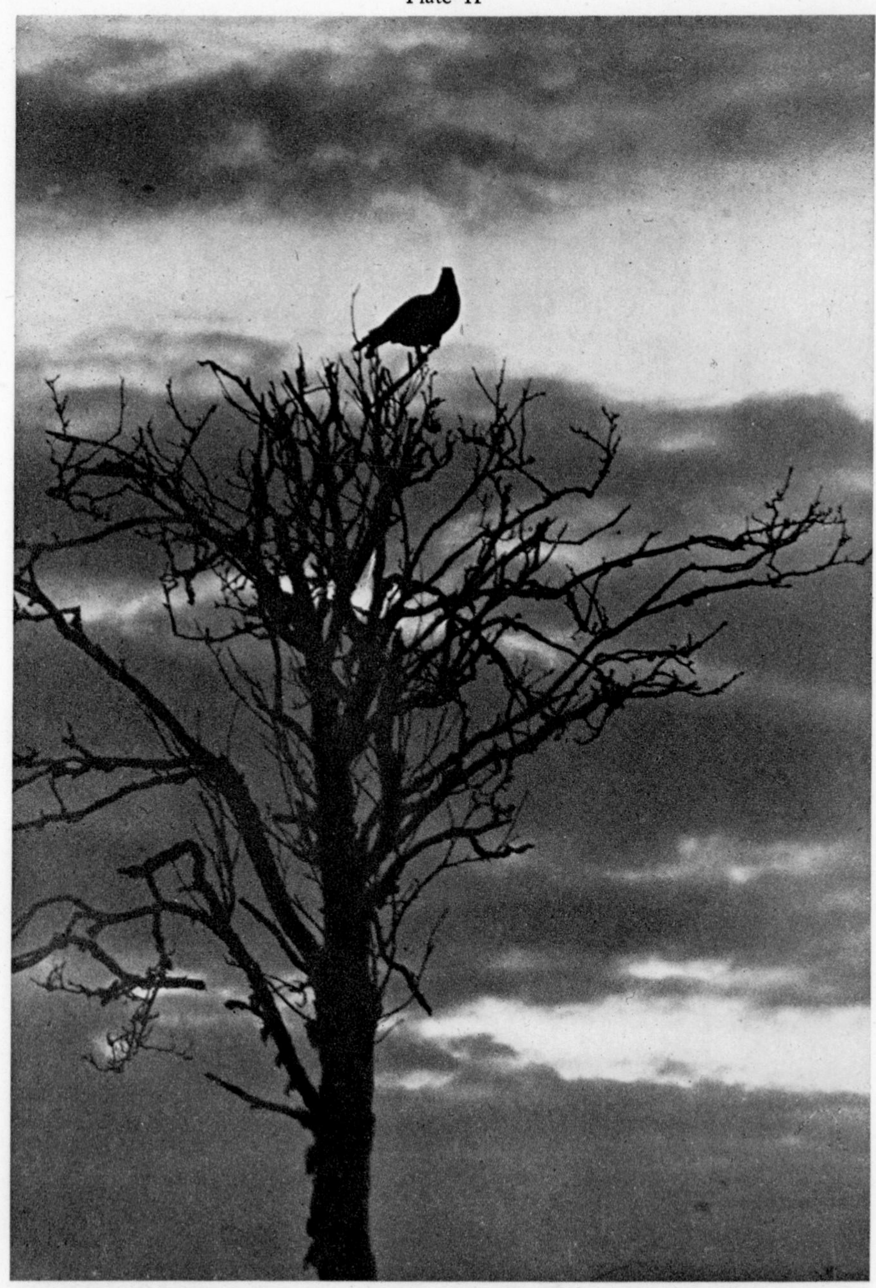

BLACKCOCK. Strath Spey. April 1939. R. G. FENNAL

preserving on a different footing. It abolished the property qualification (this, by the way, still holds good in Scotland and Ireland, legally at anyrate) and entitles anybody to kill game so long as he pays a duty to the Inland Revenue and has permission to go on land in search of it. No one, with one or two exceptions that may be ignored, can shoot game without a licence, and the licence must be obtained before any shooting is done. On the other hand, a gun licence (which costs 10 shillings a year as opposed to £3 a year for a game licence) is all that is required to use a gun provided it is not used to kill game.

For the purposes of the Game Act, hares, pheasants, partridges, grouse, heath or moor game, black-game and bustards are game. A licence is also necessary to shoot woodcock, snipe, quail, landrail, conies (rabbits) and deer, but these are not game. Nor are swans, geese, wild duck, teal, wigeon and capercaillie. These come under the Wild Bird Protection Acts for protection. What heath or moor game may be I do not know, and nor, I fancy, does anybody else. And bustards are extinct in Britain.

Deer, though they are not game, do require a licence before they can be taken or killed (except by hunting with hounds) under the Game Licences Act, 1860. But they can be killed on enclosed land without a licence by the owner or the occupier or his licensee. On the other hand, they are included as Game in the Agricultural Holdings Act when questions regarding compensation for damage arise. Again, hares (which are game) and rabbits (which are not) are included in the Ground Game Act. And rabbits, which are not game, are included in the Excise Licence to kill game but are excluded from the close seasons for killing game. In England and Wales you cannot shoot (in peace-time) a grouse, a pheasant or a partridge on a Sunday nor a pheasant or a partridge on Christmas Day. Blackgame are not protected on Sundays. And it is quite possible to find plenty more contradictions. Furthermore, poaching, strictly speaking, seems to be applicable only to game and rabbits. The Game Act, it will be seen, is not very easy to understand, and the position is not made any easier by such things as the Law of Trespass (particularly with regard to boundary questions), which is very technical indeed. The Game Act was passed in 1831 at a time when the capercaillie was extinct and the bustard was not. Almost everything in England has changed since then, but the Game Act remains (though the bustard is now extinct and the capercaillie is not), and, though that is very English and old-fashioned and conservative and pleasant, it is high time an Act bearing a closer relationship to facts as they are was placed on the Statute Book.

This book, however, does not deal with the law, which I do not pretend to understand. Nor does it deal, except incidentally, with shooting (I am *not* a good shot anyway) nor with the duties and cares of gamekeepers and gamekeeping. There have been any number of books written about both, and a list of some of them will be found at the end of this volume. This is a natural history book, giving facts about the birds and beasts that should interest sportsmen, and all too frequently do not. Necessarily, it is in many ways a compilation, but the views and opinions expressed are in every case (unless explicitly stated to be those of somebody else) my own personal views and opinions based upon my own personal experience.

B. V-F. *Winchester 1943*

THE GAME BIRDS

CHAPTER I

THE RED GROUSE

The British Red Grouse (*Lagopus scoticus scoticus* (Latham))
The Irish Red Grouse (*Lagopus scoticus hibernicus* (Kleinschmidt))

THE TWELFTH . . . the words conjure up a picture of the Scottish moors. Do you remembers these lines by Patrick Chalmers?

"Now, when the sportsman is flitting from market and Mammon,
Now, when the courts, swept and garnished, stand silent and lone,
Now, with the challenging grouse, and the sea-silver salmon,
August, of mountains and memories, comes to her own;
Would you gaze into the crystal and see the long valleys,
Braes of the north and the rivers that wander between,
Crags with whose coating the tint of the ptarmigan tallies?
Come up to Euston to-night about 7.15."

Chalmers was an Angus man, of course, and a bit biased you might think. But those lines are true enough for all shooting men; indeed, grouse and Scotland are pretty well synonymous in the minds of most people.

It would, however, be a great mistake to suppose that the red grouse is confined to Scotland. There is, for example, an Irish red grouse. But the red grouse has a very limited range. Originally it was confined to the British Isles and was found nowhere else in the world. That may not be true now. Some years ago a few were introduced into the Ardennes district of Belgium and the Eifel district of Western Germany, and after a year or two were reported to have settled down well. But it is by no means certain that they have survived, and for all practical purposes the red grouse may properly be regarded as a truly British bird. It is a bird of the heather, of the upland moors and the peat bogs. Of the two forms that occur in our islands, the British is found in and west and north of Carmarthen, Brecon, Monmouth —but, according to the *Handbook of British Birds*, it is probably extinct in Glamorgan and Pembrokeshire—Herefordshire, Shropshire, Staffordshire, Derbyshire and Yorkshire (but not in the East Riding). Outside this range it is well-established on Exmoor, but this is the result of introduction. Introductions have been attempted in many other counties—notably Surrey, Norfolk and Suffolk—but have not proved successful. In Scotland it is generally distributed on the mainland, and is also well established in the Inner Hebrides and Orkney, but is absent from Shetland, where all attempts at introduction have failed. The Irish form is found in Ireland from Kerry to Antrim and in the Outer Hebrides.

A word on these subspecies. The distinction between the British and the Irish forms is one for museum naturalists only, for, though the Irish bird tends in its winter plumage to be paler than the British, the difference cannot be distinguished in the field, no matter whether in England or Wales or Ireland or Scotland; the red grouse at a glance appears a dark red-brown bird (at a distance it looks black) with, if you can get near enough to see them, whitish feathered legs. Sub-specific status is very, very rarely discernible in the field. In any case, differences in colour as a guide to such status would be most misleading in live birds in the open country. And particularly would it be so in the case of the red grouse, for no bird is more variable in its plumage. Indeed it has been said, not altogether unreasonably, that it is always changing its plumage. And to make matters still more confusing the cock and the hen both moult twice in the year, and at different times.

A typical cock in breeding dress might be described, I think, as dark chestnut-red, barred with black, the bars being coarse on the crown and fine on the back and chest. The breast of such a bird is blackish. But I am not sure that it is not over-optimistic to speak of a typical cock. Ogilvie-Grant, who made an exhaustive study of a great many skins over a period of years, recognised three male types and no less than five female types, and he believed that, generally speaking, these types depend upon locality. They may be briefly summarised as follows:

In the male there is a red, a black and a white-spotted type.

(1) *The red type.* General coloration a rufous-chestnut without any white marks on the breast. Birds of this type are to be found mainly in the western counties of England and Wales, Scotland, the Hebrides and the lower grounds of Ireland.

(2) *The black type.* This is rare, and is in any case not a sharply defined form. The black feathers are dominant but are sprinkled with red and white-spotted feathers. Birds that were almost wholly black were obtained by Ogilvie-Grant from Yorkshire, Dumbartonshire, Stirlingshire, Perthshire, Sutherland, and Caithness.

(3) *The white-spotted type.* The feathers of the breast and sometimes of the head and the upper-parts are tipped with white. Most of the birds of this type have come from the north of Scotland, and the type is probably characteristic of really high ground.

In the female there are five recognisable types : a red, a black, a white-spotted, a buff-spotted, and a buff-barred.

(1) *The red type.* This is relatively rare in females and occurs over the same geographical range as the red type in males.

(2) *The black type.* This is as uncommon in females as in males, and occurs in the same areas.

(3) *The white-spotted type.* Occurs as in males in the Highlands.

(4) *The buff-spotted type.* This is the most common coloration in females. The feathers of the upper-parts are tipped with white or pale buff. This coloration does not occur in males.

(5) *The buff-barred type.* This is the characteristic coloration of the females in Ireland. The upper parts are coarsely barred with buff and black. This plumage does not undergo any appreciable change throughout the year.

From the above it would seem that the type, if not fixed by the locality, is at any rate very closely related to the locality. While I would not pretend for one moment that my experience of plumage is in any way comparable with that of Ogilvie-Grant (I have never examined a long series of skins), I think it would be most unwise to make any such assumption. My own experience is limited and confined to observation in the open. Yet in this limited experience I have come across the white-spotted type in Breconshire : the reddest bird I have ever seen I shot in Sutherlandshire : the blackest bird I have shot was in Montgomeryshire, and that bird was almost wholly black. At the same time my own experience has been that the red type is almost as characteristic of Montgomeryshire and Central Wales as the white-spotted type is of the Highlands, and the red type female is not so very uncommon in this area. I do not believe that the significance of these variations in type is as yet fully understood. That climatic conditions play a considerable part seems evident, but it seems possible to me that the protein content of the food taken (a subject that has received little study as yet) may also be a powerful factor in determining variation.

The moults complicate this plumage variation still further. Broadly speaking, the cock is in summer plumage from the end of May or beginning of June until the beginning of October, and in winter plumage from mid-October until mid-May. The hen is in summer plumage from April until August, and in winter plumage from August until March. In June, exceptionally at the end of May, the male goes into a sort of eclipse. This is really the commencement of the complete moult, and it begins with the inner primaries while the body feathers are still growing. The new white leg feathers commence to come in July, and it is while they are appearing that the claws are shed. This shedding of the claws has never, so far as I know, been satisfactorily explained. This complete moult ends normally in October, but may last into November or even December. A gradual moult, which is often temporarily arrested, of the feathers of the upper-parts, the head and neck, and the greater coverts and secondaries commences about the end of April as a rule, but may begin as early as the first week in June. This is not a complete moult, for the under-parts, the wings and the tail are not affected. It will be noticed that the complete moult and the partial moult proceed more or less in opposite directions. The moults of the hen are similar but commence earlier. I think that sufficient has been said to show that, what with the great variation in type and moults or partial moults going on pretty well throughout the year (and not sticking too close to any time-table), the red grouse from the plumage point of view can be very confusing.

The red grouse is monogamous. That does not mean that it mates for life: it means that, normally, a cock has only one wife in the breeding season. The time for pairing (and this, of course, affects the early close season for grouse) depends on the weather. In a mild winter grouse will pair in December or January. There is always some sparring between males in the autumn, and they may even take up territory as early as the end of October. Sex chases have been observed as early as the first week of November. But none of this means that pairing actually occurs so early. The males of all the grouse family seem to have a burst of what might be called false sexual activity in the autumn, which never amounts to more than a bit of sparring, some self-important strutting to and fro; the chivvying of some luckless hen or hens. I think it may be taken that December is the earliest month for grouse to pair off properly. In the autumn and winter it is the habit of the bird to form into flocks or " packs ". In an early season you will often find that after a few days' shooting the coveys tend to " pack ", and always the young birds tend to do so earlier than the adults. Further, hens seem to pack more readily than cocks. There are always a few cocks, generally some old gentlemen, who will not pack at all, just as you may find an odd family party or two hanging together even so late as the end of November. The birds roost—" jag " is the correct word in connection with grouse—in these packs in the heather, but they do not do so in such close formation as partridges. Generally they are a foot or two apart, and I have noticed that a pack at roost tends to adopt a semi-circular formation facing the wind. If there is heavy snow they escape smothering by treading it underfoot as it falls. In some districts there are hen packs and cock packs (I have noticed this in Denbighshire and Perthshire), but I do not think that segregation of the sexes is the rule among red grouse. If there is severe weather late in the season, after they have commenced to pair, the birds will often pack again.

The courtship of the red grouse is a most interesting affair. As the bird is monogamous, there is no regular tournament as there is in the display of black grouse, and you might think that with so wary a bird it would be very difficult to watch the courting activities of a pair. In point of fact, however, the red grouse is comparatively easy of approach during his courtship, for he is so intent upon charming the lady of his choice that he is not over-concerned with the presence of mere humans, and I have watched the courtship of a red grouse cock from a distance of not more than fifteen feet. I was lucky perhaps, but anyone who takes a little trouble should be able to watch the display from a distance of a few yards. Cock grouse, as I have already said, take up territories, and during the breeding season these territories are more or less actively defended, and so are quite easy to find. The owner of a territory tends more and more as time goes on to display from a definite point in the territory, and, as he also uses this spot as a " vantage point " from which to crow at the owners of neighbouring territories, it is easy to find the special point and mark it. The rest is merely a matter of approach and fieldcraft—and luck.

The first signs of awaking sexual activity may come quite early on in mild weather. Cocks that are to all appearances still completely neuter will suddenly at the end of their flight fly up almost perpendicularly, descending in a downward curve with outspread wings to the accompaniment of much crowing, and then when on the ground challenge each other, by means of crowing, from some eminence. The next moment they will be feeding amicably together again. Sometimes after this comes a tendency towards isolation and the acquisition of a territory, though this territory may not be, and probably will not be, the one finally adopted. But gradually these territories sort themselves out and regular display centres are adopted. Once this has been done the cocks become very busy challenging one another by crowing and making the typical display flights, and also by sparring with one another. There is very little real fighting (I have never seen any), but sometimes one cock will fly after and into another in the air. It is at this time, in my experience before any female has come on the scene, that on occasion a joint display occurs. It is a display which has some features in common with that of the black-cock, but it would be idle to suggest that at one time the red grouse was also polygamous and that this is a relic of far-off times. In this joint display, which I have seen only once, but which Nethersole-Thompson has watched frequently, several males approach one another with lowered heads and drooping wings and " curious cries " (they are quite unlike the normal display cries) before returning to their respective display centres, usually without any sparring or fighting having taken place. Males certainly come into the breeding season before females, not infrequently some considerable time before, and when the females, just entering the breeding season, wander into the male territories they will be wooed by several cocks, and sexual flights will occur in which the hen is pursued by two or more cocks. Later on pairing will occur, but there is always a period of varying length between pairing and actual mating, and during this period sexual flights and pursuit of the female on the ground by the male are common. These flights are always the same. The cock flies close behind the hen, and the pair veer and " jink " from side to side at some pace. But the flight is never on a zigzag course, but always straight, and is never of very long duration. I do not think I have ever seen one that covered much more than a quarter of a mile, certainly not so much as half a mile. On alighting the cock, with lowered head and fanned erected tail, continues to pursue the hen. Then without any warning the two will commence to feed. At this period, that is before consummation,

Plate III

BLACKCOCKS "lekking." Strath Spey. April 1939. G. B. KEAREY

GREY HEN and eggs. Inverness-shire, 1943. G. B. KEAREY

Plate IV

PTARMIGAN HEN incubating eggs. Cairngorms slopes, 1940. JOHN MARKHAM

PTARMIGAN COCK. Argyllshire. July 1942. C. E. PALMAR

should the pair alight anywhere near an unmated cock he will immediately join in the ground display, but he will not pursue them when they fly away. Should they alight near a mated cock they are regarded with indifference. It happens not infrequently that after pairing there is a spell of severe weather. When this occurs all breeding activity ceases and the birds return to packs. I do not know if they resume the original pairings with the return of milder weather or not. Nethersole-Thompson has records of one pairing over more than one season, so it is probable that some at least do. But then some red grouse may not be monogamous. There can be no fixed rule.

Once the pair is established in a definite territory the ground display of the cock changes. This is the display that I have watched from close range. The perpendicular finish to the flight ends and a perpendicular spring into the air from the ground is substituted. This display is invariable. As the cock ascends he cries *ur-rak* (I take the *Handbook's* interpretation of the sound: everybody probably hears it slightly differently, I know I do, and so the official interpretation is obviously the best); as he descends he cries *rak-rak-rak*, and when on the ground he stands in a stiff upright position and utters *go-bak-bak* in a rather guttural voice several times with increasing speed. (This *go-bak-bak* is not very similar to the "becking" *go-bak*, which is an explosive challenging sound that may be delivered impartially to other cocks or humans.) The display on the ground is not so stereotyped. There is a formal pattern in which the cock advances towards the hen with a rather high-stepping mincing gait—rather as if he were walking on hot bricks and hoped no one would notice that he was not very comfortable—with tail fully fanned and erected, wings drooped and the neck stretched out to a positively astonishing extent. The female, of course, takes no notice of this. Sometimes she just continues feeding, in which case the cock may become very excited and stamp on the ground. Sometimes she may just continue sitting down, in which case the whole thing falls rather flat. Sometimes, still apparently oblivious, she may crouch close to the ground, in which case coition may take place. In every case in which I have observed coition the hen's action immediately prior to it has been the same. She has been crouched close to the ground and apparently quite unmoved by the advances of her mate. Suddenly she stretches her neck, and "points" her beak to the ground (I think it actually touches the ground, but I cannot be sure) and the cock mounts. I have never seen any false treading such as is common with moor-hens, coots, and pheasants. I have twice seen cock grouse peck at the hen's cloaca during display in just the same manner as turkeys.

Before the actual mating, for a fortnight or perhaps three weeks before, there is a good deal of symbolic nesting. The female makes a number of false "scrapes" and sometimes the male encourages her by making one or two himself. Unmated males will also make scrapes. The nest proper is no more than a scrape lined with a few bents. Eggs may be laid as early as the end of February, but the latter half of April is the most usual period. A clutch may number anything from six to eleven eggs, buffish in ground colour freshly blotched with chestnut or a rich red-brown. In a normal season clutches average about seven, in a good season eight. It might be thought that this early nest on high ground would be fraught with many dangers from inclement weather. Undoubtedly nests are lost in severe weather—and May in the Highlands is a tricky month—but the losses are not so severe as might be supposed. Grouse eggs can withstand very considerable exposure, and hens will continue to sit in heavy snow, even when completely buried in snow, and not only to sit, but to bring off successful hatches. Very severe weather just after the chicks are hatched is another matter. It should be remembered, however, that the red grouse breeds in its first year.

The hen lays at intervals varying between 24 and 48 hours. She does not lay invariably in the early morning as is commonly thought. In my own experience the most usual time is between 10 a.m. and 3 p.m. Normally incubation proper does not begin until the final egg has been laid. The period of incubation is approximately twenty-four days. Nethersole-Thompson timed incubation as twenty-three days, hatching on the final day occupying six hours. But incubation has been timed for as little as 21 and as many as 26 days. The hen sits very closely, leaving perhaps three times in the day to feed for periods averaging about an hour. When flushed from a nest a sitting hen leaves without fuss and generally flies right away. When leaving the nest in the ordinary way to feed the hen walks from the nest and does not take wing until she is a considerable distance from it. The cocks keep very quiet during incubation (they do nothing to help), and it is very rarely indeed that a cock gives the position of a nest away. When the hen leaves to feed the cock joins her some distance from the nest and sticks closely to her until the time for her return.

But if the male does not do much to help the female during the tedious business of incubation, he is very helpful once the young are hatched. He is very quick to give warning of possible or impending danger, and he stages wonderful "injury-feigning" exhibitions to distract attention from the young. The female will also stage these exhibitions, and some hens will even attack the human intruder or a dog, running forwards very fast with neck outstretched and hissing loudly, sometimes right up to the offender. Young red grouse—they have the longitudinal stripes common to the young of all the grouse family—are extraordinarily precocious. They leave the nest immediately, at most an hour or so after, the last of the eggs has hatched, but they do not leave their parents. In my experience both cock and hen stay close to their young, and the hen will brood them periodically, even during the daytime, but never for very long at a time. Although the actions of the cock will tell you whereabouts they are, young grouse are very hard to find in the heather, and they are pretty well impossible to watch at all closely. It is not, therefore, surprising that we really know practically nothing about the early days of the bird. I have seen young birds, not more than a day or so out of the nest, pulling at heather, and by the time they are a week or so old they make a pretty good job of it. I have seen young birds at the same age picking about for grit. At seven days old they can flutter off the ground and most of them can fly, if not very far, by the time they are a fortnight old, which is astonishing progress for such big birds. They are wonderfully quick and clever, almost from the moment of hatching, at catching insects. Insects, in fact, form a large proportion of the food of young grouse. Beyond this, the only thing that I know about them is that I have never seen one being fed by its parents.

The food of grouse, as might be expected in a bird that holds so important an economic position, has received much careful and expert study. In particular the Grouse Disease Committee examined about 1500 crops. Dr. W. E. Collinge, who examined about 112 crops, found that 77·5% of the food taken is vegetable and 22·5% animal.

The staple food of the red grouse is heather (*Calluna vulgaris*). This is the common ling, and grouse eat the shoots, flowers and seed heads. But many other foods are eaten—including berries, bog-myrtle, dwarf willow, grass rushes, clover, bracken, violet and grain—some of them in considerable quantities. But heather remains always the main food of the grouse. The Grouse Disease Committee considered that the following was a pretty accurate monthly dietary of the red grouse for the year :

January :	*Calluna* shoots 64%, *Calluna* seedheads 27%.
February :	*Calluna* shoots 75%, stalks and buds of blaeberry, leaves of cowberry.
March :	*Calluna* shoots 97%, stalks and buds of blaeberry.
April :	*Calluna* shoots 93%, and very little else besides.
May :	*Calluna* shoots 82%, and rather more various.
June :	*Calluna* shoots 82%, and various.
July :	*Calluna* shoots 53%, and an increasing amount of various.
August :	*Calluna* shoots 60%, some *Calluna* flowers.
September :	*Calluna* shoots 63%, *Calluna* flowers 16% and various.
October :	*Calluna* shoots 42%, *Calluna* flowers 30% and various.
November :	*Calluna* shoots 39%, *Calluna* flowers and seedheads 33% and various.
December :	*Calluna* shoots 60%, *Calluna* seedheads 27%.

It will be seen that the percentage of food derived directly from heather is very high throughout the year ; so high that it is often stated that a constant supply of heather is an absolute necessity for the survival of the red grouse. This is not so, however, for it has been put on record by the Grouse Disease Committee that grouse that have never so much as set eyes on a sprig of heather will live and flourish for years. Nevertheless, the grouse is normally a bird of the heather, living for the most part on and in heather, and it is true to say that a constant supply of heather is essential to its well-being. Insect food is taken mainly in the first two weeks of life, and is probably not absolutely essential to life after the first week. Grit, however, is essential. Grouse, in common with other game birds, depend largely on the nature of the grit they take to aid them in the digestion of their food. In other words, the health of the grouse is dependent to no small extent on the nature of the grit they take, and they need a constant supply to be taken with their food every day. They find it on the moor in the form of quartz grit and felspar, but they will also take minute fragments of such rocks as granite and gneiss. But quartz is essential and they seem unable to exist without it. The gizzards of grouse nearly always contain quartz, even though there may be no quartz on the moor on which the bird is shot, which means that if quartz is not available on the spot grouse may travel daily, and sometimes considerable distances to get it. Young grouse begin pecking about for grit within a day or so of being hatched, so necessary is it. The grit which is taken into the gizzard remains for some considerable time, so the larger grits in the gizzard of an old bird become smooth and

PLATE 3

BLACKCOCK LEKKING

Oil painting by Allen W. Seaby 1943

PTARMIGAN

Water colour by A. Thorburn 1908

From J. G. Millais' NATURAL HISTORY OF BRITISH GAME BIRDS

polished. Some of the smaller grits, together with sand and other indigestible items, are ejected daily in the droppings, and these have to be replaced with the daily intake of food. Heather and quartz grit, then, are essential to the red grouse. The moor owner cannot do anything about the latter, but a proper understanding of the former is as essential to his well-being as it is to that of the red grouse. But the question of heather is tied up with other problems in the management of red grouse, and before I come to these there are other aspects of the bird's feeding economy which require attention.

Do grouse drink? There has long been controversy on this point. Most moor-owners seem to be of the opinion that grouse do not require water, while opinion among gamekeepers seems to be about evenly divided. It does seem to be the case that in the early stages of their life grouse do not require water or at least do not require to drink. But later on they undoubtedly do need water, and I think undoubtedly need to drink. I have never seen a grouse drink, and I do not know anybody who has. But Charles St. John, a very close observer, was of the opinion that they did (and suggests that he had seen them do so), and Abel Chapman, who knew as much about the red grouse as anybody else and a great deal more than most, was firmly of the opinion that they do. It is beyond dispute that in dry weather grouse will leave the drier parts of a moor for the well-watered parts. They do not apparently visit the burns—which means no more than that they are not seen to do so—but this does not necessarily mean that they do not drink. And the fact that examination of the alimentary canal has always failed to reveal traces of water, and that the contents of the crop are always found to be dry, need mean no more than that the bird does not drink when its crop is full. It might well drink during the long periods of the day when the crop is empty.

And when do grouse feed? Abel Chapman in an article in *The Field* in August, 1884, stated that they feed in earnest only once a day, and then during the last hour before dusk. The statement was questioned at the time by Lord Walsingham, who was a very fine shot but not an equally fine naturalist. It was categorically denied by the Grouse Disease Committee, who stated in *The Grouse in Health and Disease*: "Our observations make it quite clear that such is not the case. Grouse feed, off and on, throughout the day; but it is only during the evening that the crop retains the food that is required during the night." And they followed this bald statement up with a table giving the weight in grains of crop contents of shot birds and the hour in which the birds were shot. I give this table here :

Hour of collection.	Weight of Crop Contents of each Bird in Grains		Average Weight in Grains		
	April to November	December to March	April to November Average	December to March Average	Combined Average for 12 months
6 a.m.	1	10, 10	1	10	5½
7 a.m.	8	No specimen	8	No specimen	8
8 a.m.	No specimen	20	No specimen	20	20
9 a.m.	1, 8	10	4½	10	7¼
10 a.m.	3, 18, 19, 4, 4, 20, 9	No specimen	11	No specimen	5½
11 a.m.	18, 2, 16, 27, 20, 14, 3, 13, 24, 40, 28, 36, 43, 34, 11	5	22	5	13½
Noon	12, 14, 2, 11, 18, 6, 7, 15, 21, 7, 1, 6, 15, 24	120, 10	11⅓	65	38
1 p.m.	18, 36, 62, 29, 32, 2, 3, 5, 13, 13, 18, 12, 19, 0	No specimen	19	No specimen	19
2 p.m.	26, 45	70, 60, 20	35½	75	55¼
3 p.m.	50, 173, 98, 213, 334, 27, 7, 12, 17, 26, 18, 14, 2, 6, 8, 28, 52, 24, 48, 31, 1, 5, 68, 31, 32	110, 110, 80, 180, 358, 200, 369, 50, 380, 250, 320	53	217	135
4 p.m.	15, 1, 4, 4, 246, 50, 17, 32, 50, 43, 50, 46, 8, 4, 2, 43, 3	339, 429, 239, 369, 429, 599, 280, 280	36	370½	208¼
5 p.m.	8, 1, 1, 2, 1, 254, 66, 18, 5, 32, 23, 17, 7, 23	150, 210, 200	32½	186⅔	109½
6 p.m.	37, 93, 114	10, 349, 290, 20, 409	81	214	147½

And that, you might think, settled the point. Abel Chapman, however, was quite unabashed and remained entirely unconverted. Indeed, he went so far as to describe the Committee's report on this one point as "half-baked". And I would stress again that Abel Chapman knew the red grouse on the moors by his home as few men have known it. To all intents and purposes he lived with it, day in and day out, throughout a long life, and in addition to being a first-class shot and an expert fisherman, he was a very good naturalist, a very good naturalist indeed, and an exceptionally observant and acute man. He remained, Committee or no Committee, quite convinced that the red grouse feeds in the evening.

Now Chapman did not say that the red grouse eats nothing at all before the hour preceding dusk. He said they do not feed until then. There is a difference : all the difference between "elevenses" and lunch. And I think if you examine the figures given in the table you will agree that they do not damn Chapman as thoroughly as they were intended to do. In fact the reverse : so far as they go (and they do not go nearly far enough) they bear him out. Take the winter figures—they could be much more complete—and then consider, forgetting all such monstrosities as summer-time and double summer-time—when dusk falls in the Highlands. The summer figures are merely unconvincing, astonishingly so for a scientific enquiry, for they cease at six o'clock, which is very much too early for the grouse. You will find an exception or two in the summer figures, but there are exceptions in every form of life (I know a man who has only one meal a day and that at 4 p.m., when he eats enough to fill three ordinary men), you will not find anything to show that Chapman was wrong. And if you consider the figures for the morning you will find much to show that he was right. The Committee got over the fact that full crops in a red grouse were very, very rarely found in the morning or forenoon but were commonly found in the late afternoon or evening, by postulating a hastened digestive process in the early part of the day. They said that in the early part of the day the food passes rapidly from the crop to the gizzard and on to the digesting tracts in the gut proper, and the crop is thus left almost empty ; whereas in the evening the bird feeds heavily in order to store up food for the hours of darkness. I do not know how that strikes you as a theory : it strikes me as very unconvincing indeed. I know of no proof to support it in any way at all. I know of no proof that the digestive process of the grouse undergoes a radical change during the course of the day. But I do know, as did the Committee and Abel Chapman, that the crops are full in the evening and empty in the morning and early afternoon. That has been the case with all those birds that I have shot and examined. And I do know that the only grouse I have seen feeding (it is not quite so difficult to watch them feeding as the Committee believed) have been feeding in the evening. So I believe, with Abel Chapman, that the red grouse, unlike other birds, *feeds* only in the evening.

Abel Chapman is also credited with the discovery that grouse burrow under the snow in the winter, and will live in these burrows for a very long time. He made no such claim himself, and in point of fact the discovery was made years before his time, and was first published in England, I believe, in 1867 by Lloyd in his *Game Birds and Wildfowl of Sweden and Norway.* Lloyd was dealing with the capercaillie, the blackcock and the willow grouse, a nearly-related species. Chapman was, I think, the first man to draw attention to the fact that the red grouse has the same habit. That they do burrow under the snow, and live in these burrows, was ignored by the Grouse Disease Committee, and doubt has since been cast upon the habit. It is said that in severe weather the grouse will leave for districts less affected, and one is left to surmise that they all leave. Undoubtedly some do emigrate under such circumstances: some undoubtedly do burrow out warrens under the snow. Abel Chapman saw such burrows. George Bolam, who knew the Border moorlands almost if not quite as well as Abel, saw them. Even I, and I am but a visitor to the moors, have seen them. Once only it is true; but why should I have seen anything exceptional? The reason that the habit is not better known than it is is not far to seek. Few men spend much time on the moors during heavy snow.

Do grouse migrate? It depends, I suppose, upon what you mean by migration. In very severe weather, as has already been said, some grouse do leave the highest ground for more clement districts. It is even probable that under such conditions the very "tops" are always deserted. In the exceptionally severe winter of 1894 they flocked to the turnip fields. MacPherson, in his volume in the *Fur and Feather* series, says: "When snow and sleet have driven them down from the hills they will then fly long distances. It is not at all unusual for Red Grouse to cross the Solway Firth at a point where the estuary measures two miles in breadth, and I have known them fly longer distances. They often cross the valley of the Tees, flying about a mile from one hillside to another." But that, I think, cannot be taken to indicate more than local movement, and a somewhat restricted local movement at that. Millais mentions flight between the island of Hoy and the Orkney mainland, which is a distance of about five miles, and also flight from Thurso on the Scottish mainland to Hoy, which is a distance of about eleven miles across the Pentland Firth. Harvie-Brown mentions a pack crossing the Moray Firth; this involves a flight of over forty miles. These, too, are movements that can be called migratory. If they do not constitute migration (which indicates, to

Plate V

G. B. KEAREY

The only British photograph of a COCK CAPERCAILLIE. Abernethy Forest, 1934

CAPERCAILLIE HEN incubating eggs. Abernethy. 1942. G. B. KEAREY

Plate VI

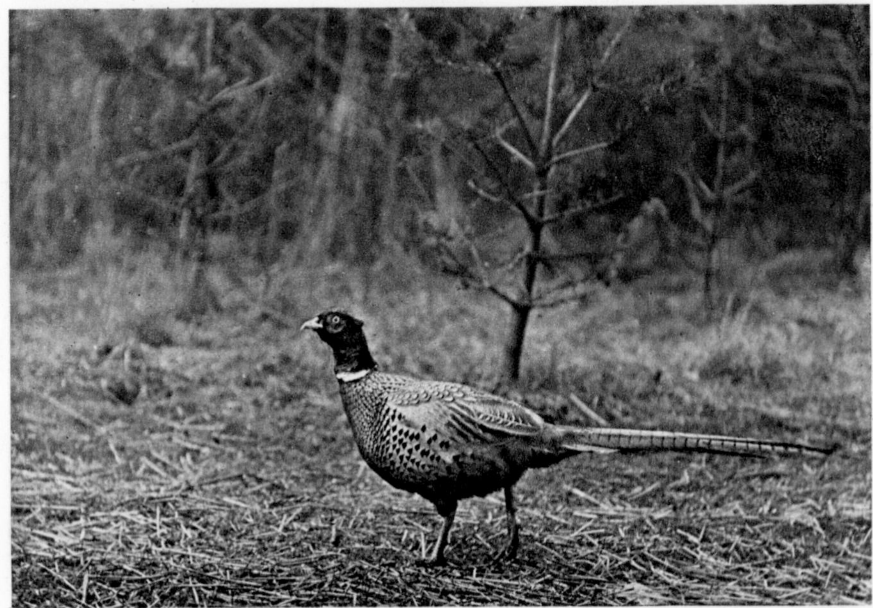

COCK PHEASANT. Yorkshire. February 1937. W. W. NICHOLAS

HEN PHEASANT and chick. Breconshire, 1929. ARTHUR BROOK

me at least, a seasonal return journey) they constitute emigration. And we have, of course, no proof that there is not a return journey or that the journeys witnessed were not in themselves return journeys.

Grouse migration has long been a subject of great interest to moor-owners and naturalists. In 1913 Mr. H. F. Witherby instituted a ringing scheme. It was an unfortunate year in which to begin such an enquiry. In all, in 1913 and 1914, some two thousand young birds were ringed and there were 234 recoveries. Of these only twenty-eight were shot at a distance of more than one mile from the spot where they were ringed. In no case was the distance from the place of ringing more than twenty miles, and in general the distance was about three. Since then there has been another enquiry, of the Committee of which I am a member. We have ringed a great number of birds, but we have had only some 2 per cent of them returned, and all the returns have been from or very near the moor where they were originally ringed. Two per cent is too small a return upon which to base final conclusions, but the cumulative evidence of the Witherby scheme and the Grouse Migration Inquiry scheme is certainly against any definite or seasonal movement among red grouse. And yet we know that there are movements *en masse* among grouse for which we cannot account, for which there appears to be no sound reason, no reason at all that we know of. Such movement occurred in 1913 when the grouse of the moors of the Border Counties left them, and could not be traced elsewhere. And again in 1915 when those same moors filled up once more with grouse that came from no one knows where.

But then the grouse is a bird that sets many problems. The biggest is Grouse Disease : so big a problem, indeed, that it gave rise to a Parliament Committee of Enquiry, and the publication of the massive and wonderfully detailed two-volume monograph, *The Grouse in Health and Disease*. We owe almost all we know about grouse disease to the work of the Committee, but it would be idle to pretend that it solved the problem.

Grouse, like all other game birds, indeed like all other birds, die from many different causes. They may be shot or trapped or poisoned : they may die from natural causes (of which old age is the least common) such as egg-binding : they may die from disease. The two most deadly diseases are coccidiosis and strongylosis.

Coccidiosis is *not* " grouse disease ". It is a disease which attacks many other wild and domestic animals. It is of common occurrence in rabbits, pheasants, domestic poultry, pigeons, and it probably occurs in many of the small wild birds. Coccidiosis is caused by a parasite which is picked up by the young grouse in their food or water. Birds severely afflicted by coccidiosis become weak and listless, their droppings show all the signs of acute diarrhœa, and they die suddenly. The parasite has a most complicated reproductive phase within the grouse, and is then evacuated to be picked up once more with food or water. So far as grouse are concerned it is a disease confined mainly to young birds. Birds aged six weeks or more seem to be able to throw it off. But for young grouse it is a deadly disease. Poultry farmers and pheasant rearers can do a good deal to cope with an outbreak, the gamekeeper on a moor can do nothing, for he cannot get at the affected birds. Indeed he cannot know if the young birds on his moor are affected or not. He may sometimes guess from the appearance of droppings : he can know only after it is all over, when he finds his coveys small or non-existent. Even when chicks die on his moor in large numbers he will in all probability be quite ignorant of the fact. A dead grouse chick is not easily seen in heather.

Strongylosis, which is grouse disease proper, is a very different matter. No keeper can remain in ignorance of an outbreak on his moor. The evidence is only too plain. There are dead and dying birds all over the place. In a severe outbreak a moor may be emptied of its stock.

Strongylosis is a disease caused by a parasitic threadworm, *Trichostrongylus pergracilis*. This is a narrow hair-like worm, between $\frac{1}{3}$ and $\frac{3}{5}$ of an inch long, and dirty white in colour. And it is present, almost without exception, in the caecum of every grouse. There may be only a dozen or so, or a score : but there may be as many as 10,000 in one bird. Now when the caeca become so congested they are unable to perform their proper function, and the grouse is unable to receive proper nourishment through them. (What actually happens is that the longitudinal ridges of the caecum—there are eight or nine of them—become greatly thickened, because the amount of blood held by them is excessive, and the lining becomes inflamed.) The bird loses in weight and condition, and in many, if not most, cases it dies. There is very little difficulty about identifying a diseased bird, for the loss of condition is obvious, and often the bird is unable to fly. Death from strongylosis is by no means one hundred per cent, but even in those birds which recover the breeding capacity is usually severely impaired.

Now, this is the life-story of the strongyle worm. Its larvæ hatch in the droppings of the grouse, climb to the green tip of a young shoot of heather; a grouse nips off the shoot and swallows the strongyle, which passes into the caecum. Here it grows to the adult stage, when it immediately pairs and the female lays her eggs in the caecum. The eggs pass out in the bird's droppings, the larvæ hatch out, climb to the tips of the heather, and so on. At certain times of the year this reproductive process in the strongyle is extraordinarily rapid. Here is a time-table given in *The Grouse in Health and Disease*:

April 1. Egg in morula stage passes out of Grouse in soft droppings.
,, 2. Larva hatches out and lives in droppings of Grouse or in moist earth.
,, 5. First moult or ecdysis.
,, 8. Metamorphosis, larva now in actively migrating form.
,, 9. (or after) Larva ascends to tips of heather; if there is no mist, rain or dew ascent will be postponed.
,, 10. (or after) Encystment or drying: this represents the first stage of the second moult—and indefinite interval may intervene here.
,, 10. Larva swallowed by Grouse, and completes second moult.
,, 11. Reaches caecum of Grouse.
,, 13. Completes raw hypothetical third and fourth moult, thereafter becomes adult and sexually productive.
,, 14. Lays eggs in caecum.
,, 15. Eggs pass out of caecum.

It will be seen that moisture is absolutely essential to the development of the strongyle. There are not many days in the spring when moisture is absent from the moors. Strongylosis finds the most suitable conditions for its development in just those months in which the grouse are least able to resist it. Deaths from strongylosis reach their peak in May, but this mortality is, of course, the result of infection that begins earlier in the year.

Since every grouse is infected with strongylosis one might expect every year to be a grouse disease year. There is some grouse disease every year, but outbreaks on a large scale are periodic. It is evident that since all grouse carry the disease, the greater the number of grouse on a moor the greater the infection, and since in the vital months good feeding is certain to be restricted to certain areas of the moor—i.e. the heather will not be of uniform quality all over the moor—the greater the concentration of infection. Grouse disease in epidemic form only occurs when the moor is carrying too large a stock of birds.

It is not in any way an unnatural phenomenon. If grouse increase beyond what the moor will sustain, the food supply falls off, the chance of infection increases, and grouse die in large quantities. There will follow a year or two of small populations, and then the moor will regain its normal population. Only when that population again exceeds the normal will there be another outbreak. That, in simple language, is what happens, and that is all there is to it. There is nothing new about grouse disease. Woodruffe Peacock says that it was known "as a slight and local trouble" in 1797. MacDonald, in his *Grouse Disease*, says: "It is now (1883) eighty years since the alarm of 'Grouse Disease' was sounded in this country." Howard Saunders, writing in *The Zoologist* in 1887, records that there was a severe outbreak in the Reay country of Sutherland in 1815. Speedy, in his *Sport in the Highlands and Lowlands of Scotland*, says: "The first time 'Grouse Disease' attracted special attention was in 1838. Prior to that date it was not unknown in Scotland; but it had not assumed the proportions of a malignant epidemic. Even in 1838 and for several years afterwards, it was much milder in its results than it has latterly become. In 1867 it seems to have developed a most destructive form, attracting very general attention. Prior to that it was comparatively local, decimating the birds in certain districts, and leaving other districts untouched." In the MS. records of Bolton Abbey it is first mentioned as a "fatal disorder" in 1882.

But though grouse disease has been recorded for 150 years, it has in its *epizootic* (epizootic is the word used to indicate disease temporarily prevalent among animals—the animal equivalent of epidemic) form been known only since the grouse has become an important item in the economic management of estates in England and Scotland.

The history of grouse-shooting is a short one. A hundred years ago there was no regular grouse-shooting season. Grouse were shot, of course—generally over dogs, though there was some driving on Horsley Moor as early as 1803—but grouse shooting as a sport that attracted high rentals did not commence till the advent of the breech-loader and the railway. Lang gave the shooting world the breech-loader in 1853, and at that date grouse shooting may properly be said to commence. And from that date sheep farming declined. Owners found tenants who could afford much more to shoot grouse than farmers could pay to graze sheep. Gamekeepers came to the moors and the shepherds could no longer do as they desired. The shepherds used to burn the heather over large stretches of hillside : the men who came to shoot grouse found that the heather carried the grouse, and so they stopped the shepherds burning it. To begin with that did not matter because there was lots of young heather where the hills had been burned. But soon it did matter. There was no food for the sheep except on those moors where the farmers had acquired the shooting as well as the grazing rights, and there was no food for the grouse where there was no food for the sheep. On those moors where there was no burning the grouse began to die off—at first it was thought that this was due to disease, but it was due primarily to lack of food—and in 1872 and 1873 disaster swept the moors. But on the moors that carried sheep and were burnt regularly the grouse did not die. So the shooters commenced burning the heather. That was the first lesson in moor managment.

But owners soon discovered that the rich men who came from the south wanted to do much more than just shoot grouse : they wanted to shoot lots and lots of grouse, grouse in hundreds. The more grouse on the moor, the higher the rent obtained. And so moors were managed so as to produce the greatest possible number of birds. Very careful protection was afforded them ; improved conditions of food were brought about by heather-burning and drainage ; and, so far as possible, all birds and beasts that might seriously endanger their lives were destroyed. By these artificial means the moors were much more heavily stocked with grouse than was the case under natural conditions. And to these artificial means the incidence of grouse disease in its epizootic form is often attributed. That is invariably denied by shooting men. The Grouse Disease Committee uphold the shooting men. They may be right, of course, but I am not at all sure that they are. One thing at least is certain : Grouse disease as an epizootic has occurred frequently only after the imposition of these artificial conditions on the moors, and it has not lessened since the Grouse Disease Committee published its findings.

The main argument against artificial care is based on the supposition that there is a balance in nature. It is said that if all, or almost all, the birds and beasts that prey upon the grouse were not destroyed the moors would be improved. As at present the whole aim of every moor-owner is to upset the balance in favour of the grouse it is rather an academic argument, and one which I do not propose to go into fully here. But it is not one that can be discussed lightly. The Committee, while admitting that there was among gamekeepers too great a tendency to destroy indiscriminately, dismissed the argument somewhat abruptly and poured scorn on the idea that, generally speaking, the predator kills off the weak birds and so helps to maintain a healthy stock. The argument they produced in support of their rebuttal of this theory—namely, the peregrine falcon striking at the centre bird of a covey, and the robber of a hen roost—is unconvincing in the extreme. The fox may take, and generally does take, the fattest bird in the hen roost, but the fox on the moors (and foxes and carrion crows are the two most deadly enemies of the grouse) is dealing with a wild and wary bird, and he certainly does not concentrate on the fattest and healthiest bird. He takes what he can get, and it is rarely the strongest bird. The peregrine falcon undoubtedly strikes at the centre of a covey. But which bird flies at the centre. I do not know, but in my experience it is generally the cock that leads the covey in August, and in winter the strongest and fastest bird probably flies first. Nor do peregrines invariably strike at coveys.

I think it is beyond dispute that the common idea is that if you have " vermin " on the ground, whether animal predators such as foxes, stoats, and weasels, or feathered predators such as hawks and eagles, you will have no game. Hence you kill the predators. It is a foolish idea. The Island of Hoy provides a most excellent example to the contrary. On this island there are no gamekeepers, and no ground predators—no foxes, stoats, or weasels. But there is an abundance of predatory birds : great skuas, peregrines, hen-harriers, greater and lesser black-backed gulls in large numbers, plenty of hooded crows, several pairs of ravens, some of the lesser hawks, and every now and again a visiting eagle. Yet there is a good stock of grouse, resident and breeding. This stock varies a little with the dryness or wetness of the spring and early summer. It does not vary with the stock of predatory birds. Nor have I ever heard of grouse disease as an epizootic on Hoy, and I can vouch for the vigour, strength, wariness and general well-being of the grouse.

In my own view the gamekeeper whose chief concern is to kill all the " vermin " on his ground does his master no good service. But it must not be taken that I am against the destruction of " vermin " altogether. Obviously under artificial conditions some destruction is inevitable and essential. When it is taken too far it does much more harm than good, for, combined with other causes, it leads inevitably to disaster. And it should be remembered that a single outbreak of disease will carry off in one month many more birds than a host of predators would account for in a year, with a much greater financial loss to the owner. And the effects of a bad outbreak are felt over more than one season, while the effect of the predator is purely temporary.

It is quite clear that moor management has led to a vast increase of stock, more than the ground can carry under natural conditions. It is also quite clear that artificial conditions have now advanced too far to warrant any return to the natural, even were such a course economically advisable, which it is not. The modern moor manager is not, therefore, concerned with any such theories as the " balance of nature " or with such basic laws as those of natural selection and the survival of the fittest. He is concerned with making the best of the moor, as he knows it, to suit his own special requirements. And his special requirement is the largest possible stock of grouse with, if he can manage it, no outbreak of disease. Now, we know that when the ground is carrying a greater stock than it should carry disease breaks out. Overcrowding means both insufficient food and the spreading of disease. The birds must, therefore, be kept down by shooting to a proportion the moor can sustain. In other words, the stock must never exceed the available food supply by any great number. That is the ideal. That it is extremely hard to attain is shown by the frequency with which grouse disease breaks out in its epizootic form.

Moor managers endeavour to increase the food supply by regular burning of the heather. This necessitates the employment of considerable additional labour and is very rarely, if ever, done on a sufficiently large scale. And here the manager comes up against another enemy —the heather beetle, which annually attacks and destroys a considerable acreage of the all-important food supply. At the outbreak of war an enquiry, instigated by the British Field Sports Society, was in progress. The Committee has not published its final report, and so far at any rate the heather beetle has defied all attempts at its control. Happily, like all insect plagues, it is subject to great variation in numbers. Probably the best preventive would be extensive drainage coupled with burning on a short rotation. But what effect the former would have on the moor in other directions is problematical. The moor manager has another enemy in the sheep tick. The sheep tick has been, and is, the subject of investigation by more than one scientific body. It can be a serious menace to a grouse moor, indeed a tick-infested moor will not let. Older birds are not killed by ticks very often. though they are undoubtedly weakened, but young birds, say up to six weeks old, are killed. The tick is most active in spring and early summer, the dangerous season for grouse, and as many as 140 have been taken from the head and neck of a single grouse.

The sheep tick is not confined solely to sheep ; it is carried also by hares, rabbits and red deer. I have heard it suggested, quite seriously, by a moor-owner that the only way to get rid of tick is to exterminate all the mammalian inhabitants of the moor. You would have to do more than that: you would have to exterminate the mammalian inhabitants of a good many moors, and you would have to prohibit the movement of possible hosts into the cleared area. You could do that with the sheep, and you could do it (with a good deal of difficulty) with the deer : you could not do it with either hares or rabbits. Greatly reducing the numbers of these animals would not be sufficient—a reduction in the number of hosts does not necessarily mean a reduction in the number of ticks—you would have to exterminate. Even if this were possible, which, thank heaven, it is not, no amount of tick-free grouse would repay for the loss. Grouse are a great economic asset to Scotland, but even in those areas they are not the be-all and end-all of life. It has also been said on many occasions that grouse and sheep do not go together, that you must have one or the other. I do not myself agree with that view at all. I do not believe that grouse and sheep interests are necessarily conflicting. I do believe that a well-managed grouse moor will support, and benefit from, a very fair head of sheep. Properly managed they do no damage to the heather, and their droppings, which are fertile breeding places for insects, are quite definitely of great value. Grouse and sheep, incidentally, regard each other in the friendliest light, and sheep-walks provide natural runs for grouse-chicks.

The great trouble remains grouse disease, and the root of that trouble lies in the fact that the moors are continually forced to carry stocks far in excess of their capabilities. The figures speak for themselves. The record bag of grouse was obtained on 12th August, 1915, when on the Littledale and Abbeystead beat in Lancashire eight guns shot 2,929 grouse. On the following day the same guns on another beat shot 1,763 birds, and on the next day, with an additional gun, 1,279 birds. That is a total of 5,971 grouse in three consecutive days. The bag for the season was 17,078 grouse, and these were obtained from an area of about 17,000 acres. As grouse shooting it was magnificent, I have no doubt. As a record it is most impressive. But no one with any real knowledge of the grouse and its requirements can pretend for a moment that 17,000 acres can support more than 17,000

Plate VII

RED-LEGGED PARTRIDGE by nest. Suffolk, 1936. ERIC HOSKING

ERIC HOSKING

COMMON PARTRIDGE. Cock helping hen dry newly-hatched young. Suffolk, 1935

Plate VIII

GREY LAG GEESE. DAVID HAIG-THOMAS

GREY LAG GOOSE incubating eggs. North Uist, 1937. A. R. THOMPSON

birds (all the birds on the moor were not shot) in full health. I will not give further records—you will find them all in Sir Hugh Gladstone's magnificent *Record Bags and Shooting Records*—but it is worth pointing out that Broomhead Moor in Yorkshire has produced 2,843 grouse in one day (August 27th, 1913), and on another (August 30th, 1893) 2,648 birds. Broomhead is only about 4,000 acres, but it has in one season produced 5,000 grouse !

Economic conditions in the future will, I imagine, prevent any wholesale return to the old ways. I cannot but believe that this will be all to the good in the long run for the grouse, for the grouse shooter and for the moor-owner.

THE PTARMIGAN

The Scottish Ptarmigan (*Lagopus mutus millaisi* (Hartert.))

THE PTARMINGAN can truly be said to span the top of the world. From northern Scotland it is found right round the world, in Europe, in Asia, in America, and outside this northern range it is found only in the Alps and the Pyrenees, in the high mountains of central Asia, and in Hondo, the main island of Japan. It is essentially a bird of the high places, the snows and the cold winds. It is resident in Spitsbergen, within four hundred miles of the North Pole.

There are many local races of the ptarmigan, of which our bird is one. It is confined to Scotland, and of recent years its distribution here has been considerably restricted. It used to occur in Galloway, Dumfries, Peebles, Kirkcudbright, Wigtownshire, the Orkneys, Arran, Lewis and Harris, but is now extinct in all these districts. There are still a few in Jura, Islay and Mull, and rather more in Skye. To-day on the mainland it is found on all the high mountains from Ben Lomond northwards. Millais was of the opinion that it was gradually disappearing from western Sutherland and Caithness, but it has not disappeared from those districts, and I do not think there has been any diminution in numbers recently either there or elsewhere. In Scotland it is very definitely a bird of the high tops, occurring generally at heights of 2,500 feet and upwards, though locally it may be found at 2,000 feet, and in Islay even lower than that. As the red grouse is a bird of the heather, so is the ptarmigan a bird of the barren ground and broken rocks.

The ptarmigan may always be distinguished by the white wings and white underparts of the body. In winter, of course, it is quite unmistakable because it then adopts a pure white plumage. (As a matter of fact, the tail remains black tipped with white, but as it is practically concealed by the white upper tail-coverts this is not noticeable.) But, except for the winter plumage, it would be difficult to say what a typical ptarmigan looks like. The red grouse is confusing enough, and it has only two seasonal changes of plumage. The ptarmigan has three such changes and, with the exception of its winter coat, is no more punctual in its moults than is the red grouse. Indeed, except for the period when it is dressed in white, it would not be untrue to say that the ptarmigan, like the red grouse, is always changing its plumage.

Broadly speaking—and I would stress that there is no punctuality about these changes and that plumage variation is enormous rather than considerable—the seasonal changes are something like this :

April to July (the breeding season). The *male* is a dark bird. The upper parts and the flanks are black, finely mottled and barred with reddish-grey on the back, the rump and the upper tail-coverts. The chin and the throat are white. The breast is brown, generally a rather reddish-brown. The rest of the underparts are white. The tail black, tipped with white. And above the eye is a large vermilion wattle. The *female* is a buffish bird. The upper parts are black spotted and barred with buff and white. The flanks are a rich golden yellow coarsely barred with black. The wings are white. The wattle above the eye is much smaller than in the male. In July the light edges of the feathers of the upper parts become worn and faded, giving the bird a much darker appearance than in May.

August to October (the autumn dress). The *male* is a grey bird. The upper parts and the flanks are grey barred and vermiculated with black and white. (Sometimes some of the black feathers of the breeding plumage linger on the scapulars and succeed in giving the bird a rather piebald appearance.) The throat and the sides of the head are more or less white, barred with black. The wings and the whole of the breast and underparts are white. The *female* is like the male, but sandy-grey rather than grey.

November to March (the winter dress). The *male* is a pure white bird, save for a black stripe behind the eye, black lores, and the black tail feathers, which to all intents and purposes are concealed by the upper tail-coverts. The *female* is also a pure white bird, but can always be distinguished from the male (if not in the field at least in the hand) because she has no black on the head.

These changes in plumage are each acquired by a complete moult. Sometimes between early June and the end of September (and it may be at any time between those extreme dates) the feathers of the legs in both male and female are moulted and renewed, and the claws (as in the red grouse) are also shed. Nestling ptarmigan are very like nestling red grouse except that the crown of the head is rather darker.

The ptarmigan is, like the red grouse, monogamous, and, like the red grouse, it joins with others into packs in the autumn. This movement begins later than in the grouse, however, rarely commencing much before the end of November, and I have never heard of any tendency to pack by sexes. But packs, never large in number, may sometimes be observed throughout the summer. These are formed of unmated males (I do not *think*—I am not sure—that the ptarmigan breeds in its first year like the red grouse), and sometimes towards the end of the summer may be joined by a few mated males. Normally, however, family parties stick together until well into November. You can always pick out the cock in these family parties at a glance. Ptarmigan walk like grouse, with rather round backs and depressed tails, and the females walk with a decided roll. But the male is always more upright, and in place of the roll he struts. In a family party this is most noticeable. In the winter packs all the birds walk with a roll, and at a glance it is impossible to distinguish the sexes.

I have noticed some sexual activity in the males in autumn, the false sexual activity common to the grouse family. A male, perched upon a rock (the males are very fond of perching on outstanding rocks), will challenge, with jerky bows and a sound that is very like the snore of a fat man who has had too much to drink, another male perched upon another rock, but I have not observed any actual sparring and have not myself seen any sexual chases in the autumn. Once I watched in autumn a male displaying in a very half-hearted manner to a female, who was in company with another male and four young birds. The whole family party ignored the demonstration. I have not personally noticed any proper sexual activity nor any tendency to take up a territory before March, but it may well begin earlier than that. We know very little about the courtship of the ptarmigan. The bird lives in difficult, and often inaccessible, country and courtship and display occurs early in the day, beginning at dawn, or perhaps just before dawn, and very rarely continuing after 10 a.m. To watch it properly means spending a night, many nights, out on the mountain at heights in excess of 2,000 feet in weather that no one, not even the most rabid devotee of the Highlands, could call pleasant. It has been done, of course—I have done it myself for the matter of one occasion—but it has not been done often enough to secure a full and

PLATE 5

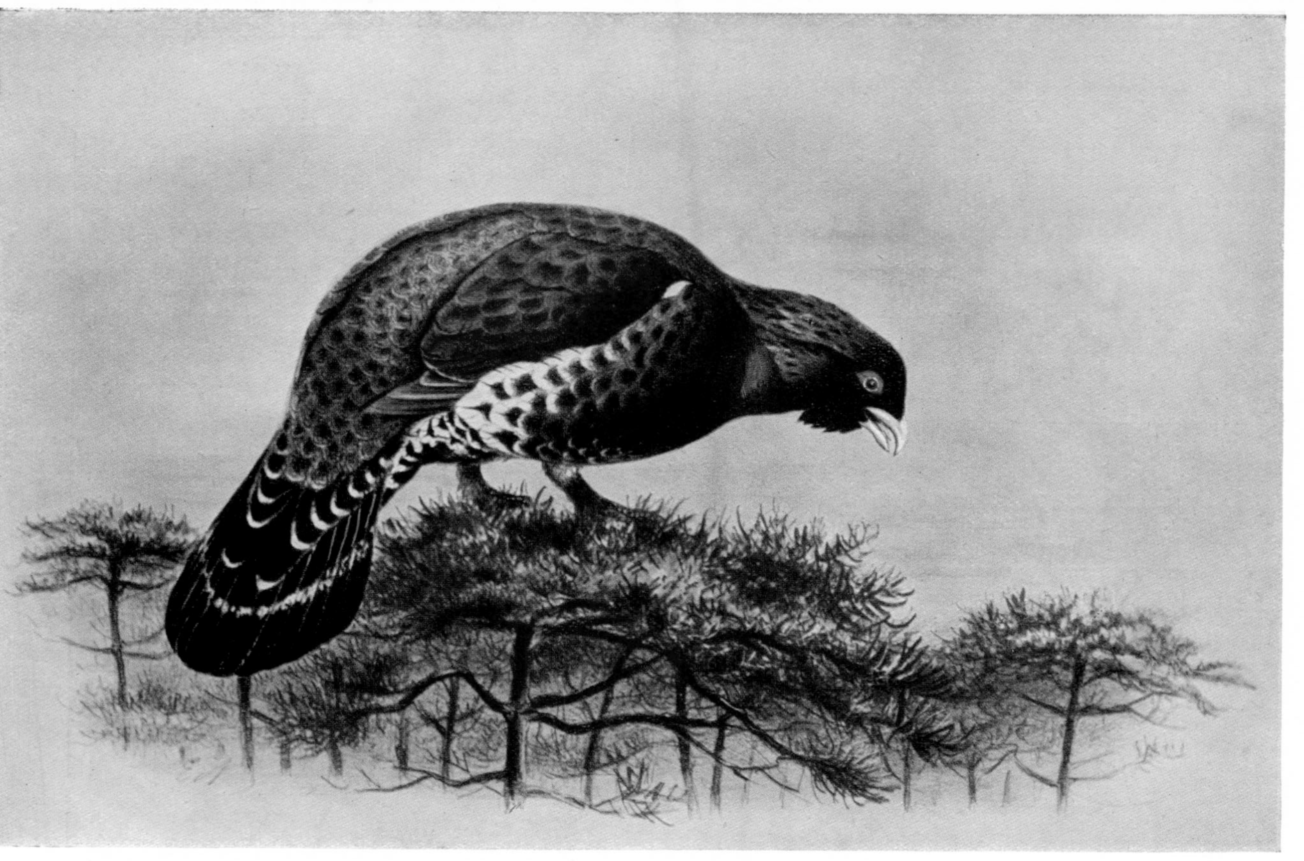

CAPERCAILLIE

Coloured lithograph by Edward Neale

From Edward T. Booth's ROUGH NOTES ON BIRDS 1881-1887

PLATE 6

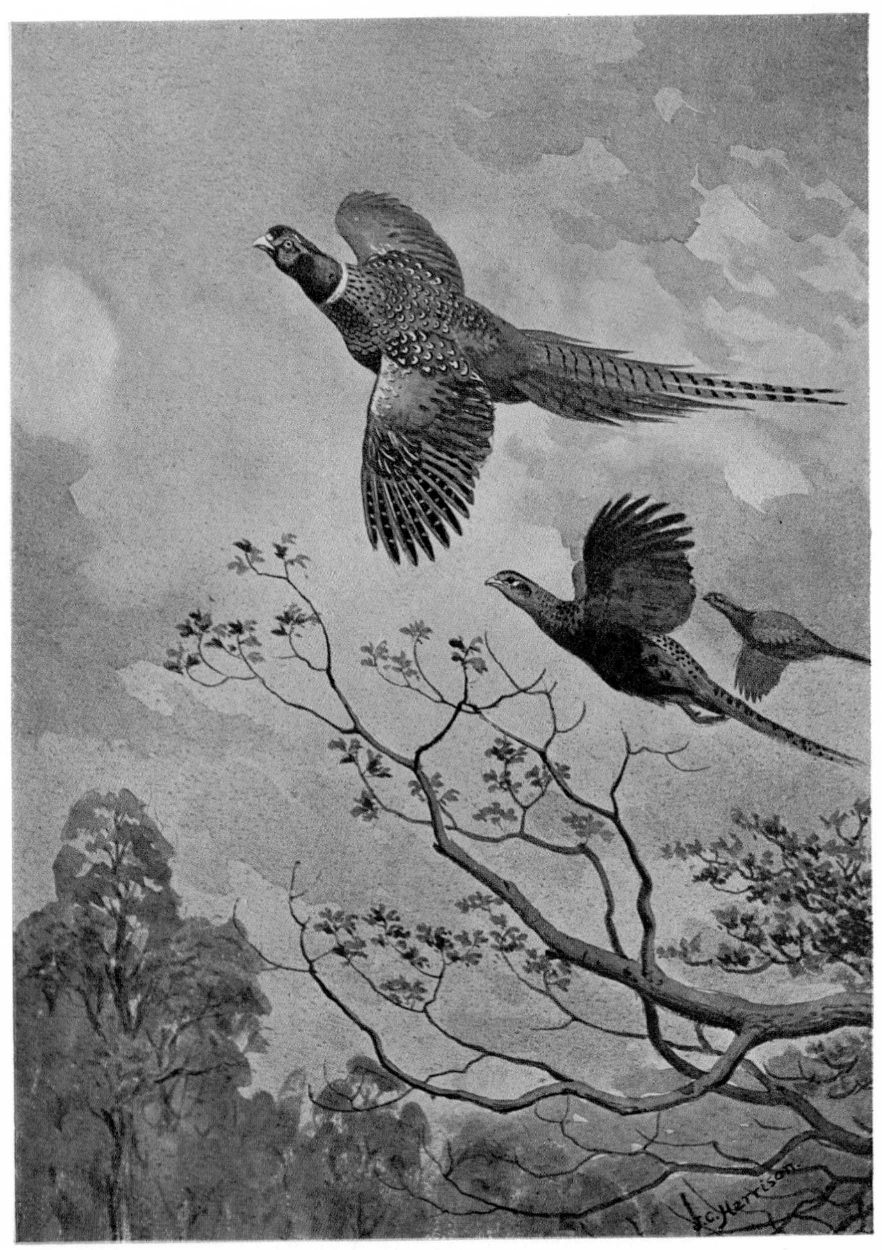

PHEASANTS

Water colour by J. C. Harrison

detailed account of the courtship and display. So you will find the bird books, when they do not ignore the subject altogether, evasive on the point: nor do I pretend that I can add anything to such knowledge as we possess. In general, courtship and display follow the same lines as in the red grouse (red grouse and ptarmigan occasionally interbreed), but it is, I think, a rather more belligerent affair so far as the cocks are concerned. Actual fighting is rare among red grouse—sparring and threat is sufficient—but among ptarmigan it occurs, I believe, fairly frequently, if not regularly. In display the male behaves in much the same manner as the cock red grouse, springing perpendicularly into the air—and descending on spread wings, uttering a cry on alighting that the *Handbook* translates as *er-ook-oora*. It sounds nothing like that to me. Sexual chases are conducted at what amounts to ground level, the male following the female very closely and the pair twisting and turning over the rocky surface at remarkable speed. On the ground the male chases the female, spreading and erecting his tail and drooping his wings. The female runs away from him, but stops every now and again to feed. This rather nonplusses the male, but in a moment or two he springs into the air perpendicularly and the business starts all over again. I have not observed coition in the ptarmigan.

The nest (as a rule it is very rarely found below 2,000 feet, and most usually between 3,000 and 4,000 feet) is just a hollow scraped by the hen in stony ground or among crowberry plants. Generally it is unlined, but occasionally a few bits of grass, some lichen or a feather or two may be put in. The eggs, usually five to nine in number, but sometimes as few as three or as many as twelve, are on the average a little smaller than those of the red grouse, but are so like the latter that they can only be distinguished by the expert. Incubation, which is undertaken by the female alone, varies between three weeks and a month. The cock is a good mate and watches over his hen closely during the incubation period. He gives warning of the approach of danger, circling round the intruder and crying, and then flying to his look-out post and calling loudly, and when the hen comes off to feed he displays to her as vigorously as he did during their courtship. You might think that his circling and crying at the approach of danger would give away the position of the nest. It does no more than tell you that there is a nest in the vicinity. The hen ptarmigan harmonises perfectly with her surroundings and sits very closely. Nests are next door to impossible to find and are as a rule come across only by accident. There are many stories of the tameness of the ptarmigan on the nest (tameness is the wrong word : the ptarmigan is not in the least tame : she sits very closely, and will leave only on the greatest provocation at the last possible moment : bravery would be a better word), and I have myself stroked a ptarmigan on her nest. Should she be put up, the cock will immediately fly down to her, and the two will remain in the neighbourhood, trying their hardest to attract the attention of the intruder.

The young, even for grouse, are extraordinarily precocious. They leave the nest as soon as the last egg is hatched, and can move very quickly at once. Nethersole-Thompson says they can fly at ten days old. Millais was of the opinion that they could fly within a few hours of birth. It depends, I suppose, on what you mean by flight. They can certainly get off the ground and cover a good many yards long before they are ten days old. Cock and hen stay close to the young, and off and on during the day the hen will brood them for short periods. The chicks feed a good deal off insects, which they catch themselves, but they also take young grass shoots and blaeberry leaves. The parents teach the young to feed and to begin with pull and break up the vegetable matter for them. Both cock and hen are very solicitous for their young. Both will go through "injury-feigning" tactics to draw off danger. Nethersole-Thompson has seen the hen jump into the air to draw off a dog, and I have seen a cock run right up to a dog in an attempt to distract attention from the young. The young make rather a plaintive whistle when lost or in distress. This whistle is easy to imitate, and by use of it a hen ptarmigan (but I have never heard of its being effective on a cock) can be drawn right up to one's feet. Seton Gordon has done so on many occasions, and I have brought a hen ptarmigan up to within a few feet of me by doing so.

Like all game birds, ptarmigan are very fond of dust-bathing, and of basking in the sun. Their flight is similar to that of the red grouse, but is, I think, faster, and they can (even when quite young, about the size of thrushes) swing up and down precipices without apparent effort. The food, when the bird is adult, is almost entirely made up of vegetable matter, although insects are not ignored, and is taken in the early morning and in the evening during the hour before dusk. There may be an odd snack or two taken during the daytime, but there is no feeding in the proper sense of the word. Large quantities of quartz grit are taken. In the winter they will burrow into the snow for food, and it is only the most severe weather that will drive them to the lowlands. (They do come off the highest tops in the winter, but it is rare, even in what we would call a severe winter, to find them below 2,000 feet. Though there may be, and probably is, some movement from hill to hill there is no real migration, the only seasonal movement being this vertical change of residence.) I do not know if there has ever been any argument as to whether ptarmigan drink or not. The *Handbook* ignores the point, and this might be taken to imply that they do not. It may be of interest, therefore, to mention that I have seen them drink. This was early on a May morning in 1922, and on the plateau running towards Ben Muich Dhui. There are several large flat boulders here with round hollows worn in them. Some of these hollows are quite deep, and they all, deep or shallow, hold rainwater. It was at one of them that I watched a cock and a hen drink, and a little later another or the same hen. From the droppings on this and several other boulders, both on this plateau and elsewhere, I should imagine that they are frequently resorted to by ptarmigan for purposes of refreshment.

Normally eggs are laid towards the end of May, exceptionally it may be earlier, but eggs may be found late in July. These are not a second brood — the ptarmigan is single-brooded — but if the May clutch is unfortunate a second may be laid either in June or July. Nesting in May at such altitudes is fraught with many dangers. Many clutches and many broods of young must be destroyed by late snowstorms or inclement weather of one sort and another. Then a heavy toll of the eggs is taken by crows and gulls (the hoodie often takes the egg away to water before it eats it), and the raven is not averse to a meal of egg, though it does not search for them in the painstaking manner of the crow. Stoats will also take both young and eggs, and the golden eagle and the peregrine prey on the birds, but ignore the eggs. For protection against eagle and hawk the ptarmigan relies entirely upon its wonderful protective plumage, which harmonises exactly with the surrounding country both in summer and winter. So long as it stays still it is safe. It may escape by flight, but this is a much more hazardous business. It is often said that the eagle can see the ptarmigan on the ground, protective plumage notwithstanding. But this is not so. I have often watched the golden eagle soaring over a hillside containing ptarmigan. After a while he comes diving down and immediately ptarmigan will spring up and try to escape by flight, and one of them will be struck down. I am sure that the dive is not made at a bird that has been seen, but solely to put the birds up.

Ptarmigan have a great fear of the eagle and seem unable, with few exceptions, to stay still and hidden. The golden eagle, however, does not, despite the fact that it takes many ptarmigan in a year, greatly reduce the numbers on its territory. I know one ptarmigan hill that is, and has been for more than twenty years, within the territory of a pair of golden eagles. The number of ptarmigan on that hill has certainly not lessened in that period, though over the twenty years there has certainly been some fluctuation in numbers due to the exigencies of the climate. The peregrine is not a severe enemy. Undoubtedly it takes a few each year, but my experience of mountain peregrines is that they hunt the valleys in preference to the mountains for food.

As a game bird the ptarmigan sets no problems. The ground they occupy is, with few exceptions, the highest ground in deer forests. This means that early in the season it is occupied more often than not by bands of stags that it is essential to leave undisturbed, and later when the bands break up the stalking season is in full swing and it is not possible to wander about the hills letting off a gun at the birds. Further than that, the pursuit of ptarmigan entails activity of a distinctly athletic nature—the sportsman would have to climb rocks and cross much treacherous ground with his gun at the ready—and it has not many devotees. Those that go to the high ground for their sport prefer deer-stalking. Ptarmigan have been driven, and give, I understand, excellent sport, but the bags are never big. The record bag is 122, achieved on August 25th, 1866, by a single gun " walking up " ; the record bag for driven birds is 120, to several guns, but the more usual figures achieved are well under forty. Twenty brace is a good bag indeed.

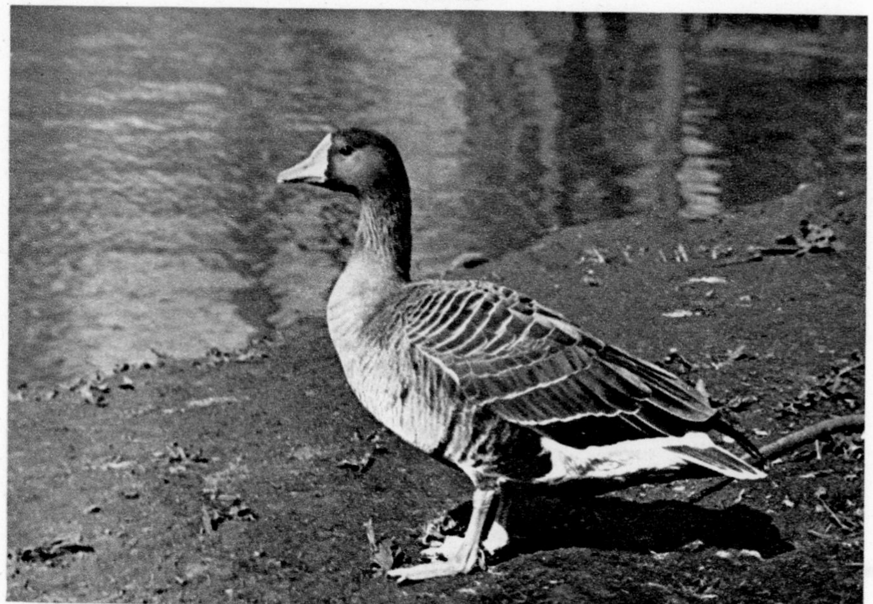

WHITE-FRONTED GOOSE, captive. Northampton. April 1937. OLIVER G. PIKE

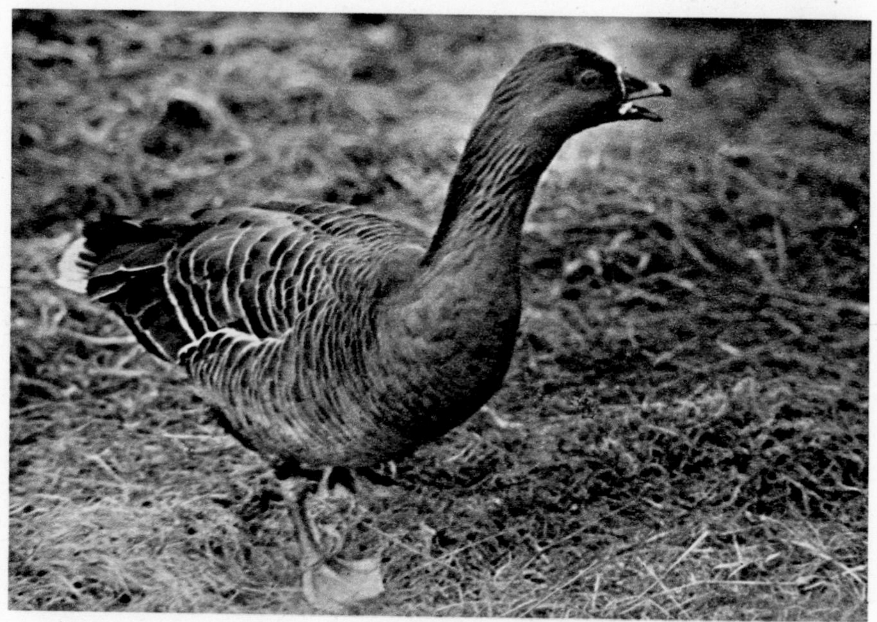

PINK-FOOTED GOOSE. Whipsnade Zoo. February 1937. OLIVER G. PIKE

Plate X

GREATER SNOW GOOSE. Greenland. 1938. DAVID HAIG-THOMAS

SNOW GOOSE. Greenland. 1938. DAVID HAIG-THOMAS

THE BLACK GROUSE

The British Black Grouse (*Lyrurus tetrix britannicus* (Witherby and Lönnberg))

LIKE the Scottish ptarmigan our black grouse is an island form of a species that, in suitable localities, is found throughout Europe (south of 70° N.) and northern Siberia. Closely allied races are found in south-eastern Russia, southern Siberia, Mongolia and Western Manchuria.

Our bird is confined to Great Britain, and has been steadily decreasing in numbers for many years. It is now extinct in Wiltshire, Dorset, Hampshire, Kent, Surrey, Sussex, Berkshire, Buckinghamshire, Norfolk, Suffolk, Leicestershire, Nottinghamshire, Pembroke, Orkney, the Outer Hebrides, and Shetland. In Cornwall it is almost extinct, and it is very scarce indeed in south Devon. In many parts of Wales it has disappeared of recent years, but is still to be found in some numbers locally, particularly in Merionethshire and Montgomeryshire. In north Devon and Somerset it is still fairly plentiful, and a few remain in Herefordshire. In the north midland counties of England it is still plentiful locally (but the localities become fewer year by year), and it occurs in some numbers in the northern and border counties. In Scotland it is generally distributed on the mainland, but there, too, there has been a steady decrease in numbers (with a temporary recovery in 1925 and 1926), and it is still to be found on some of the Inner Hebrides. All attempts to settle the birds in Ireland have failed. Attempts at re-introduction have been made in many places, but always unsuccessfully. Every now and then, however, birds do turn up in places where they have long been extinct. Twice recently I have seen a single blackcock in the New Forest—in 1939 in the Puck Pits district, and in 1941 in Red Rise—and I have been told of a greyhen that was seen on Thorney Ridge in 1935. I know of no attempt to re-introduce the bird to the New Forest in recent years (I am quite sure I should have heard of such an attempt within a day or so of its occurrence), and I can only suppose that these birds were wanderers from Devonshire.

Two reasons are popularly accepted as being the cause for any decrease or extinction in birds—excessive shooting and excessive egg-collecting. (The gunners blame the egg-collectors and the egg-collectors blame the gunners.) Both occupations, when carried to excess, undoubtedly play some part, but the chief reasons for decrease or extinction in any particular species are not quite so obvious. Drainage, the construction of roads, the building of houses, changes in farming practice, increase of human populations, these are the factors that weigh most heavily in the nice balance of a wild bird population. So far as the black grouse is concerned, shooting and egg-collecting can be discounted. The chief reasons for the steady decrease in numbers are, I am convinced, the spread of the human population and the building that has accompanied that spread. Blackgame are birds of the wild, and they require ample space. But they are not birds of the moorland or the woodland, but rather of the fringe between moorland and woodland. That fringe, so far as the south of England is concerned, has practically disappeared, and it is steadily disappearing elsewhere. They were once common around the Surrey heaths, but the Surrey heaths to-day are enclosed areas. They were once common in Woolmer Forest, but Woolmer Forest has little of Forest about it to-day. They were once common in the New Forest, but the New Forest to-day is evenly divided between the Forestry Commission and the tripper. Blackgame have not been able to support the change.

When you see a blackcock you can never be in any doubt about it. The bird, with its glossy black plumage, lyre-shaped tail, and white wing bar, is quite unmistakable. The greyhen is not quite so easy. It is easy enough to recognise when dead, for it has a distinctly forked tail (a feature possessed by no other British game bird), but though this is stressed as the distinguishing character in the books it is by no means always noticeable in the bird in the wild, as many a man has found to his embarrassment on August 12th. In the wild state it is safer for purposes of identification to ignore the forked tail—but be thankful if it is noticeable—and to concentrate on size, colour and the broad white wing bar. The greyhen is a brown bird barred with black, a larger and less red bird than the red grouse, a smaller and less boldly barred bird than the capercaillie, and it has a broad white wing-bar which the other two have not got.

In eclipse plumage the blackcock is not nearly so handsome a bird. The wonderful blueblack plumage becomes a rather dingy blackish-brown, the broad lyre-shaped tail becomes merely a tail, divided with two rounded ends that have a tendency to turn outwards, and the fine large red wattle above the eye degenerates into a red streak. Young blackgame are very much like the female, but smaller. The males begin to take on their winter plumage when they are only half-grown (about the beginning of August), and then they show patches of black and white. The tail, however, is only slightly curled, and even in the autumn these young birds have not the full glory of an old cock.

The flight is the typical flight of the game bird, a series of quick wing beats alternating with glides. It is a strong and rapid flight, capable of covering long distances, and generally blackgame fly low to the ground and for only a short way. This does not hold true, however, of blackgame put up by beaters on an open moor. Then you can generally tell them from red grouse, even at a distance, by the greater height from the ground that they have attained and by the fact that they sail much more than red grouse do. On the ground they walk, slowly and sedately, and with a distinctly nautical roll. They perch much more than do red grouse, and are, indeed, fond of perching in trees. But, though they will roost in trees, they prefer to do so on the ground.

As I have said, blackgame are not birds of the open moorland so much as of the fringes of moorland. They like rough, sparsely wooded ground, plentifully bestrewn with bushes, gorse or heather clumps, or the rushy boggy ground on the borders of plantations. But you will also find them on the high rocky ground above the moors, and I think the birds that live so are wilder and more unapproachable than those elsewhere. They are also less inclined to fly, preferring to run to cover. When they do get up, they do so, like the birds of the lower ground, silently. I have never yet heard either blackcock or greyhen utter a sound when put up.

The greyhen nests where she lives, but occasionally you may find a nest far out on the open moor, as occasionally you may find (I have never done so) a nest high up in a tree. Generally, however, the nest is just a hollow scraped in the ground by the hen, and unlined. It is usually sheltered by a clump of heather or grass, but I have found nests in most exposed situations. Six to ten eggs are usually laid, sometimes as early as the end of April, but more commonly from the middle of May onwards. They are very like those of the capercaillie but a good deal smaller. Only one brood is raised, and all the work of incubation and rearing is done by the hen unaided. Like all other game birds the young are very precocious, and can run about and take insects as soon as they are born, but they show, unlike the red grouse and the ptarmigan, a marked disinclination to fly. This disinclination is becoming more pronounced. At any rate I seem of recent years to have seen fewer young blackgame on the wing than I used to do. One seems to shoot more old birds than young even in late September. I remember when I was seventeen or so that young birds got up and flew well ; now they will run to your feet if given a chance.

Courtship in blackgame is a highly specialised business, and has received so much attention from naturalists that I do not propose to do more than give a brief outline here. The birds have special display grounds, which are called " leks ". Both sexes resort to these grounds and coition takes place at them. In my experience these " leks " are always on grassy ground, and never on heather. The area is divided up between the cocks, so that each cock has a piece of ground of his own, a " territory ". The size of the territory varies considerably, depending more upon the number of birds using the lek than upon the size and aggressiveness of individuals. Within his territory the cock fights, sings (I use the word in its ornithological sense), displays, courts and copulates. He does none of these things outside his territory, and, so far as feeding is concerned, the birds feed all over the lek, ignoring territorial boundaries. These territories are male mating-territories only. They have nothing to do with nesting or feeding.

There are several well-defined display attitudes, but in all of them the tail, the blackcock's most distinctive feature, is fully spread, the wings are a little drooped and the red wattle above the eye is distended. Lack describes the appearance of the tail when seen from the front as " a black bow with the tips of the white coverts showing over the top at the centre ". At the lek the blackcock is more vocal than at any other time. First of all there is the note, which has been described as crowing (this is not always confined to the lek, though, for I have heard blackcock crow when perched in trees as early as the last day of January) and which is usually accompanied by certain formalised positions. The head and the neck are held upright and the wings are dropped, and as the bird calls it jumps into the air (sometimes it remains stationary, but I have seen this only rarely) a few inches off the ground, or a few feet with fluttering wings. This crowing seems to be a social and communal performance, directed not against other males but to telling the females that the lek is occupied and inviting them to come along. Quite a different sound is uttered by the cocks when displaying against each other. This is called "rookooing" (I think Mr. Lack invented the term) and is the blackcock's song. It is not altogether unlike the sound made by a woodpigeon, but is much more continuous. It is not unmusical and is by no means loud, though, on a still day, it will carry over long distances. It is a purely aggressive sound, directed against other males, and is made with the head and neck thrust forwards, and the neck considerably swollen. You often read of the fierce fighting of blackcocks at the lek. Fierce fighting does occur occasionally, and occasionally a bird is killed; but, even more than among monogamous birds, fighting is formalised and contact between the opposing parties is very rarely made. When it is the birds jump breast to breast striking with beak, claws and wings, and one bird trying to get above the other; but generally fighting consists of quick running advances and equally quick withdrawals without contact, and not infrequently the combat will be broken off by one bird commencing to feed just as if nothing had happened at all.

Sexual display is quite different. When a female appears hostilities cease. The hens pass over the lek—pass through might be the more correct term—and the males court them as they do so. Sometimes a male will sink down before a female (in just the same manner as a ruff) with wings a little spread and touching the ground, and remain so for several seconds. I have seen this happen several times, but it is not usual. More usually the cock, with head stretched forward, parades about the female, using very short, very rapid steps, and looking very important. Sometimes he circles right round her, but generally he turns about so as to avoid passing behind her. As he passes in front of her he tilts his tail and body towards her (making play, I think, with the white feathers), but he does not attempt to stop her. The hen, also taking short quick steps, moves forward—and sometimes through the territories of several cocks—in a succession of little runs and pauses. The circling of the cock is the prelude to coition, which is initiated by the female crouching down, but the circling does not necessarily mean that coition will take place. Sometimes a cock will circle as many as four hens at once, and sometimes a cock will do so and then find that all the hens pass on to the territory of a neighbour. Courted hens will fight each other—and these fights are not formalised—and neighbouring cocks will often interfere with coition.

The cocks start coming to the lek about the middle of March and display there regularly day after day, though the hens do not as a rule start visiting the leks until well into April. The cocks will continue to use the leks for some time after the hens have ceased visiting ; and in the autumn there is a recurrence of display, when the mature males (October is the month) come again to the leks and hold there a well-developed tournament with crowing and rookooing, but with no sexual behaviour. Normally, display at the leks is limited to two or three hours after dawn and an hour or so in the evening, but some leks seem to be occupied throughout the day in April.

Blackgame are commonly described as polygamous. I do not know what the evidence in support of this description is, and I have none to support it myself. It is generally said that the cocks fight on the leks for the females, and that each one as he collects a harem leaves with it for his own ground. The impression given is that the hens collect at the lek, watch the cocks fighting and choose the victor as husband. And pictures of blackgame usually portray one cock and four or five hens. Lack certainly does not support this view, and nothing in my experience (and I have watched many leks) supports it. I have never seen the hens gathered at a lek. The greatest number of hens I have seen at a lek at the same time has been four, and they did not all mate with the same bird. I have never seen the cocks fight while a hen has been on the lek (though I have seen one cock interfere with the copulation of another), and I have never away from the lek seen a cock with a harem. Nothing that happens at the lek, and nothing in the life of blackgame away from the lek supports the view that they are polygamous. They are promiscuous. The hens come to the lek to acquire mates. What influences their choice we do not know, but it is certainly not the fighting and so forth among the cocks, nor is it by any means the case that the most magnificent cock at the lek is the most sought after by the hens. However, the display does apparently influence them. Mating accomplished the hen departs to lay her eggs and rear her brood alone. The cock has nothing more to do with her. His only duty is accomplished on the lek. Furthermore, it has been my experience that even out of the breeding season cocks and hens do not mix. (The fact that cocks and hens may come over the guns together in the autumn does not necessarily mean that they pack together.) I understand that mixed packs do occur, but I have not yet come across one. The young stay with the hen until towards autumn. By the middle of August the young cocks, already beginning to acquire adult plumage, tend to separate and form into packs of their own. By autumn the birds are in packs, generally ten to twenty in number (Millais speaks of packs ranging from a hundred to three hundred birds : thirty would be a large pack nowadays, an indication of the decrease in comparatively recent years), and it has been my experience that these packs are composed wholly of males or wholly of females. In July and early August you will find solitary cocks in eclipse plumage, and there does seem to be a tendency on the part of old cocks and old hens to lead solitary lives.

So far as food is concerned, the black grouse is more omnivorous than the red, but is best described, I think, as a vegetarian with a fondness for heather beetle. In the winter it takes the buds of birch, the shoots and buds of larch and Scots pine, the catkins of alder, and bilberry and bog-myrtle. In summer it has a most extensive diet ranging from heather and grasses to berries, the tops of potatoes and turnips, and grain. It eats an enormous number of heather beetles, and it takes grit, of course, in quantities. It also drinks.

As a game bird it is, regarded purely from the sportsman's point of view, a disappointment. Larger and heavier than the red grouse, it is considerably faster on the wing, but it does not always fly as fast as the smaller bird. Red grouse do not mind, in fact rather like, flying down wind. Blackgame have a marked aversion to doing so. And you cannot drive blackgame. You can put them up, of course, but which way they go is entirely a matter for them. If they decide to break back nothing will stop them (and blackgame have a great fondness for circling round and returning to the spot they have been forced to leave); if they decide to fly out of the side of a drive no flanker can stop them. They are birds of determined will. Nor can you increase the stock of blackgame at will. You can try to do so by not shooting the hens—that has been tried in the past—but it does not always work out the way it should do on paper. Old greyhens can be a great nuisance on blackgame ground, for barren themselves they seem to spend an undue amount of time in harrying their younger cousins, interfering with their breeding or bullying their young. Old birds should always be shot, but old birds are extraordinarily cunning.

The record bag of blackgame was obtained on Cannock Chase,

Staffordshire, about 1860 when 252 birds were killed in a day's driving. (Forty birds would be a very good bag nowadays.) On 4th October, 1869, 247 birds were killed by eleven guns at Glenwharrie, Dumfriesshire. This bag, according to Sir Hugh Gladstone, contained over 200 cocks, and it is noticeable that wherever records are available the number of cocks far exceeds the number of hens. For example, in the largest bag obtained in recent years (on 25th October, 1910, at Auchenbrae, Dumfriesshire) of the 114 birds shot 74 were cocks. In four days shooting by this party 235 birds were shot of which 163 were cocks. There is even the record of a bag of 105 of which only 12 were hens. Granted a policy of sparing the hens these figures are yet extraordinary and suggestive. To me, at least, they suggest packing by sexes, and they seem to bear out what I have often noticed, that the greyhen is much less inclined to fly than the blackcock.

It is legal to shoot blackgame on August 20th. This is much too early. The young birds on August 20th can scarcely fly . . . and are certainly not worth shooting at. Blackgame should not be shot until October 1st.

BERNICLE GOOSE. Whipsnade Zoo. February 1937. OLIVER G. PIKE

BRENT GOOSE. Whipsnade Zoo. February 1937. OLIVER G. PIKE

CANADA GOOSE. Whipsnade Zoo. February 1937. OLIVER G. PIKE

RED-BREASTED GOOSE. Whipsnade Zoo. February 1937. OLIVER G. PIKE

THE CAPERCAILLIE

(*Tetrao urogallus urogallus* (Linnaeus))

ALONE among British members of the grouse family the capercaillie has not achieved sub-specific status. Our bird differs not at all from those to be found throughout the coniferous forests of northern and central Europe. Closely allied races are found in the Pyrenees, in Finland, in Russia, and through Siberia eastwards to Mongolia.

Although a grouse, and the largest and most handsome of grouse at that, the capercaillie in Britain is not legally a game bird. It is not mentioned in the Game Act of 1831 for the simple reason that, at the time that Act was passed, the capercaillie was extinct in the British Isles. But though it has no legal status the capercaillie has a much sounder claim to the name British than either the pheasant or the red-legged partridge, for its bones have been found in kitchen middens of times that may well be called prehistoric. The capercaillie is, in fact, an indigenous British bird, and once was distributed pretty well throughout our islands. It died out with the wide destruction of woodlands in Scotland in the seventeenth and eighteenth centuries. There is a rather doubtful record of an old cock killed near Fort William in 1815, but it is more probable that the last birds were killed in Ireland about 1760. The existing stock is descended from a few birds imported from Sweden in 1837 and 1838 by Lord Breadalbane and Sir Thomas Fowell Buxton. These birds were released at Taymouth, settled down immediately, and have since spread rapidly, which makes the extinction of the indigenous stock appear all the more extraordinary. To-day the capercaillie is well distributed over the Tay, Dee and Moray districts and as far north as the Dornoch Firth. It is beginning to penetrate Sutherland, is well-established in Argyllshire and as far south as Stirling and the Firth of Forth, and is trying to establish itself once more in Wigtownshire, Dumfriesshire, Kirkcudbrightshire, Peeblesshire, and Berwickshire. Given normal conditions there seems no reason to doubt that it would soon be south of the border agai and particularly as this present stock has not shown any pronounc inclination to stick closely to coniferous woods. It is doubly unfort nate, therefore, to have to record that the capercaillie in Scotland once again facing a crisis. War conditions are peculiarly hostile this bird, which is so closely wedded to the woods, and at the time writing (autumn, 1943), there does seem to be a possibility that, w the excessive cutting of timber, it will once again become extinct.

Its great size (a full-grown bird will weigh as much as 12 lb.) a dark colouring is quite sufficient to distinguish the cock capercai from all other game birds. The hen is not quite so easy to tell a glance from a greyhen. It is considerably larger, of course, and ha rounded tail and bolder black markings, but these things are always so noticeable in the field as they appear in the hand. The d tinguishing feature it always seems to me is the reddish patch on breast of the capercaillie, which is absent from the breast of the gr hen, and which above the light-coloured underparts is almost alw conspicuous. The cock capercaillie is an imposing bird in full pluma He looks black, but is really a dark slate-grey, with green-black be feathers, and a glossy blue-green breast, and a black tail barred w white. Above his eye is a fine scarlet wattle. The hen is buff bar with black and grey, the reddish patch on the breast coming ab underparts that are white barred with buff and black. The young both sexes resemble the hen, but the males begin to adopt the ad plumage, if a rather dull imitation of it, before the end of Septemb

Primarily the capercaillie is a bird of coniferous woodlands t hold a fair amount of undergrowth, but in Scotland it seems to quite at home, especially in winter, in deciduous woods. Its c preference seems to be for woods on hillsides, though it may oc sionally be found in the heather at a considerable distance from wo of any description. In autumn it will sometimes visit the stub fields. The flight is the typical game-bird flight, a series of rapid wi beats alternating with prolonged glides, but it flies always with neck much extended. Unlike the blackcock it is exceptionally n when put up, but once fairly on the wing it is silent. The fligh rapid—there has been much argument as to whether it is faster t that of the blackcock ; personally, I have no doubt that it is m faster—and marvellously controlled ; a cock capercaillie can we its way between the trees at astonishing speed with apparent e This is the flight of winter. The cock bird in eclipse plumage se scarcely able to fly at all. Normally, only short distances are flown, and then close to the ground, but when put up the birds will often rise to a great height and cover long distances. On the ground (and the capercaillie prefers to be on the ground in the summer and autumn) the walk is the ordinary game-bird walk with rather less of the nautical roll. As is to be expected in a woodland bird it is fond of perching and habitually roosts in trees, often using the same tree night after night.

The nest is usually on the ground, a favourite situation being at the foot of a tree though occasionally it may be in deep heather far from any trees. Very exceptionally an old tree nest of some other species is taken over, even so high as twenty feet from the ground. If on the ground it is no more than a hollow scraped by the hen and unlined, though lining may sometimes be added as the eggs are laid. The eggs, normally five to eight, are pale yellow sparingly spotted and blotched with reddish-brown. Incubation and the rearing of the young is undertaken by the female alone. As in all game birds the young are exceptionally precocious, can run and catch insects almost at birth, and can flutter at a fortnight old. Only one brood is raised in a year. The capercaillie, except in its youth, is almost entirely a vegetarian, doing no more than pick up stray larvae here and there. From October until April it feeds almost entirely on the buds and shoots of conifers. But during the summer months its diet is extensive and includes the flowers of heather and hawkweed, clover leaves, shoots of bracken, seed-pods of violet and buttercup, grass, grain, and many berries. Grit is taken in quantities, but I do not know if the bird drinks or not.

Like the blackcock the capercaillie has a specialised display. I have not had the good fortune to watch this myself, and the account I give here is condensed from the reports of those that have. As with blackgame there is a lek (though it is not properly so-called in the case of the capercaillie) at which the cock birds foregather. Display begins in April and very early in the day, as early as 2 a.m. in Poland, but usually just after dawn in Scotland, and it may be continued well into the day. Occasionally there is another session in the evening. Having selected a tree, flat-topped rock or a piece of ground (which presumably serves for the territory as in blackgame and song-birds), the cocks begin their display, at first rather tentatively, but gradually working themselves into a passion. The neck is stretched up, the tail is fanned and held vertical, and the wings are drooped and the song uttered. The noise, which is not loud for so large a bird, has been so variously described by different authors that I shall not attempt to describe it at all. One man says it is like two cats fighting, heard at a distance ! This " song " is broken by intervals during which the birds parade to and fro (if they are on the ground) and jump vertically into the air to a height of three feet or so. The cocks defend their display territories, but the fighting is largely formalised, though Millais shows that fierce fights do sometimes occur.

The capercaillie, like the blackcock, is said to be polygamous. Each cock is said to gather unto himself a harem as the result of his performance on the display ground. I do not know if it is polygamous or not. I think it is more likely that he is promiscuous. There does not seem to be any evidence that hens greatly outnumber cocks. Coition apparently takes place on the display ground, and I know of no evidence to suggest that cocks are to be seen with a harem at any time. In the breeding season the females move and feed in parties, and cocks are generally seen singly. In the winter the birds pack. I have evidence of male packs (indeed they are common) but none of mixed packs, though they may well occur.

In the extension of breeding area the initiative always seems to be taken by the females, males following on the next season. This leads to a fair amount of pairing with blackcock, and occasionally to pairing with pheasant. Pairing with blackcock is well known, of course. I am not so certain about pairing with pheasant, though in 1921 or 1922 I shot a bird which certainly seemed to be such a cross. Eric Parker, with fifty years' experience of shooting, is quite definite that this cross occurs occasionally, and so are one or two Scottish gamekeepers of my acquaintance.

The record bag of capercaillie is 69, shot by seven guns on 4th November, 1910, at Dunkeld, Perthshire. As a bird for the sportsman the capercaillie is eminently satisfying, for driven from high trees it provides to my way of thinking the most difficult shot of all birds. It is a large enough mark in all conscience, but the flight, or rather the pace, is most deceptive, and I have seen first-class shots miss apparently easy birds time after time. You get plenty of warning, too, for the crash of a cock capercaillie leaving his tree carries a long way on a still winter's day.

PLATE 7

PARTRIDGES

Coloured engraving by Philip Reinagle 1806

PLATE 8

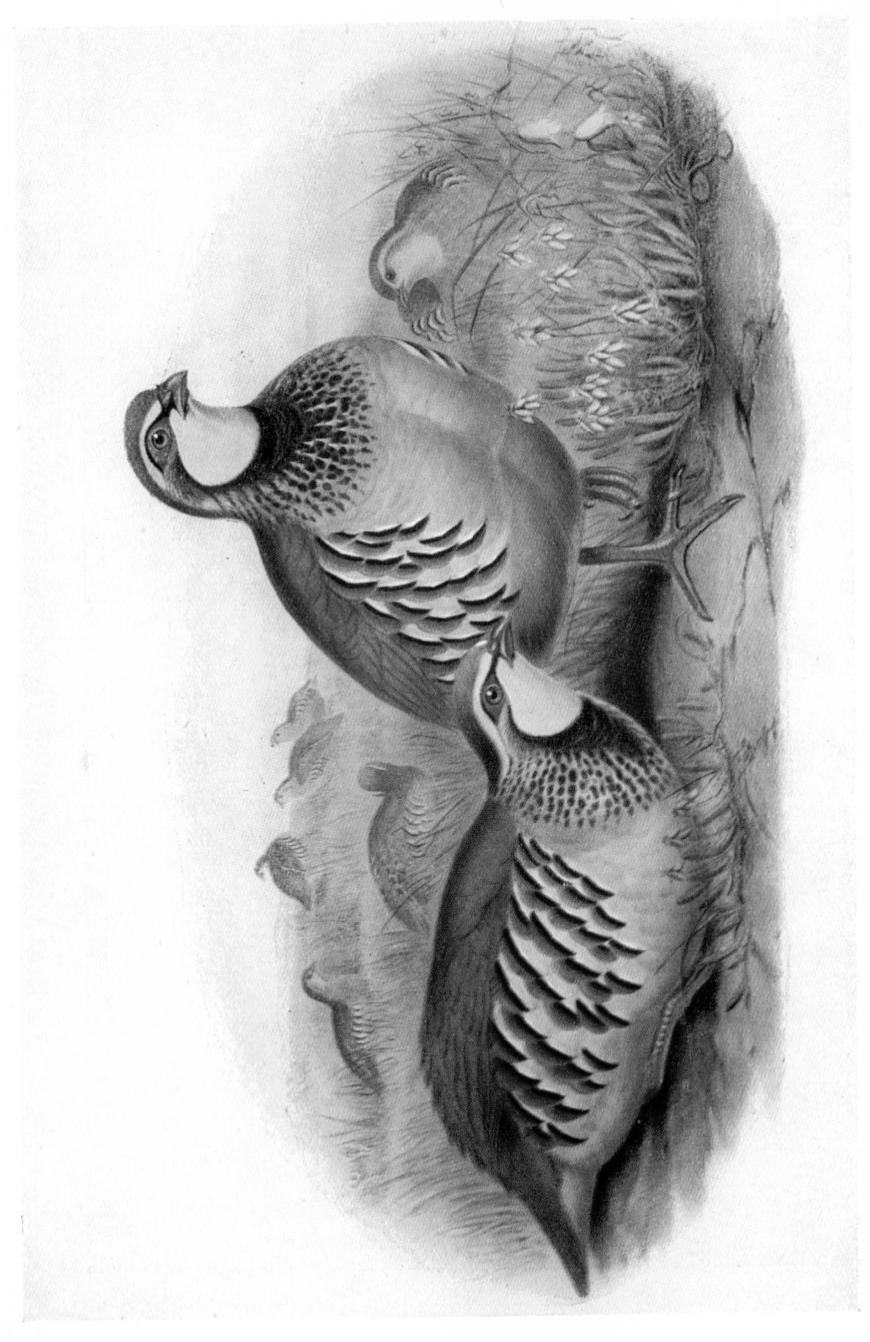

THE PHEASANT

(*Phasianus colchicus* (Linnaeus))

It is the custom nowadays, and an eminently sensible and helpful one at that, to use trinomials for the names of birds. However, the common pheasant of our countryside is always treated binominally, because the bird of our woods and hedgerows is a hybrid carrying in its veins the blood of many subspecies. There seems to be little doubt that *Phasianus c. colchicus* L. was the form first introduced into England. Later, very much later, the ring-necked pheasant, *Ph. c. torquatus*, was introduced, and mixed freely with the other inhabitant. And since then many other forms, notably *Ph. c. principalis*, *Ph. c. mongolicus* and *Phasianus versicolor*, have been introduced, and have mixed with the original stock freely : so freely, in fact, that it is probably impossible to find to-day a single *Ph. c. colchicus* in the British countryside. Nearly all British pheasants now carry a white ring, or a partial ring, round the neck, and it may be taken that all are mongrels. It is, by the way, true that all pheasants (including Reeves' pheasant, which is the one with the exceptionally long barred tail) interbreed more or less freely. Crosses with Reeves' pheasant are said to be infertile, but I do not know that that has been proved beyond dispute. In view of the character of the bar-tailed bird it would be a good thing if they were.

Having regard to this extremely mixed blood, and to the fact that no two pheasants seem to have exactly the same plumage, I do not propose to give any detailed description of the bird. Pheasants, no matter what their colour, may at once be distinguished from all other game birds by the long tail, and the cocks, no matter what their colour, are unmistakable by reason of the large red wattle completely surrounding the eye. But I must mention two varieties that turn up fairly frequently. The one is cream-coloured, and has been called (for no particular reason) the Bohemian pheasant. It seems to have become more frequent recently, and the colouring seems to be pretty constant. The other is the melanistic mutant, which has even been given a scientific name, *Ph. c. tenebrosus*. These birds seem to have appeared for the first time in 1927, and caused quite a sensation. A typical melanistic cock is a dark bird, with blackish-purple, blackish-green, Oxford blue plumage ; a typical melanistic hen is a rich dark red-brown, a colouring very similar to that of the red grouse. The cocks are rather variable in plumage, but a true melanistic mutant never has any sign of a ring on the neck. Now quite a lot of *Ph. versicolor* crosses are very dark birds, and quite a lot were sold at one time as mutants. (It takes an expert to distinguish between the *versicolor* cross and the mutant.) These birds did not breed true to type . . . in time crosses always die out, but melanistic mutants generally breed true to type.

The pheasant is not indigenous to the British Isles. It was introduced, and no one knows when or by whom. The popular theory is that it came with the Romans (*not* with Julius Caesar), and it is quite likely that it was introduced towards the end of the Roman occupation, for we know that the Romans knew a great deal about the rearing of pheasants. Palladius, in his *De Re Rustica*, which was probably written in approximately A.D. 350, gives detailed instructions for the rearing of pheasants, and some of the hints he gives are followed to this day by British gamekeepers, few of whom will have any idea that a man named Palladius was once interested enough in pheasants to write about them. But whether the bird was introduced by the Romans or not, it was certainly here well before the Norman conquest, for it is mentioned in a Waltham Abbey Ordinance of 1059. That bird, of course, was *Ph. c. colchicus* ; there is no evidence that *Ph. c. torquatus* was here much before 1785. To-day the pheasant is widely distributed throughout Great Britain in a semi-domesticated state. It does not occur in Shetland, and attempts at introduction in the Outer Hebrides have been unsuccessful. In Ireland, except where it is carefully preserved, it is scarce.

There is no type of country in Great Britain, except barren moorlands and rocky outcrops at a high altitude, where you may not meet the pheasant. I have found it, on more than one occasion, on the seashore. That is not to be wondered at in a bird that is more or less generally preserved, and as often as not artificially reared. For all that, certain types of country suit it very much better than others. In particular it flourishes on light soils, preferring such land with thick plantations and woods, with good undergrowth providing plenty of cover, and interspersed with parkland, fields and cultivation. It has a decided preference for well-watered country, and is fond of feeding in wet, rushy fields and in reed and sedge beds and in the long grass by the side of streams, rivers and lakes. In the grounds of a house in which I used to live was a small pond set on the edge of an oak and hazel copse. The ground around was so wet that it was known locally as " the marsh ". I did not rear pheasants, but I was never without them, and in some numbers. Certainly there was no day in the year on which I could not find several in the marsh, and several more in the copse. Another pond in the grounds, also set near a copse, but on higher and much drier ground, was also visited regularly by pheasants, but in nothing like the same numbers.

Even though its status—in game-preserving districts anyway—is very largely artificial, the pheasant remains a shy and wary bird, extremely suspicious of man. It is a ground bird, though not so markedly as some other game birds, taking all its food on the ground. Its normal gait is a walk, not unlike that of the domestic fowl only more stately, and it flies only on extreme provocation, much preferring to crouch in cover or to crouch in shelter. It can run extremely fast, and when running carries its tail a little above the horizontal : the faster the run the more vertical the position of the tail. In flight the neck is a little extended and the tail is spread. The flight begins with a succession of rapid wing-beats, which cause a loud whirring as the bird rises—a sound that must be familiar to every countryman—but as soon as sufficient height is gained the flight becomes typical of all game birds, a few quick wing-beats alternating with long glides. In open country the pheasant rarely rises to any height above the ground, but in woods it rises almost perpendicularly until above tree height. The flight is strong, direct and fast—but in my experience nothing like so fast as that of the blackcock. But there is an exception to this : I have seen blackcock easily outfly pheasants on more than one occasion, but I once saw a Reeves' pheasant outfly four blackcock, under what appeared to be level conditions, with the greatest of ease. Normally, the flight is of short duration, the pheasant being much happier on the ground. The *Handbook* mentions an instance of a pheasant flying across four miles of water, which must be very exceptional. I have never seen a bird fly half that distance, and I should put a mile as a long flight for a pheasant in its right senses. The *Handbook* also mentions pheasants swimming when necessary. They will also swim when it is not necessary. I have more than once seen pheasants swim across the first pond mentioned above. The pond is thirty-six yards across at its widest point and twenty-one, approximately, at its narrowest. On the occasions of which I have records — there were others — the birds swam across, covering a distance of about twenty-eight yards, when they had no need to do so at all. A gypsy poacher friend of mine, when told about this, expressed no surprise and maintained that he had often noticed it.

Though so firmly wedded to the ground, the pheasant roosts in trees. Indeed it habitually roosts off the ground, choosing any small eminence if there are no trees available. Young pheasants do not seem to take to the trees until October, but I have not known them to roost actually on the ground. If it is at all possible to roost over water such a position, in my experience, is invariably chosen. At roost, apparently considering itself safe from the attentions of ground predators, the pheasant loses much of its wariness and can be approached to within a very short distance, provided care is exercised. Indeed I have seen the gypsy already mentioned bring down two cock birds roosting next door to one another, one after the other, with a long whip, a weapon he used in the manner of a lasso with great dexterity.

The voice of the cock pheasant is a " crow ". Cocks crow at all times of the year and frequently without any apparent justification. They also crow—gamekeepers call it " cocking "—when going to roost, at which times they make an immense noise. They crow, too, when alarmed, and also in answer to a call—it is quite easy to make cock pheasants crow—or to a sound you may not be able to hear yourself. There are many stories of pheasants crowing in answer to the gunfire across the Channel during the last war, and during the Dunkirk period in this. At the time of the first big daylight blitz on London, I heard cock pheasants crowing in Hampshire, though I could not myself hear the bombing.

The cock pheasant also crows during his display in the breeding season. Every countryman knows the sound of a pheasant " drumming ". It is one of the most characteristic sounds of spring. The cock stands upright, high on his feet, with his tail on the ground, crows loudly and follows the crow with a loud, rapid, and vigorous beating of his wings. This is part of his display to the hen, and normally it begins in March. But, like so many game birds, the pheasant not infrequently has a burst of sexual activity in the autumn. I have heard

Plate XIII

SHELD-DUCK. Cornwall. May 1941. C. E. PALMAR

Plate XIV

MALLARD on frozen pond. Hampstead Heath. Winter 1938. JOHN MARKHA

MALLARD DUCK on nest. Buckinghamshire. 1936. IAN M. THOMPSON

cocks drumming in September and October before now. In addition to the drumming the male puffs up his feathers, inflates his red wattles, erects his ear-tufts and parades round and in front of the hen with quick short steps, holding his head low, trailing the wing nearest to her and spreading his tail and tilting it towards her. As to the actual process of drumming : I have often heard it said that this is done in the reverse manner to the domestic cock, who always beats his wings and crows afterwards. I do not think this is the case. At any rate in all the cock pheasants that I have watched drumming (and I have watched many) the wings have been beaten before the crow *and* afterwards. Before the crow there are two or three, but not more, beats of the wings, and afterwards there are some half-a-dozen beats. The beats before the crow are not very vigorous and are inaudible, which is why, I suppose, the barnyard cock story has gained currency. Exceptionally the bird may crow and drum at the same time. I have never come across such a case myself.

The nest, which may be in a wood, a copse, a hedgerow, a reed bed, indeed, pretty well anywhere (I have found one in my garden sheltered by a lavender bush) is a hollow scraped by the hen in the ground. Almost invariably this hollow is made under the shelter of some taller vegetation, and is usually lined with a few bits of grass or some dead leaves, but every now and again a pheasant's nest is found in such odd situations as in a squirrel's drey thirty feet from the ground, in a haystack, or, as I have known one, in the thatch of a cottage roof. The usual number of eggs is something between eight and fifteen, but much larger numbers have been recorded, these almost certainly being due to two hens. Eggs as a rule are laid in April, but I have found them in the second week in March and in the last week in September. Generally only a single brood is raised in a year, but there have been one or two records of a second, and I imagine that eggs laid from late July onwards are second layings. Incubation, which takes from three to four weeks (22 to 27 days) is by the female only (there have, however, been many records of the cock brooding) and she also tends and feeds the young after hatching. It is said that the cock is polygamous —in view of the shooting they cannot very well be anything else— but I have known several quite definite cases of monogamous cocks, and I think such cases may well be much more frequent than is generally realised. You will sometimes hear people say that the cock pheasant must be polygamous because he wears spurs (I have often heard gamekeepers say so), but that is not so : all spurred birds are not polygamous any more than all un-spurred birds are monogamous. The hen pheasant has a bad reputation among gamekeepers as a mother. There are exceptions, of course, and an occasional bird is very courageous in defence of her young, but in general the reputation is well-deserved. I have, here and there, used the term wild pheasant, meaning thereby birds not reared on the rearing field. But, compared with other game birds, the wild pheasant is, in fact, a pretty helpless creature and requires constant care. Generations of hand-rearing have contributed to this helplessness, of course, but the fact remains that after at least nineteen hundred years' residence the pheasant has not really settled down. You can see this in the nesting procedure even of wild birds. They are careless. They will nest in the most ridiculous places, they will change their minds and lay eggs in several different places, finally deciding to brood only four or five eggs, they will desert completed nests on little or no provocation or they may just forget that they have a nest or fail to recognise their own nest. And, as often as not, they will fail to take any proper care of the young after hatching. It has been estimated that from each nest, only three, or at the most four, chicks survive to the shooting season. It is not an underestimate.

The pheasant could almost be described as omnivorous. About its food and its effect on other countryside activities there has been much argument, and the literature on the subject is enormous. Dr. W. E. Collinge examined 296 stomachs and found that 62·6% of the food was vegetable and 27·4% animal. Of the vegetable food leaves, fruit and the seeds of weeds comprised 41·7%, grain 2·4%, and roots and stems 2·4%. Of the animal food insects comprised 25·9%, earthworms 8·7%, and slugs 2·8%. As far as vegetable food is concerned, they are particularly fond of acorns, hips and haws, hazel nuts, beech mast, holly and other berries, the seeds of many plants (but specially, I think, convolvulus), grain, the leaves of a great number of plants and grass. They also take oak-spangle galls and champignon fungus. They will take peas, beans and potato (and I have had them in my garden at the peas), and they like such food as apples and plums, when they can get at them. As far as insects are concerned, they take grasshoppers, ants, leather-jackets, wireworms and caterpillars. That is comprehensive enough, but they also eat, though not in great quantities, worms, snails, slugs, field-mice, lizards, small birds and young snakes. That is a very much wider range of diet than you will find in most birds, and, of course, there has been much argument as to whether from the food point of view the pheasant is beneficial to agriculture or not. I have shot a good many pheasants in my time, and I have examined a good many stomachs. I do not mean that I have examined them expertly like Dr. Collinge (I am not qualified so to do); I mean I have opened them out of curiosity to see what the contents are, being of an incurably curious turn of mind. Two Hampshire birds in particular remain in my memory. The one had been eating grain, greedily, very greedily. The other was crammed with wireworms. And that, I think, just about sums the matter up. Some pheasants are harmful to the farmer, some are helpful. But there is no evidence to support those, and they are many, who would condemn the pheasant out of hand as an enemy of agriculture from the food point of view. So far as its food is concerned, the species as a whole is beneficial. Individual birds undoubtedly do do a considerable amount of damage, but these birds are few in comparison to the pheasant population. And if the number of pheasants in any one district take to feeding in the main on grain or root crops the fault is not theirs so much as that of the landowner or gamekeeper who has raised too large a stock for the normal food supply. If this does not happen, and it has happened rather too frequently in the past, the pheasant, simply through the number of wireworms it destroys, is a friend of the farmer. Occasionally, very occasionally, you may come across a "rogue" pheasant (generally a hen that has—perhaps because she has been wounded or, more probably, as with poultry, as the result of senility—taken on the characteristics of a cock, even down to the spurs). Many years ago, when I was poultry farming, I lost a number of chicks. Finally I caught a pheasant in the act of murder, and, close season notwithstanding, put an end to its activities. It was hen turned cock.

Of pheasant diseases there are any number. Nearly all are confined to chicks or to birds on the rearing-field, and can properly be called diseases of the rearing-field, for they do not appear to attack wild birds to anything like the same extent. They are the diseases well known to the poultry-farmer—gapes, favus, coccidiosis, cramp and, worst of all, B.W.D. (bacillary diarrhoea)—and they need not concern us here. There is no disease of pheasants comparable with the scourge of grouse disease. But sometimes pheasants long since free of the rearing-field die in considerable numbers as other game birds would not die — of poisoning, generally yew poisoning, poisoning from the leaves, not the berries; and poisoning not from the leaves plucked from the trees but from clippings. It is but further proof of the helplessness of the pheasant.

CHAPTER 6

THE COMMON PARTRIDGE

(*Perdix perdix perdix* (Linnaeus))

THERE are three species of the genus *Perdix*, one of which is found pretty well throughout Europe east to the Dneiper and the other two in northern Asia. Our bird, which is indigenous, is typical of the European bird. European birds have been introduced into north America, and have settled down well in Canada and certain of the northern and western districts of the United States.

The common partridge—it is often called the grey partridge—is easy to recognise in the field. It is a rotund little bird, orangy-brown in general colour, with grey neck and underparts and chestnut-barred flanks, and in flight (the flight is the typical game-bird flight, a succession of quick-wing beats followed by a glide) the rufous tail is unmistakable. But it is not so easy to distinguish between the cock and the hen. I have lived in good partridge country all my life, and I should not care to say that I could always say which is which. In the hand, of course, it is easy enough to separate the two: the crown of the head of the cock is brown and the rest of the head and throat is a bright brownish-red; the crown of the hen's head is also brown, and so is the back and the sides; the median wing-coverts of the cock are mainly brown shading off into grey with wavy bars of black running across them, those of the hen are mainly black shading off into grey with wavy bars of buff running across them. The cock has a broad horseshoe of dark chestnut on the lower breast; in the hen this horseshoe is much less pronounced and is sometimes absent altogether. This is the feature which is usually stressed as the means by which the sexes may be told apart in the field, but it is certainly not infallible, particularly in May when the cock's plumage is much faded. Moreover, hens in their first year often have a well-developed horseshoe, while in some cocks it is not so pronounced that it can be picked out with certainty at a distance. Broadly speaking, cocks walk in a more upright position than hens, and this with the horseshoe provides a means of recognition at a distance, which if not infallible is generally safe enough. Many variations in colour occur, the most striking of which is that of the so-called " mountain ", " hill " or " fell " partridge. In this the head and neck are a bright reddish-buff and most of the rest of the plumage is a rich chestnut-red. The bird, in fact, looks not unlike a small grouse in the distance. In this variety the sexes are indistinguishable. Another variety is grey, shading off into pale yellow. In this the wing coverts of the head are almost invariably barred with black. I have more than once seen albino partridges, and once shot a cock whose horseshoe was deep black. The cock has no spurs.

Partridges are to be found pretty well throughout Great Britain and Ireland. They do not occur in Orkney or Shetland and are local throughout Scotland, while in Ireland they have never been plentiful.

" Good farming and partridges go hand in hand " ; and the old saying is not far from the truth. In the main they are birds of agricultural country, and particularly of corn-growing country and light soils. But they must have some rough ground with hedgerows or gorse or scrub for cover and do not like intensely cultivated country. On the other hand, they are never frequent in completely uncultivated country, for although they occur regularly on moorlands, heaths, marshes, hillsides, downland and sand-dunes they do so only when these border upon cultivated ground. Coast-wise partridges are very fond of the shingle, and will feed regularly on the shore well below high-water mark, but even so you will not find partridges on a coast that is far from cultivated land.

Like the pheasant the partridge is essentially a ground bird, taking all its food from the ground. Its normal gait is a walk, with neck drawn into the shoulders and rounded back (the cock, as I have said, appears a little more upright than the hen, due, I believe, to carrying the head less drawn into the shoulders), and the bird can run very fast when occasion arises. When a patridge is suspicious its head is raised and the rounded back disappears ; and when the bird is running for cover it does so with neck extended and back straight. Partridges would always rather run than fly, and if there is no cover within running distance, and they are not unduly frightened, they will crouch close to the ground rather than run. When so crouched they are astonishingly difficult to see, as anyone who has walked or ridden over partridge ground at all frequently will know well enough. When put up they rise with a whirr of wings and fly swiftly and strongly, but rarely fo any great distance—a mile is about the limit. Though I have seen some pretty high partridges in Norfolk, they prefer to fly low, skimmin over the hedge-tops, and the flight with its quick changes of course an variations in speed is extremely deceptive. For one thing it appear very much faster than it actually is. In point of fact, the partridge the slowest of our game birds on the wing, though that is not easy t believe when shooting driven birds : it certainly does not make then any easier to shoot ! Partridges do not often perch. Rarely they ma do so on a wall or a fence (I have once seen one on a fence, and it too me some time to realise that it was a partridge), and exceptionall they have been recorded as perching in the lower branches of tree during a period of heavy snow. But normally they stick to the ground resting under hedgerows or bushes or in longer grass, and they roo on the ground at night. Shore partridges often roost on the shingle inland partridges choose grass or other ground vegetation and, in m experience, do not roost under the cover of hedgerows or bushes. I winter several coveys may come together to roost, and you may fin as many as forty birds together in one roost or " jug ". There ha been a good deal of argument about these roosts. Most people, natu ralists, shooting men, and gamekeepers, who have given the subje any attention (and the partridge from the natural history point view has not received the attention it deserves), are agreed that th members of a covey when they roost usually do so in a rough circ with the heads outwards. Millais, on the other hand, maintained th the birds sit with their heads inwards, and stated quite definitely th this view was based on personal observation. Millais was a good an careful observer, and his opinion on any point connected with gam birds deserves attention and respect. For all that, I find it very dif cult to believe, for it is quite evident that such a position has ve serious disadvantages. For one thing it would make it very muc harder to detect approaching danger, for another it would make an quick " get-away " impossible, for a third it would mean that some the birds would roost back to wind. I have personally no evidence support Millais' opinion, and I have lived almost all my life in goo partridge country. Direct observation of partridges at roost is ne door to impossible. I have never managed it myself, and I do n know of anyone who has. The view that they " jug " in a circle, hea outwards, is based, I gather, upon observation of the droppings roosts. I have examined a good many roosts the morning after, an my own observation does not support the view. So far as the droppings I have seen prove anything, they prove that partridges normally jug in a very rough arc facing the wind. In a high wind I am quite sure that they forsake this formation for a tight bunch facing the wind. The droppings at a roost after a night of high wind give support to this view every time. It is the normal practice of all birds to rest facing the wind (the pheasant will sometimes roost back to the wind, but then the pheasant is a semi-domesticated and remarkably foolish bird), and though I have not seen partridges roosting, I should be astonished to find that any partridge ever roosted in any position other than facing the wind.

The voice of the partridge has been compared to the sound of a rusty key being turned in a lock, a very apt description of the call of the cock. The *Handbook* interprets this as *kar-wit*, *kar-wit* or *kirr-ie*, *kirr-ie*. This is the call of the cock at all times, and especially when alarmed, but when a covey is flushed all the birds seem to give it when once on the wing and before they have really settled down to the business of flying. As they rise, however, the sound is different, a harsh and rapid cackling. The cock has many other notes, however ; when communicating with the hen, and she with chicks at foot, he uses a low hissing call that Millais has described as *zut-zut* ; he has another note, something like *ark-ark-ark*, which he uses only when on the ground, and which I have come to associate with some very particular danger, perhaps the presence of a fox. The hen calls to her chicks with a series of low chuckles just in the manner of the barnyard fowl, and the chicks cheep just like barnyard chickens. There are many other partridge notes. I have heard a long clear whistle, in January particularly, which has taken me years to trace to the cock, so utterly un-partridge-like is it. There is a note like *Kup*, *Kup*, *Kup* which is associated in my mind with hot days in late August, and there are many others. Indeed, I think the partridge has the largest vocabulary of all our game birds.

The partridge is monogamous. Pairing in a mild winter may take place as early as the last week in December (I have seen sparring between cocks on Boxing Day in Hampshire), but January 12th may be taken as the approximate date in normal English weather. Then the coveys, which have remained together since the previous breeding season, break up and the cocks set about securing territories.

These territories are large. The hardest time of the year, the period when food is hardest to find, is ahead, and that the more ground they can secure the better the chance they and their mates will have of entering the breeding season in good health. I do not know if partridge territories in February have ever been accurately mapped, but I should say that the average territory measured some ten acres. Inexperienced birds probably have to put up with less. The winning of territory leads to a certain amount of fighting between the cocks. From my own experience this fighting between cocks is related solely to the acquisition of territory and not to the acquisition of mates. Millais says that during the fighting the hen runs round the combatants in an excited manner, raising and lowering her body and flapping her wings. I have never been fortunate enough to witness a dispute over a hen myself. In those fights between cocks that I have seen, and I have seen not a few, the birds have always appeared to me to be paired already. On more than one occasion I have seen two hens present, and they have taken no notice at all of the sparring cocks, and I have also seen hens assailing each other at the same time as the cocks. The territory, once established, is not guarded very closely —it would be impossible for a pair to guard ten acres adequately—and there is a good deal of poaching, but for all that there does seem to be some recognised boundary, for on the approach of the owners the intruders will generally retire without attempting to dispute the ground. In a really severe February, however, such as those of 1940 and 1941, territories seem to go by the board. I well remember seeing twenty-four birds searching a hedgerow for food near Winchester in February, 1940, and I had watched territorial fights in just that area some weeks previously. These fights between males are for the most part purely formal affairs. There is a good deal of bluster and very little and frequently no actual contact. Occasionally, however, they will come together, striking with bill, feet and wings but without doing any serious damage. I do not think there has ever been a record of a bird being killed in a fight.

Courtship is quite different. There have been records of large numbers of birds coming together for a sort of communal courtship, in which, after a good deal of running about and some sparring, pairs have gone off together. And there have been records of a sort of formalised dancing by several birds together. I have not been fortunate enough to witness either of these performances. I have once, in March, watched two males performing a sort of "partridge lancers" the while two hens looked on. In this case the birds kept a pretty consistent ten yards from each other, the while they chased one another

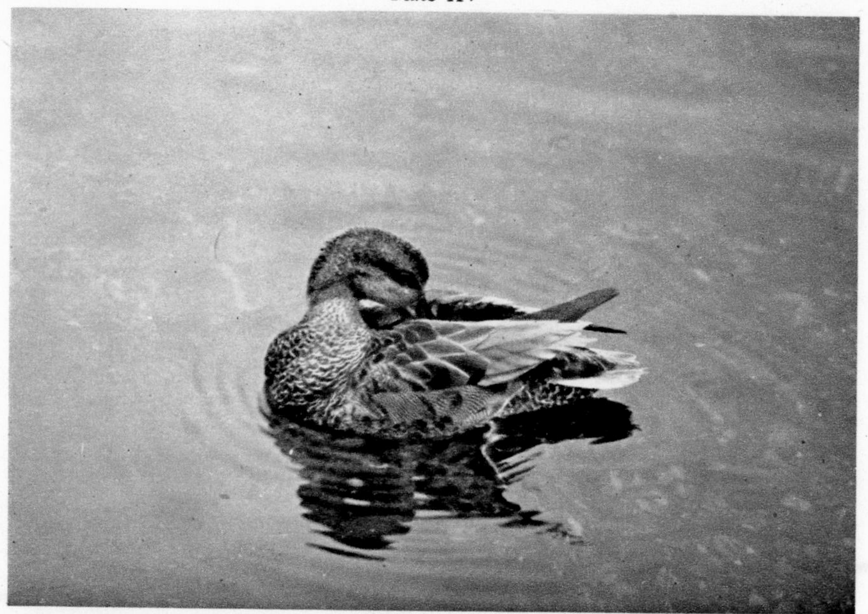

GADWALL DRAKE. St. James's Park. January 1938. OLIVER G. PIKE

TEAL DRAKE. Bedfordshire. May 1937. OLIVER G. PIKE

Plate XVI

WIGEON. Argyllshire. December 1941. C. E. PALMAR

WIGEON, duck and drake. St. James's Park. December 1940. OLIVER G. PIKE

in a rough circle. After the one bird had chased the other round the circle once or perhaps twice, they would then about turn and repeat the performance. The circle got smaller and smaller until the birds faced each other, when they indulged in some polite bows and a spring or two just off the ground between the bows. The whole performance must have lasted ten minutes or so, and broke up without any warning and for no apparent reason. In courtship I have watched the male, crouched very low to the ground and with neck extended, chasing the female, keeping always right on her tail, and I have watched the male parade before the female with short mincing steps and the wing nearest her drooped with feathers extended. He did this in a semicircle around her, but never actually went behind her. The hen gives the signal for coition during the crouching run display of the cock by stopping and tilting forward with bill to ground, and I think actually touching the ground. I have never seen any false-treading of the hen by the cock.

I have found a partridge's nest with four eggs on 10th April, but this is exceptionally early. Generally speaking, they begin to nest at the end of April or in the first week in May. Very occasionally you may find a nest in an odd or foolish situation, in a haystack or between the sleepers on a railway siding, and as these nests are invariably recorded in the Press the partridge has acquired something of a reputation as a careless nester. This is very far from the truth. It is my experience that the average partridge chooses the site of her nest with extreme care. The usual description in the natural history books—a mere scrape in the ground, made by the female, and lined with dry grasses and dead leaves, situated in the bottoms of hedgrows, on waste ground with bushes, in fields of grass, grain or clover—does less than justice to the bird, who spends, I am sure, much time in selecting just the right place. The hen partridge, deservedly, bears a very high reputation as a mother; why should she then be careless over the nest in which her young are to be hatched? I have found many partridges' nests, a great many, and very, very few that have been carelessly placed. But few people who find a nest stop to consider why it has been made in that particular place, and remarkably few people can find their nests; most of them just stumble across them by chance. It is my belief that the dominating factor in the choice of a site is protection from the wind. This comes first, and secondly, nests are placed so as to catch as much of the early morning sun as possible. You will find that it is, ninety-nine times out of a hundred, waste of time to look on the north side of a wood, hedgerow or bank for a nest. If the prevailing wind of the district is westerly it is waste of time to look on the west side of any such feature. And if the prevailing wind is easterly you will find that the nests are cunningly placed so as to take advantage of any shelter and still get the early morning sun. Then again, the nest is much more than a mere scrape in the ground. True, the hen just hollows out a scrape, but you will very rarely find a waterlogged partridge's nest (you will often find a waterlogged pheasant's nest), so some attention must be paid to drainage. And again, in 90% of the nests you will find that over them, forming a sort of arch, is a small branch or a twig—usually blackberry in my experience, but then blackberries are common in my district—and this is not the result of chance. That twig affords some protection from above, and later on when the leaves are out they afford protection to the sitting bird not only from the sun but from prying eyes. And finally, to this mere scrape in the ground there are two entrances; a " run " in on the one side and a " run " out on the other. After, say, the middle of May it is much easier to find the " runs " than it is to find the actual nest, though in point of fact it is not so hard to find partridges' nests as many people seem to think. The number of sites where there is likely to be a nest is strictly limited on any area of ground, so that once you have some knowledge of the ground the area to be searched is greatly lessened. A partridge's run is very like a rabbit's, but if you find the run on a bank you can generally tell the difference: rabbits run straight up the bank, the partridge diagonally. And a partridge's run through grass is rarely as straight as that of a rabbit.

Usually something between 8 and 20 olive-brown eggs are laid, but sometimes you come across nests containing a much larger number, which probably means that two hens have used the same nest. I have found white partridge eggs more than once. The eggs are usually laid on consecutive days, and most partridges seem to lay between 10 a.m. and noon. Incubation, which is by the female alone, begins on the day after the last egg is laid and takes about twenty-four days. Only one brood is raised in a season. During the laying of the clutch the hen covers up the eggs with grass or other material, and sometimes this habit will enable you to find a nest that you would otherwise pass by, for it frequently happens that at the time she lays the grass is dry on top but damp underneath. When she scratches the grass over her eggs she not infrequently turns it over so that the damp side is uppermost, and some damp grass in the midst of dry is astonishingly noticeable.

The young all hatch within an hour or two, and are as precocious as other game-bird chicks, being able to run almost from the moment of hatching. It is now that the cock first begins to show that he is a good father, for he will often brood the first chicks hatched, but as soon as the brood is complete the hen takes over. The young can flutter at ten days old, can fly a little way at sixteen days, and quite a long way at three weeks. The parents stick close to their children all the while, and when danger threatens, the mother, in particular, is very brave. For that matter she is very brave from the moment that she begins to sit tightly on her eggs. Once that has happened she will very rarely desert, will sit tight through the heaviest thunderstorm, and through the closest attentions of a prying human. I have many times stroked a sitting partridge, and more than once have had to lift a bird sitting on pot eggs from her nest. But this sort of bravery passes unnoticed. It is when the young are about that it strikes even the casual observer forcibly. Then if you walk into a family party the cock gets up first and generally flies forty or fifty yards away. Immediately the hen will get up with a lot of frightened noise and flop down a few yards from you as if she had a broken wing. Flapping along, broken wing and very lame, she will endeavour to draw you away from the chicks, and with the uninitiated she is generally successful. As soon as she is satisfied that the chicks are safe she will fly around calling to them. If you have a dog with you she will invariably work round behind you, for it is essential to draw the dog off, and if it is not a very well-trained dog she runs a considerable risk with her broken-wing trick, since she cannot be sure how fast the dog can run nor how far he can spring. Sometimes she will in defence of her chicks actually attack. A farmer friend of mine has seen his collie driven off by a furious hen who flew at the dog and actually buffeted it about the face with her wings.

About the food of the partridge there seems nowadays to be a considerable difference of opinion. Dr. W. E. Collinge, who examined 132 stomachs some years ago and many more when he was working for the Committee of Enquiry into Partridge Disease, found that 59·5% of the food was vegetable and 40·5% animal. A. D. Middleton and Helen Chitty, a few years later, examined 429 stomachs and found that the food was practically entirely vegetable : seeds and grain in autumn, and nearly all grass and green leaves in late winter and spring. They found that only during the summer months did animal food, mostly ants and their pupae, occur in significant quantities, and then it amounted to only 11·8%, and they found that this held true even for the chicks from the age of three weeks. James W. Campbell, examining twenty stomachs in September and October, found that vegetable matter comprised 99·4% of the food taken. When experts disagree so radically, what is the poor layman to say? But I imagine that very few farmers and very few gamekeepers will accept Middleton, Chitty and Campbell's findings without reservations. Now, the partridge is a bird of regular and conservative habits. Any gamekeeper will tell you so, and I have proved it myself year in and year out for many years in good partridge country. He has a firmly rooted love for his own ground; where he is bred, there or thereabout will he live out his days. He knows his ground intimately, and he has on it fixed places for certain things and fixed hours for doing those things. And this conservatism makes it very much easier to watch his habits. If you do watch at all closely you will soon know that you can, unless the ground is altogether too heavily shot over, find the same birds in the same place day after day. Many and many the time I have noticed this: many and many the time, day after day for days on end, I have seen the same covey in the corner of the same field at the same time. They dust bathe in the same spot at the same time day after day, take their siesta at the same time each day in another, have their special roosting place. They have their regular times for feeding, as regular as our own. Only when food runs short do they modify these regular habits a little, and even then it is noticeable that so far as they can they continue to visit certain parts of their territory at certain fixed times. It is for the observer a most helpful characteristic. Now every farmer, every gamekeeper, and every shooting man knows that during January, February and March partridges feed along hedgerows. They do so because they know that it is in the hedgerows that they will find seeds blown by the wind. And every farmer and every gamekeeper knows that when the land is freshly ploughed in February or in March the partridges will be on the newly-turned earth, and that as likely as not they will stay there until it is almost dark. They are certainly not there for fun, and they are almost certainly not there for seeds. They are there, I feel sure, for insects, for wireworm and leather-jackets. Indeed, from the crop of one partridge killed late of a March evening no fewer than 261 larvae of the crane-fly have been taken, and I have always under-

PLATE 9

QUAIL

Water colour by A. Thorburn 1908

From J. G. Millais' NATURAL HISTORY OF BRITISH GAME BIRDS

stood that they are even more partial to the larvae of *Bibionidae.* The *Bibionidae* is a family of two-winged flies belonging to the same section as the gnats, midges, mosquitoes, daddy-long-legs, etc. St. Monk's Fly or the March Fly is a well-known one. The colour is very often black, but the females may be reddish-brown. And then, if you happen to live near a field of swedes, you must have seen partridges pecking at the highest leaves of the plant and then moving on to the next. They are very deliberate about it. Swedes generally carry a good number of insects, and if you go into the field and examine the leaves after the birds have left you will find that they have not been eaten, that probably they have not even been marked. The birds were after the insects only. And finally, in country where sheep are still kept—it is unfortunate from the farming and the shooting point of view no less than the partridges that sheep are not kept nearly so frequently as formerly—you will notice that there are usually some partridges in the neighbourhood of the folds, and I believe this is because sheep encourage insects. Against all that you have those 449 stomachs, and you will be a brave man to ignore them. In support of it you have Dr. Collinge's findings. And you can take your choice. I think myself that the great increase in the use of artificial fertilisers may account for some at least of the difference.

A number of diseases attack partridges, and in addition they are often heavily infested with lice, which sometimes cause so great a loss of vitality, particularly among chicks, that in inclement weather when it is not so easy to take a dust-bath birds die from weakness. Of the diseases, B.W.D., gapes and pneumonia sometimes cause serious local losses. But the two most serious diseases in the partridge are coccidiosis and strongylosis. Both occur in epizootic form, and both in recent years have become much more prevalent. Coccidiosis is common to many birds, strongylosis seems to attack only the red grouse and the partridge in epizootic form. But strongylosis in the red grouse and the partridge, though the result is very similar, is caused by different, though very closely related, worms. The worm that attacks the red grouse is *Trichostrongylus pergracilis*, that which causes death in the partridge *Trichostrongylus tenuis.* A very bad outbreak occurred in the last two months of 1930 and the early months of 1931, so bad indeed that a Committee was set up by *Country Life* to enquire into the disease and to find, if possible, a means of prevention. The Committee came to the conclusion that the disease took on an epizootic form as a result of inbreeding, too large stocks for the food supply, and certain meteorological conditions. Wet seasons, they found, favour the parasites, prolonged drought killed both eggs and larvae. partridge country you cannot take the same measures as on a grou moor, and it seems that the prevention of inbreeding (if that is, fact, a cause) and the provision of sufficient food for the stock are t only methods that can be adopted to prevent the disease developi into a scourge.

It is easy enough to hand-feed along the hedgerows in winter in normal times you can provide any amount of grain in that way but provision of sufficient food means more than that. It means th the land must not carry too great a stock for its natural resourc And what stock of partridges should the land normally carry? It a question of the utmost importance, since too heavy a stock in pa tridge country no less than on grouse moors is the chief reason for t spread of strongylosis, but it is one which is, I fancy, asked by all t few owners of partridge shootings nowadays. I have heard it said th the absolute maximum that the most favourable land can carry fifteen pairs per hundred acres, while very ordinary land (land co prising, say, 95% of grass) should manage to carry five pairs p hundred acres. I think those figures are as accurate as one can ho for, and taking them as a fair standard, one can safely say that many of the smaller shootings during the ten years immediately p ceding the outbreak of war the land was grossly overstocked.

The prevention of inbreeding, and the partridge through its ve conservative habits would seem to be prone to inbreeding, is ea enough. Eggs can be exchanged between the various nests on t ground or with eggs from distant parts of the country, and this frequently done nowadays. Eggs can also be imported from the Co tinent, but this is a risky business. Birds can also be imported from t Continent, and large numbers of Hungarian partridges have be imported. Many unkind things have been said about the Hungari birds, and many owners will have nothing to do with them. I ha had no personal experience of rearing them, but it does seem that th take a long time to settle down. The climate of Hungary is very c ferent from our own, and on this score alone it would seem that th are better suited to north America, where, indeed, they seem to ha done well. In England they do not do well on heavy soils or in d tricts with a heavy rainfall, but they have done well in some distri with a light soil and a comparatively low rainfall. Introduced bi often take a very long time to settle down, and, despite all that I been said in disparagement of these Hungarian birds, I cannot but think that they are well worth persevering with.

Modern farming practice has, of course, affected the partridge grievously. Before the advent of the machine reaping was done by hand, and no matter how carefully it was done a large number of ears of corn were left on the ground and a much larger number of grains were shed. There was always feed in plenty left on the stubbles. The first reaping machines left the corn in long rows to be collected by hand and tied up in rough bundles with a wisp of straw. The workers always missed a few ears, and in handling the bundles a certain quantity of grain was always shed. Times were harder for the partridge, but there was still feed on the stubbles for the seeking. But the modern reaper-cum-binder-cum-everything-else leaves practically nothing behind. The stubbles are bare, and, furthermore, they are now often ploughed in immediately after the harvest. Then again, the absence of sheep from the land, an absence that has been growing more pronounced year by year, has undoubtedly had a great effect. In the old days of rotation, when flocks of ewes were folded on roots and then corn-cropped the following spring, insect life always abounded. And if you think that had no effect on the partridges, look at the results from Lord Ashburton's estates when Marlow was head keeper and that way of farming was practised. Farming practice has altered in many other ways too. Under certain systems hedges have been cut down, and the partridge is thus robbed of shelter, and in many cases inner hedges have been grubbed up altogether. This lack of hedges has not only meant lack of shelter but also of nesting sites. The birds have been driven more and more into the open, with the result that many more eggs are destroyed and the sitting bird falls a much easier victim to the fox. Again, up to the outbreak of war arable acreage was decreasing year by year, more and more land was going down to grass, and mechanisation was increasing. I am quite certain that the partridge did not like the increased acreage of grass, but I think the increased use of the tractor cut both ways. It has meant that the ground is covered more quickly, and there is therefore less disturbance for the birds, but it has also meant a great decrease in natural manure and a great increase in the use of artificials. And finally, there has been for some years past a steady, and recently an enormous, increase in the acreage of sugar beet. Partridges do not like sugar beet and seem to avoid it whenever possible.

What has been the effect of artificial fertilisers? The Committee on Partridge Disease was quite definite about the use of artificial " This cannot by any stretch of the imagination be in any way ben ficial to partridges, while dressings of some artificial manures, esp cially sulphate of ammonia and some potato-spraying mixtures, a extremely detrimental, and in some cases fatal. Even when the u of artificial manure does not supplant farmyard manure, it probab tends to neutralise the beneficial results on insect life, so necessa to the welfare of the young partridge." I think that possibly nine o of ten shooting men would agree with that view. But Mr. A. Middleton said in an article in *The Field* that he knew of no clear ca of birds being poisoned by eating chemical manures distributed the land in the usual way, and he gave figures to show that inse are not destroyed or reduced by the application of these dressings. do not know, myself. I do know that liming the soil appears to hav beneficial effect on partridges, but I find it hard to believe that so of the stuff I see put down nowadays does either the partridge or t insect any good. If the partridge does not eat insects it does n matter, of course.

The record bag of partridges was secured at Holkham, Norfo on 7th November, 1905, when 1,671 birds were killed by eight gu Bags of over 1,000 partridges in one day have been obtained on ma occasions, while at the Grange, Hampshire, in four consecutive da shooting in 1887, 4,109 birds were killed, and in three consecuti days in 1897, 3,533 birds were accounted for.

Plate XVII

EIDERS and families. DAVID HAIG-THOMAS

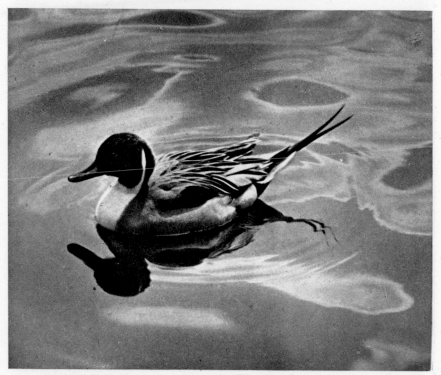

PINTAIL DRAKE. St. James's Park. January 1940. OLIVER G. PIKE

Plate XVIII

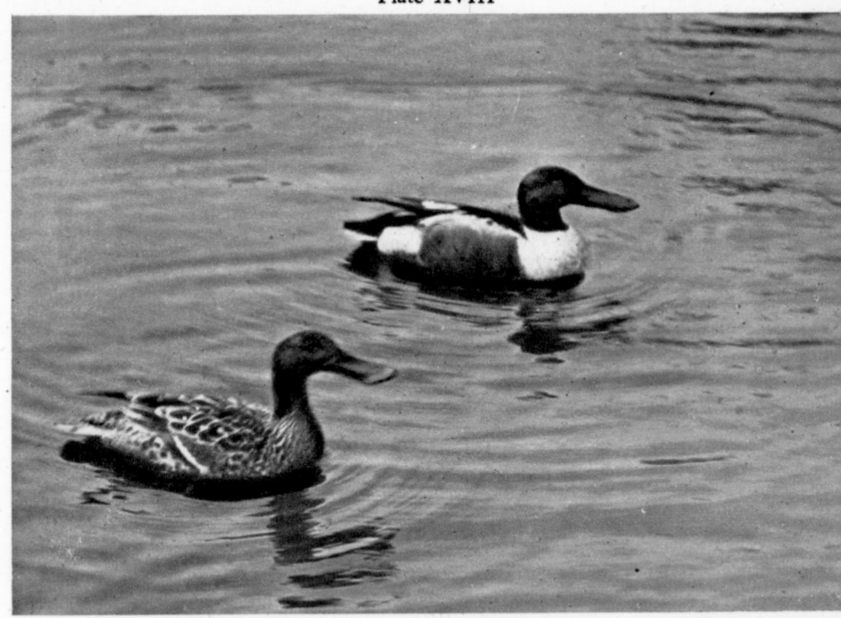

SHOVELER duck and drake. Norfolk, 1937. IAN M. THOMSON

SHOVELER duck on nest. Norfolk, 1940. G. K. YEATES

THE RED-LEGGED PARTRIDGE

(*Alectoris rufa rufa* (Linnaeus))

THE RED-LEGGED partridge, commonly called the French partridge or simply the Frenchman by the shooting man, is not an indigenous British bird. It is a species normally confined to a rather restricted, and I think decreasing, range in south-western Europe, being found in France (south of the Loire), the lowlands of Switzerland and northern and central Italy, and in Corsica and the Balearic Islands. It was originally introduced into England about 1673, when a few birds were released at Windsor and at Richmond. This introduction was unsuccessful, and about 1770 it was re-introduced near Orford in Suffolk. It has since been introduced at many places, and is now well established from Yorkshire southwards, and is abundant in some parts of the country.

A larger bird than the common partridge, it is quite unmistakable when in the hand, and at short range it can at once be distinguished by its white cheeks and throat, which are bordered by a black band, its flanks which are most beautifully barred with black, white and chestnut, and its red bill and legs. Seen thus it is a most striking and beautiful bird. But at any distance these outstanding features are not noticeable, and it is then very hard to distinguish from the common partridge, no matter whether it is on the ground or on the wing. On the ground the walk is roundbacked, and on the wing the flight is the typical game-bird flight, and the rufous tail, characteristic of the common partridge, is present also in the Frenchman. The young have none of the gorgeous markings of the adult (these are not acquired until November) and look very like young common partridges, except that the plumage is rather more spotted than striped. In the field the sexes are indistinguishable. In the hand the cock can always be recognised by the presence of spurs or rather, since they are knob-like and not sharp, of protuberances on the tarsus.

The red-legged partridge likes very much the same sort of coun as the true English bird, but with a particular fondness for sa heaths and chalk downs, and is not so firmly wedded to cultiva country. Though it has a marked preference for light soils, it d occur on marshy ground and I have found a nest in a reed bed. L the common partridge it likes coastal shingle, and birds that live the coast feed regularly well below high-water mark, even follow the sea out to the limit of the ebb. It is a much more restless a nervous bird than the common partridge, and even less inclined fly, indeed it will sometimes run for great distances rather than t wing. Once on the wing the coveys tend to scatter. The flight is l but there is no change of direction though variation in pace occ as in the common partridge, and this coupled with the fact that flight is actually faster than that of the smaller bird, without appe ing to be so, makes the Frenchman a very sporting target. The when disturbed or when put up by beaters is a sharp *kuk-kuk*, under these circumstances the red-legged partridge usually ma less noise than the common. Though so nervous and restless the r legged is also a bird of fairly regular habits, and makes a poin visiting certain places on its ground regularly and usually at the sa time each day. It seems to feed, however, more or less haphaza throughout the day with closing hours of evening as the main ti Unlike the common partridge it perches frequently, and is fon sitting on a fence or wall or on a low bush or the lowermost bran of a tree and viewing the surrounding countryside. Roosting pl seem to be changed frequently—indeed a different place may used night after night, all the suitable sites on the ground being u in turn—and in my rather limited experience the bird prefers roost off the ground. Roosting of coveys seems to be in a close bu (judging by the droppings) even when a tree is chosen. A cove red-legs, ten strong, once roosted in the rhododendrons bordering drive to the stables for eight nights in succession. They moved d the drive a few yards each night—you could tell where they roosted by the droppings—and the whole covey roosted in the s bush on each night. On no night was ever more than one bush u

Pairing commences later than in the common partridge. I h not noticed birds paired before February 8th. The display of the leg does not seem to have been studied at all—at least the *Hand* is silent on the point. I have not seen any sparring between cocks, I imagine that it must occur. The display note of the cock is an mistakable sound which has been described as suggesting a labouring steam engine (a very good description in my opinion) and rendered as *chucka-chucka*, *chik-chik-chika*, *wa-shack-shack* by various naturalists. The hen has a very similar but much softer note. In courtship (I have watched this on one occasion) the male and the female run more or less side by side, the male a little in the rear, and about two feet apart. The pair I watched ran forwards about fifteen yards, turned and came back, and repeated this several times. There was also a good deal of mutual bowing and the birds touched bills on two occasions during it. Unfortunately a wandering dog then broke up the meeting. I have not watched coition.

The nest, a hollow scraped in the ground, is usually placed in hedgerows, on the edge of copses, in growing crops or on rough open ground in the shelter of a bush or hillock, and is lined with grasses, dead leaves and so forth. But the red-leg is much more inclined to nest off the ground than the common partridge, and seems to be especially fond of the angle of a cut hayrick. It has, too, a pronounced tendency to nest in a rickyard or an orchard close to a house (I have had a nest within twenty feet of my dining-room), and these apparently unsafe sites generally prove to be quite safe. For some reason the farmyard cat leaves the red-legged partridge nesting close to the house or in the rickyard alone, and in my cat-infested area the bird nesting in my shrubbery was not molested and brought off a brood of twelve.

The eggs, usually from nine to sixteen in number (but sometimes up to twenty and twenty-eight have been recorded), are creamy-buff rather sparingly spotted with reddish-yellow. They are not laid on consecutive days, and sometimes there is a long interval between layings during which they are left uncovered. I found the first egg in my shrubbery nest on April 21st and examined the nest every day thereafter. This first egg was laid on or before April 20th, judging by the bird's habits, for the remainder were laid on the following dates: April 22nd, 24th, 26th, 30th, May 2nd, 4th 7th, 9th, 11th, 13th, 15th. They were invariably laid between 9 a.m. and 1 p.m., which means that she laid approximately every forty-eight hours. The *Handbook* gives 36 hours approximately. Incubation by my hen took 25 days and was undertaken by herself alone. At least I saw no other bird, as far as I know, and certainly there was no change-over in my presence. But the cock red-leg does help with incubation on occasions, and there is, according to the *Handbook*, some evidence that hens will lay clutches in two separate nests, incubating one herself while the cock incubates the other : in such cases the broods are usually kept separate, each attended by both parents. My hen was not so lucky, but she had an attentive mate for all that, for I used to hear him calling her off the nest every evening, the call sounding like *Hik-yoa*. He always called from the other side of the shrubbery, which merged into a small copse with a large field behind it. As the time of hatching approached the hen sat very closely, and would allow me to stroke her. On the morning the chicks hatched she was sitting tight at 9 a.m. (though some had hatched, for I could hear cheepings and see one bit of egg). When I returned at 1.15 p.m. the nest was empty and the family had gone. They remained about the place, however, for some weeks—it was this covey that roosted in my rhododendrons—and took dust baths in one of the beds. I saw the chicks many times, generally just after lunch, during the first three weeks of their lives and some days before that they could fly a little.

The food of the red-legged partridge is apparently composed almost entirely of vegetable. I am pretty sure, however, that in June and July a good many insects are taken by both adults and young.

The Frenchman has never been popular with shooting men. Its strong aversion to flying can be a great nuisance when birds are being walked up, for a covey of red-legs will start running all over a field of roots as soon as the guns enter and so scare the common partridges badly, making them run also—and seriously interfering with the shooting. But I think that when the partridges are driven the Frenchman has two distinct points in his favour. Firstly, he will often break up the coveys of common partridges, sending them forward in twos and threes, and secondly, he offers very good shooting himself. From the rearing point of view the Frenchman stands above reproach. Birds will bring off large broods time and again, and even in seasons when for one reason or another the common partridge has fared badly, the Frenchman will remain unperturbed. Furthermore, the red-leg will bring a very large proportion of its brood to maturity.

THE QUAIL

(*Coturnix coturnix coturnix* (Linnaeus))

OUR only migratory member of the pheasant family, the quail, is so scarce that it may be ignored as an English game bird. So far as we are concerned, it is a summer visitor, arriving at any time between the end of April and the beginning of June and usually leaving again in September or October, but occasionally it may spend the winter here. It breeds in Europe from the Mediterranean to the White Sea and also along the African coast from Morocco to Egypt, and it spends the winter in the Mediterranean region and south to tropical Africa as well as in Arabia and India. A few birds still breed regularly in southern England, but over most of our islands it is now only an irregular visitor, never arriving in any numbers and rarely attempting to breed.

In general appearance it looks like a very small and delicate common partridge, rather lighter in colour and with pronounced longitudinal streaks, which are not, however, very noticeable at any distance. It prefers rough grassland to any other form of country, but if this is not available will live in mowing grass if it is not too tall, or in clover, or in young corn. It does not occur in woodlands or in tall or thick vegetation. In autumn it visits the root fields. Outside these preferences its habits are very much those of the common partridge ; it walks like a partridge and flies like a partridge. The flight is low and by no means fast, and it will not fly, except on the greatest provocation, and then only for a short distance. It does not perch—at least there is no record of perching—and it is not so gregarious as the partridge. Family parties—bevies is the correct term—stay together until autumn, and it is said that migrants arrive in small parties. I have never heard of anybody in this country putting up a bevy of quail. In England quail are almost invariably put up singly—usually only by dogs. You are, in fact, much more likely to hear the quail than to see it. The call of the male is unmistakable, and is usually, and aptly, rendered as *wet-my-lips*. You may hear this, if the quail are in your neighbourhood, any time from the latter half of May until the end of July, and at night as well as during the day.

There seems to be no data as to display, and though the cocks are supposed to fight fiercely for territory and the hens, I do not think this has ever been observed in England, which does not mean, of course, that it does not occur. The nest is the typical game-bird nest, a hollow in the ground, scraped by the female and lined with a few bits of grass. It may be placed in a hedgerow, or in a grass field, or among growing crops, or on rough grassland. The eggs, usually from six to a dozen (but sometimes up to eighteen) are smaller than the partridge's, yellowish-white in colour, and either heavily blotched or lightly spotted with chocolate and brown. Incubation is by the hen alone, and normally only one brood is raised in the season. Incubation takes about three weeks, and the young can fly before they are three weeks old.

It is generally said that the quail used to be quite plentiful in Britain, and the reason for its scarcity, or at any rate the main reason, was supposed to be the excessive netting that used to take place along the shores of the Mediterranean during the spring migration. The quail has always been regarded fondly by the gourmet, and no questions were asked as to how the bird met its end. Thousands and thousands of quail were netted annually, and this must have had a great effect on the numbers. Netting is now severely curtailed and has been abolished altogether on some stretches of coast. But though this was done some few years ago now, the quail has certainly not increased in England. It may be that the sixteen or so years that have passed since the restrictions on netting came into force have not been long enough for the bird to re-establish itself on the limits of its range. I am not, however, at all convinced that the quail has been plentiful in England at any time in the last hundred and fifty years or so—it was certainly both plentiful and to all intents and purposes resident in Ireland as recently as 1850—and I am sure that it has never been even constant as a migrant, except in small numbers to favoured localities, during the last century or so. Colonel Peter Hawker, who was an ardent and indefatigable shooting man, and who kept a record of every single day's shooting (almost all of it in Hampshire) from his sixteenth year until he died in 1853, that is fifty-one seasons in all, shot in all that time only 58 quail. In twenty-eight seasons he did not shoot a quail at all, and seven of those seasons were consecutive. In all the years from 1833 to 1846 he shot only one quail, and that was in 1836, and the most he ever shot in one season was eight in 1847. That does not support that quail in this country have been plentiful at any time since men started to shoot in earnest, and it is notable that Sir Hugh Gladstone does not give any figures for quail shot in Britain in his book.

I have never shot a quail (frankly, I do not want to shoot a quail), and I have only once seen a live quail in England—near King's Somborne in Hampshire on August 26th, 1929.

THE WILDFOWL

CHAPTER I

THE SWANS

THREE species, all of the genus *Cygnus*, occur regularly in the British Isles: the mute swan, the whooper swan, and Bewick's swan. They may at once be distinguished from the geese and ducks by the white colour and the long neck, which in each species accounts for half the total length.

THE MUTE SWAN (*Cygnus olor* (Gmelin))

The mute swan is commonly regarded as an introduced and semi-domesticated species like the pheasant. There is, however, no evidence to support the theory of introduction. The bird is almost certainly indigenous in East Anglia and probably elsewhere. It was brought into a semi-domesticated condition by capture and pinioning, and from the 13th to 18th century all mute swans in England were the property of the Crown; but they have never been regarded as royal birds in Scotland. Licences (under which marks were issued) were granted by the Crown to certain communities and individuals to keep swans. During the 18th century the custom of marking died out and is now observed in a very limited degree, only on the Thames, Yare and Wensum. In general, throughout the British Isles, despite the readiness with which individuals will come for food, the mute swan has reverted to a purely wild state. It is because of this and the fact that it does on occasion fall to the wildfowler's gun that it is included in such a book as this.

The name must not be taken to mean that the bird has no voice. It is very much more silent than other swans but it has a voice, and

Plate XIX

POCHARD. Sussex. December 1943. C. E. PALMAR

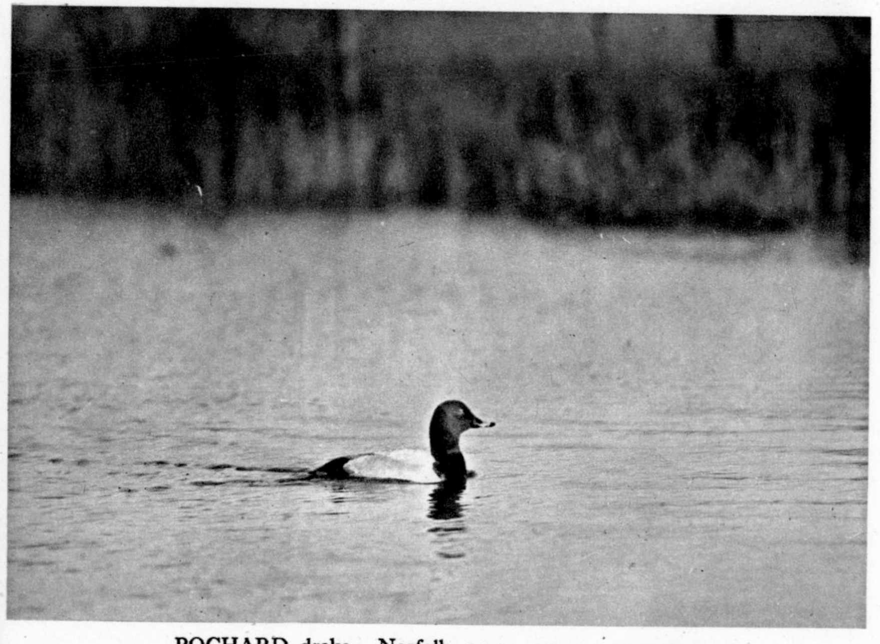

POCHARD drake. Norfolk, 1937. IAN M. THOMSON

Plate XX

TUFTED DUCK. Sussex. November 1936. C. E. PALMAR

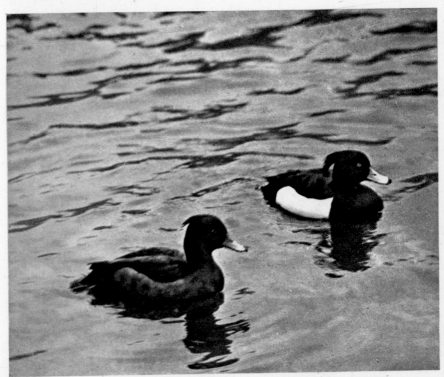

TUFTED DUCK AND DRAKE. Middlesex. December 1939. OLIVER G. PIKE

a number of distinct notes. It hisses, and this is the note most frequently heard. When irritated, or when advancing in defence of its nest or young, it utters a snoring grunt. It has also a shriller note, almost a whistle, and this is sometimes combined with the snoring grunt to produce a loud resonant note, which is usually described as trumpeting. I have only once heard a swan trumpet, and I do not believe that trumpeting is usual even in wild birds. Nor have I ever heard mute swans calling on the wing, though Danish wild-fowling friends have assured me that in Denmark they utter their whistle on the wing comparatively frequently. Cygnets have a shrill peeping note, and are much more vocal than adults.

The mute swan may be found on almost any sort of open or slow-flowing water so long as it supplies a sufficiency of vegetable food at a depth that can be reached. So you will find full-winged, but usually comparatively tame birds, on quite small ponds in town parks, but you will also find mute swans living on the more or less sheltered stretches of our coast line, and these birds are very rarely at all tame, and not infrequently are as wary as wild geese. The bird feeds by dipping its long neck into the water, but it will also "up-end" after the manner of ducks, and it also has the duck-like habit of wagging its tail. Semi-domesticated birds, or rather birds living on artificial waters, are extremely aggressive towards other birds, and will attack ducks and sometimes kill them, but wild birds, particularly those living on the sea-shore, seem to be of a much more friendly disposition, and I have noticed no inclination on the part of duck to avoid their company under these conditions. Outside the breeding season mute swans are sociable and live in small parties.

It is frequently, indeed commonly, asserted that mute swans pair for life. I do not know what evidence, if any, there is to support this assertion so far as wild birds are concerned. Nests are sometimes used, it is true, year after year, but I am by no means convinced that they are used by the same pair year after year. Hereditary nests or hereditary nesting sites are common in many species of birds in my experience, and it has always seemed to me that the mute swan is such a bird, and that the cob each season brings his mate to the nest or the nesting site that has been his property for many years. Pairing takes place in August and September, though the winter parties do not break up until March or later ; there is no courtship display as such. There is an aggressive display, generally by the cob in the breeding season, but this is too well known to need further description. On land the gait is a peculiarly clumsy walk, but it is altogether wrong to say that the bird cannot move quickly on land. I have had a terrier killed by a cob in Hampshire, and this bird moved altogether too quickly for the dog. Excluding semi-domesticated colonies such as Abbotsbury and individuals living on such restricted areas as town park ponds, the mute swan nests on islands, in reed-beds, even occasionally on level grass, but always near water. The nest is a large structure of reed stems, rushes and other vegetable matter and is circular in shape. It may be used for several years in succession, but is normally used only for one season; but a nesting site once adopted is not lightly given up, the nest being built on or about the same spot year after year. Both birds take part in the building of the nest and both birds incubate. From five to eight eggs, greyish-blue in colour, are laid, apparently on alternate days, and incubation lasts about five weeks. Only one brood is raised in a year, and the young are not fully fledged until they are about five months old.

The mute swan is the biggest of our swans, for though not quite so long as the whooper swan—averaging some 58 as against 60 inches—it is much more heavily built. Distinction on the water is easy. The mute swan swims with its head held in a graceful S-shaped curve, and the bill is orange with a black base that has on it a prominent black knob, which is bigger in the cob than in the pen. Both the whooper swan and Bewick's swan have the bill yellow at the base and black at the tip. Flight in all swans is very similar, with neck extended and the wing-beats slow, regular and powerful, but at the same time the flight of the mute swan is quite unmistakable because the wings make a loud throbbing sound which can be heard a long way off. I have never seen mute swans fly in other than an oblique line. They sometimes fly at considerable heights, but in Hampshire when coming in off the sea they are rarely at a greater height than thirty feet. I have had them come right over my head at this height of an evening, and the loud musical throb of the wings is very impressive. So, too, is the speed of the flight. At thirty feet on a January evening the mute swan is a large enough mark: it is by no means an easy one.

The Whooper Swan (*Cygnus cygnus* (Linnaeus))

Though a few pairs breed in Scotland every year (and a pair attempted to nest in Norfolk in 1928) the whooper swan is in the main a winter visitor to our islands, arriving in October or November and leaving again in late March or April. It is very common in winter in the Outer Hebrides, and is more frequent in Scotland and northern England than elsewhere in England or Wales. In Ireland it is scarce. Though most uncommon in southern England a few birds turn up in Hampshire on the Beaulieu and Lymington rivers every winter, and in hard winters, such as those of 1940 and 1941, the numbers on these rivers as elsewhere in England and Wales are larger.

On the water it is easy to distinguish the whooper from the mute. The neck is held straight and the bill is black at the tip and bright yellow at the base, this yellow running down into the black in a wedge at the sides. The flight is similar to that of the mute swan, but the wings do not make a throbbing sound—only the swishing sound common to large birds in flight. You cannot hear whoopers on the wing at any distance (unless they are calling), and even at close range the wings do not make much more noise than do those of a large duck. The whooper is much more vocal than our other swans ; indeed, it is a noisy bird. The commonest call is that from which it gets its name, the loud bugle-like *whoop-pa*, the second syllable being higher-pitched than the first, and the call repeated anything up to half-a-dozen times in succession. The call is much louder on the wing than on the water. There are many other notes, particularly a loud harsh crow or croak, uttered when alarmed on the water and generally, in my experience, a preliminary to flight.

In winter you will generally find the whooper on the sea coast, especially in estuaries or sheltered bays. But it will come inland to lakes, up the larger rivers and even to flooded fields, indeed, to any sort of water that might be frequented by the wilder type of mute swans. In 1940, during the very hard spell in February, a party of six whoopers came to the small pond in Cranberry near Winchester and drove away four mute swans that were in residence ; and in 1941 I saw a party of four on flooded land in the Itchen valley. I saw the 1941 party only once, but the 1940 birds were on the pond for ten days. They went out to sea every morning and returned every evening (the whooper's movements in this sense are influenced as are those of ducks by the tide and the moon) and in their flight they adopted, on each occasion that I saw them, a V-formation. Over the land they flew high, which surprised me, for on the coast I have never seen them flying out of gun-shot range, the must usual elevation in my experience being about forty feet.

In the breeding season whoopers frequent the lochs of moorla
and tundra, small ponds high up on hillsides or mountains, and t
swamps and valleys of the arctic. The nest is a large heap of moss
and marsh plants, held together with mud, with a shallow depressi
in the middle. The same nest may be used year after year with a litt
fresh material added each season. Both birds assist in the buildin
but only the female incubates. Five or six creamy-white eggs a
laid, apparently on alternate days, and incubation takes between fi
and six weeks. The young are fully fledged in about two months.

I have never watched the courtship of the whooper swan, and ha
only seen them in parties outside Iceland, while in Iceland I ha
only seen birds with young. Pairing evidently occurs much later
this species than in the mute, and I do not know that any signs of
have been observed before March. Such courtship display as the
is seems to be on the usual bowing lines, and the whooper is said
be much more excitable or emotional at this period than the mu
The aggressive display (which I have watched) is quite differe
from that of the mute. The wings are not arched over the back, b
held partly spread sideways, the neck is lowered and stretched mo
or less parallel to the ground, and the bird hisses. I have watched
whooper attack a dog in this manner, and it moved over the grou
much quicker and much more gracefully than the mute. It did n
however, reach the dog, a collie, for the latter was altogether ov
come by the sight of the bird and did not stand upon the order of
going. But in general the whooper is much less aggressive than t
mute, those I have seen in Hampshire never interfering with oth
birds.

Unlike almost all other wildfowl the whooper swan is compa
tively easy to approach. It appears to have no sense of smell, or
any rate not to object to the scent of man, and one can approach qu
safely down wind. It has, however, exceptionally keen eyesight. Ev
so, it will often allow of quite close approach before getting up, a
on the wing, too, it is often astonishingly indifferent to the presence
man. I have had a whooper fly past me at a distance of not more th
fifteen yards when I was standing on a sand-hill and plainly visib
I watched this bird coming for something like half-a-mile, and I ca
not believe that it did not see me. It made not the slightest attem
to alter course, however.

PLATE II A — PHEASANT SHOOTING

Coloured aquatint by Henry Alken 1820

WILD DUCK SHOOTING — PLATE II B

Coloured aquatint by Henry Alken 1820

BRENT GEESE

PINK-FOOTED GEESE

Coloured lithograph by John Gould 1871 From his BIRDS OF GREAT BRITAIN

Bewick's Swan (*Cygnus bewickii bewickii* (Yarrell))

This, the smallest of our swans (the total length is only 48 inches), is purely a winter visitor, arriving, as a rule, in November and staying until March or April. Its winter distribution in these islands is more westerly than that of the whooper. It is scarce in the Outer Hebrides, and more frequent in England and Wales than in Scotland. In Ireland it is a regular and sometimes abundant visitor. My main experience of the species has been on the Solway Firth and in Galway, but I have seen it on more than one occasion in Hampshire, and I think a few birds probably visit the Hampshire estuaries every winter.

On the water Bewick's swan looks much shorter and more goose-like than the whooper, and this coupled with the fact that the yellow at the base of the bill is much less extensive and never extends in a wedge into the black at the front of the bill makes distinction fairly easy. If you see the two together there can be no possibility of error. The flight is the same as the whooper's, but I have never seen Bewick's fly in any sort of formation, and I have seen a good many flights on the west coast of Ireland. The call, too, is distinctive, as loud perhaps as the whooper's, but much more like the honking of geese, a monosyllabic *wawg-wawg-wawg* (that, at least, is how it sounds to me) uttered half-a-dozen times in succession. When alarmed on the water a sharp barking *wow-wow* is uttered, and almost invariably this is the preliminary to flight. When on the water and undisturbed, the birds are very chatty, and there is a continual musical babbling from a feeding flock.

I have never seen any signs of an aggressive display—it is said to be similar to that of the whooper—nor of courtship display. All the birds I have seen have been in parties, probably family parties, for it is known that the young remain with their parents through the first winter, and some of these parties have been large. I remember a Galway flock that certainly numbered over 200. I stalked this flock—and found it as easy to approach as a party of whoopers, but in my experience Bewick's swan once on the wing is a wary bird, flying at a greater height than the whooper, each bird, while keeping to the same general direction, following its own inclination. I cannot imagine Bewick's swan flying steadily towards and past a man standing up and plainly visible, as did the whooper mentioned previously.

THE GEESE

NINE species of geese—seven of the genus *Anser* (the grey geese) and four of the genus *Branta*—have been recorded in the British Isles, but of these only six, three of each genus, occur regularly. In all geese the bill is high at the base and about the same length as the head; there is a nail at the tip of the upper mandible, the wings are long and pointed, and the tail is short and rounded.

The Grey Geese (Genus *Anser*)

In all grey geese tooth-like serrations are visible along the cutting edge of the upper mandible. All the grey geese bear a strong resemblance to the common domestic goose, and are extremely confusing in the field, a fact which is not sufficiently stressed in the majority of bird books. It is quite impossible to distinguish species when the birds are flying high and not calling, nor is it easy when they are on the ground and at any distance, since in general habits and behaviour they are much alike, and in all of them the colouring is very similar. At reasonable range whether on the ground or on the wing an experienced wildfowler can distinguish between typical adults without difficulty, but there is often considerable variation in plumage, which is confusing, and immature birds are always difficult to identify. As a rule a dead goose is easy enough to identify, but I have known much argument among highly experienced wildfowlers over the identity of a dead bird. In view of all this I shall outline briefly the main characteristics by which the various species may be distinguished. The distribution of all our geese (and especially is this true of the grey geese) is constantly changing. The notes on distribution given here, therefore, must not be taken to indicate more than a broadly accurate record of the position at the time of writing.

THE GREY LAG GOOSE * (*Anser anser anser* (Linnaeus))

A resident and winter visitor. The largest and heaviest of the grey geese, having a length of 34–36 inches and a wing spread of about five feet. Almost exactly like the domestic goose (of which it is the ancestor) but less heavily built. Head and neck grey : plumage ash-grey with breast and underparts lighter. Bill bright orange with nail ivory to white. Legs and feet flesh-coloured. Large stout bill and heavy head noticeable both on the ground and in flight. Pale grey fore-wing and pale grey rump are conspicuous on the ground and sometimes (but not always) are conspicuous in flight. The wings when folded do not reach beyond the tail. In the field the general colouring appears grey-brown. The call is a deep, sonorous, loud *gnong-ong-ong*, not unlike a pack of hounds in full cry. It is an unmistakable sound, and to *my* ear the most thrilling music in nature.

At one time the grey lag used to breed in many parts of eastern England and Scotland. It now breeds only in some districts of Caithness and Sutherland, in one or two localities in the northern districts of western Ross-shire, in some of the Outer Hebrides, and in one of the Inner Hebrides. As a breeding species it is undoubtedly decreasing in numbers. As a winter-visitor, arriving from the end of September until the middle of November and staying until late March or April and occasionally well into May, it occurs chiefly in Perthshire and Stirlingshire and along the coast from south-west Scotland as far south as Anglesey, and locally in small numbers in Kintyre and Ayrshire. Along the east coast from Northumberland to Suffolk it is chiefly an autumn and spring passage-migrant in small numbers, though a few birds do stay through the winter. Elsewhere it is an irregular visitor in small numbers and can properly be called rare. I have known it on the Hampshire coast, but only at long intervals

* The word lag has no connection with leg. It is a contraction of laggard, and denotes the grey goose that stays behind when the others go. The grey lag used to breed in many more places in Britain than is now the case and has played a big part in our history, as witness such poems as :

" What of the shaft?
The shaft was cut in England,
A long shaft, a strong shaft,
Barbed and trim and true.
So we'll drink all together
To the grey goose feather
And the land where the grey goose flew."

and :

" Oh where be these bold Spaniards that make so brave a boast oh !
They shall eat the grey goose feathers, but we shall eat the roast oh ! "

and generally in very severe weather. In Ireland it is a winter vi
in considerable numbers to Mayo, the Shannon estuary, Kerry, V
ford, Wicklow and Down. Until the beginning of the century the
lag was undoubtedly one of the least common of our geese, but s
approximately 1905 the number of winter visitors to south-wes
Scotland and down our north-western shores as far as Anglesey
particularly to the Solway marshes has increased considerably. C
ditions on the Solway marshes have altered of recent years, howe
The grey lag nests on moorland among heather, and shows a dec
preference for nesting on islands. The nest is placed in a hollo
the ground, and is built of heather twigs, grasses, mosses, and so fo
and roughly lined with down and small feathers. Four to six crea
white eggs are laid towards the end of April or in early May,
incubation, which is by the goose alone, takes about four weeks. C
one brood is reared in a season, and the young take about two mo
to become fully fledged. The grey lag does not breed in its first sea

THE PINK-FOOTED GOOSE (*Anser fabalis brachyrhynchus* (Baillon)

A winter visitor. Smaller than the grey lag, having a total le
of 26–32 inches. The bill is relatively short and strong, and is b
with a pink band, the nail being black. The legs and feet are f
coloured to pinkish-purple. The wings when folded reach beyond
tail. In the field the dark head and neck contrasted with the
body are characteristic. This is the greyest-looking of all our
geese. The call is *ung-unk*, and is not so deep as that of the grey la

The pink-foot arrives about the end of August or in early
tember (but occasionally as early as the second week in July),
stays until the end of April or early May. It occurs in many dist
on the east coast from Dornoch Firth to Norfolk, and on the west c
of the Clyde area and from the Solway Firth south to the Ribble
is a regular visitor to the Severn from September until the en
December, but is rare there after Christmas. In the Inner Heb
it occurs in small numbers, but is unknown in north-western Scotl
In England, elsewhere than in the areas mentioned above, it is
gular or occurs only in small numbers, and in most districts it is sc
There have been only twelve records in Ireland. There can be no d
at all that the number of pink-feet visiting us has increased of re
years, and that the species has enlarged its area of winter reside
They now flight regularly over the town of Yarmouth to the ma

Plate XXI

WOODCOCK returning to nest. Larch wood, Radnorshire, 1938. ERIC HOSKING

COCK SNIPE helping hen dry newly-hatched young. Radnorshire, 1938. ERIC HOSKING

Plate XXII

CURLEW. Strath Spey, 1939. JOHN MARKHAM

CURLEW at night on water. Flashlight. Radnorshire. March 1936. ARTHUR BROOK

west of Breydon Water from their roosting places out on the Scroby sands, and not so very long ago (before World War One) they were rare in this neighbourhood. They now visit the marshes of East Sussex (near Rye and Pevensey) in most winters, though still only in small numbers, and they have turned up in small numbers on the shore around Lymington, Hampshire, for the last six years or so.

The Bean Goose (*Anser fabalis fabalis* (Latham))

A winter-visitor. Large and more heavily built than the pink-foot, having a total length of 28–34 inches. The bill is orange-yellow and black, with the nail black. Two types occur * : one with bill mainly black with an orange-yellow band, the other with bill mainly orange-yellow and sometimes entirely so save for the black nail. The legs and feet are orange or orange-yellow. This the brownest of all the grey geese. The call resembles, according to Peter Scott, the baa-ing of sheep, and I think this is a very good description, but the bean goose is the most silent of all geese.

The bean goose arrives from early October and stays until late March or April, and exceptionally until May or June. It occurs chiefly along the east coast from Northumberland to Suffolk, though only in small numbers in the Wash, and very locally in Norfolk. It is a regular visitor in considerable numbers in Ayrshire, and visits one locality in south-western Scotland. Small numbers regularly visit Aberdeenshire, North Uist and Sussex. Elsewhere it is irregular and scarce, and is unknown in northern Scotland and the Scottish islands, except North Uist. It is very uncommon in southern Ireland, but is not uncommon in the west where it has, I think, increased during the last few years. Taken all round, however, the bean goose in England is the least common of the regular grey geese. In the last twenty-odd years I have shot only four, three of the yellow-billed variety and one of the black orange-banded type.

* The yellow-billed type is the most frequent in the British Isles. Many naturalists consider that the two types represent distinct species, that with the bill mainly black with orange-yellow band being named *Anser segetum* and the yellow-billed type being named *Anser arvensis*. This view is not accepted by the authors of the *Handbook*. There is certainly much variation, and all sorts of intermediate stages occur. The pink-foot and the bean goose are regarded by the authors of the *Handbook* as geographical races of one species, and if you regard all the black-nailed geese as one species this is obviously correct. Much work remains to be done on the systematics of the bean geese. In my own experience, however, there does seem to be some difference in habit between the two types of bean geese ; *segetum* being fonder of arable land, *arvensis* fonder of rough pasture. The two seem to choose different roosting places also, the former sticking close to salt water, the latter seeming to prefer fresh water.

THE WHITE-FRONTED GOOSE (*Anser albifrons albifrons* (Scopoli))

A winter visitor. This is the smallest of our regular grey gees having a total length of 24–30 inches. It is also the most easily reco nisable of the grey geese, having a prominent white patch at the ba of the bill and black barring on the breast. The bill is pinkish and t nail white. The legs and the feet are orange. In the field it appea a darker bird than the grey lag or the pink-foot, but rarely so da as the bean goose, and always of more slender build. The call is al quite characteristic and unmistakable, being higher pitched th those of other grey geese and having a laughing quality that on heard will never be forgotten. It is best described, perhaps, as *Ko lyow*. Immature white-fronted geese, however, are very difficult identify.

The white-fronted goose arrives from early October and stays un the end of February or early March, but exceptionally as late as Ma It occurs mainly in the Inner Hebrides, South Uist, the Severn estua and Ireland. Locally, but in some numbers, it visits the Solway are Norfolk, Northamptonshire and the coast of South Wales. But it al occurs regularly in small numbers in many other parts of the countr and exceptionally in large numbers in places where it is normal uncommon, as, for example, the Hampshire coast which was visit by a large flock in January, 1940. Next to the pink-foot the whit front, particularly on the west coast and more particularly in t Severn area, is our most common grey goose. In the Severn area t pink-foot have mostly left by Christmas, and in their place co thousands of white-fronts. In Norfolk, too, the white-fronts do n arrive much before Christmas, while I, personally, have never se them on the south coast where they are irregular and uncommo before the middle of January.

In addition to the above, all of which visit our islands regular the following geese have been recorded: the lesser white-front goose (*Anser erythropus* (Linnaeus)), the snow goose (*Anser hyperbor hyperboreus* Pallas), and the greater snow goose (*Anser hyperboreus atla ticus* (Kennard)). The lesser white-front is a very rare vagrant. Al Chapman's brother Alfred shot one on Fenham Flats, Northumbe land, in September, 1886, and another was shot on the Wash January, 1900. These are the only two records about which there no doubt. The bird is quite distinct from the white-front, having larger white patch and a swollen lemon-coloured ring around t eye, and it is also smaller and more lightly built. But these characteristics may not always have caught the attention of wildfowlers, and, as it breeds regularly in northern Norway, it may have occurred here more frequently than has been recorded. It is not possible to distinguish between the two snow geese in the field. The snow goose has been recorded more frequently than its larger cousin, which has not yet been recorded from England, though it has been shot in Scotland and Ireland. The snow goose (though some may be *atlanticus*) seems to be coming to our western shores more frequently of recent years, and has also been recorded from Essex, Norfolk and Hertfordshire. Snow geese are pure white birds with black primaries, the bill is red with a white nail, and the legs and feet are pinkish-red. It is about the size of the pink-foot, the greater snow goose being a little larger and a good deal more heavily built. I once shot a pure white goose out of a skein of pink-foot on the Solway and got very excited about it, but it proved to be an albinistic pink-foot.

THE BLACK GEESE (Genus *Branta*)

The black geese are in general very much like the grey, but no teeth or serrations are visible on the cutting edge of the upper mandibles.

THE BERNICLE GOOSE * (*Branta leucopsis* (Bechstein))

A winter visitor. A boldly contrasted black, white and grey bird that can easily be identified at long range. The total length is 23–27 inches. The crown, neck and breast are black, the whole of the face and forehead white, but with a black stripe running from bill to eye. The upper parts are grey with black bar bordered with white. The rump is white, the rest of the underparts pale grey, and the tail black. The bill, legs and feet are black. The call is unlike that of any other goose, a shrill monosyllabic bark, rapidly repeated.

The bernicle goose arrives from the end of September and stays until the end of April or early May. So far as we are concerned the bernicle is almost entirely a bird of western distribution, though it

* The *Handbook*, and most other bird books, call the bird the Barnacle Goose. Almost all wildfowlers call it the Bernicle. I use the latter because I believe it to be the older and the correct name. The name Barnacle came from the old legend that the barnacles attached to a ship's bottom turned into geese in due course. Bernicle comes from Hibernicula, i.e., the Hibernicle or the Irish goose. The bird is widely known among fishermen and wildfowlers both here and abroad as the Irish goose, and it is this bird that gave the name wild geese to the Irish exiles. In any case all wildfowling literature speaks of Bernicle, not Barnacle, and the bird interested the fowler long before it interested the ornithologist.

does turn up fairly regularly on passage in Northumberland. It is regular visitor to the Inner and Outer Hebrides and the Solway, bu has undoubtedly decreased in all three areas. Elsewhere in Englan and Scotland it is scarce and irregular and along the south coast it i extremely rare. In Ireland it is a regular and abundant visito to the western and northern coasts, but irregular elsewhere. I hav seen a flock that must have numbered several thousands in Count Sligo.

The Dark-breasted Brent Goose (*Branta bernicla bernicla* (Linnaeus))

The Pale-breasted Brent Goose (*Branta bernicla hrota* (Muller))

Winter visitors. The smallest and much the darkest of our gees The total length is 22–24 inches. The whole head and neck is blac with a small white patch on the side of the neck. The upper parts a dark grey-brown with light edging to the feathers. The upper brea is black, the rest of the under parts are dark slate-grey and not notic ably lighter than the breast in the field. The upper and under ta coverts are pure white. The bill, legs and feet are black. The pal breasted brent is in every way—size, habits, voice, flight and so —the same as the dark-breasted, but with the under parts below t black upper breast much paler and shading off into white. There a good deal of variation and sometimes the under parts are almo white. The two forms occur in mixed flocks, but usually fly separatel In flight the white stern is very conspicuous. The call is a very guttur monosyllabic croak, something like *Krowk*.

The brent goose arrives in the main from the end of October, a stays until the end of March, but exceptionally birds may come in early as August and stay as late as June. The distribution of the for has not been worked out at all fully. The dark-breasted form see to predominate on the east coast from Northumberland to Essex a occurs also in Kent and along the south coast to Dorset, and a along the south Wales coast. It appears also to be predominant Tay and Forth. It is scarce and irregular in south-west and w England, in Wales (except for the south coast) and in Solway. T main distribution of the pale-breasted seems to be in western Sc land and Ireland. In Ireland I have never shot a dark-breasted br nor have I seen one, but on the south coast—in Hampshire and

Chichester and Pagham harbours—both forms occur as they do on the South Wales coast and in Suffolk and Northumberland. I cannot give any guide to the proportion of dark to pale-breasted birds in these areas. On the south coast I should say that I have shot about equal numbers of each, but, so far as memory serves, more pale-breasted than dark in South Wales and more dark-breasted than pale in Northumberland. Movements of brent geese seem to be more closely related to the weather than is the case with our other species.

The Canada Goose (*Branta canadensis canadensis* (Linnaeus))

A resident. This is by far the largest of our geese, having a total length of 36–41 inches. It is a grey-brown bird with a black head and neck. There is a sharply defined white patch on the sides of the head, extending from the chin to behind the eye. The wings and the upper parts are dark brown, the flanks and sides lighter brown, the breast dirty white, the upper and under tail-coverts pure white, the tail black. The bill, legs and feet are blackish. The call is a very loud and resonant *ah-honk* with a distinct break in the middle, and the second syllable higher-pitched than the first. No confusion is possible with any other British goose save possibly the bernicle, and that is much smaller and has a completely white face and a black breast.

The Canada goose was originally introduced and is known to have been domesticated in England since the middle of the seventeenth century. Now, like the mute swan, it is in the main feral. As it nests chiefly by private lakes its distribution, though wide, is still rather local and artificial during the breeding season, but it has recently shown a tendency to explore new sites. It prefers to nest on islands in lakes and ponds, but if these are not available it chooses marshy ground. Occasionally it nests in colonies of considerable size (all geese have a tendency towards colonial nesting), but usually in small parties of two or three pairs. The nest is a hollow in the ground lined with grasses, dead leaves and so forth, and also with down and feathers. Five to six, but sometimes as many as ten, creamy-white unglossed eggs are laid in early April, and incubation, which is by the goose alone, takes four weeks. The gander remains on guard in the neighbourhood of the nest throughout incubation, and I have known a gander attack in defence of a sitting goose. Only one brood is reared in a season, and the young are fully fledged at six weeks old. In England the Canada goose is widespread except in the north, west and south-west, where, as in Wales, it is rare. In Scotland, it is well established in the Tay and Forth areas, but has decreased in Moray and seems to be more or less unknown elsewhere. It is well established in counties like Antrim, Down and Dublin, but it is scarce elsewhere in Ireland. There is a considerable movement in winter, sometimes in flocks of no small size, and during the winter months distribution is much more general, though the tendency of this winter movement seems to be in a southerly direction.

In addition to the above, the red-breasted goose (*Branta ruficollis* (Pallas)) has been recorded on a few occasions. Two in 1766, one in Northumberland in 1818, one in Essex in 1871, one in Gloucestershire in 1909, and one in Pembrokeshire in 1935—these are substantiated records. There have been a few others that are rather more doubtful. The bird is, however, kept in captivity in this country and imperfectly pinioned examples may wander from time to time.

THE HABITS OF BRITISH GEESE

THE GREY AND BLACK GEESE that visit our shores differ considerably in their habits, and must be considered separately. In all the grey geese the choice of habitat is very similar and the grey lag goose, which is the only true British goose, may properly be taken as the criterion in this respect. Habitat so far as the breeding season is concerned may be ignored as only the grey lag breeds in the British Isles. Outside the breeding season the grey lag frequents the salt and fresh marshes and marshy grasslands and bogs generally in the neighbourhood of estuaries and low-lying coasts, but also near lakes and rivers and flooded country, and sometimes many miles inland. It is also fond of visiting cultivated land, and in particular fields of young grain, beans and stubble. This it does in the daytime, usually retiring at night to shoals or sandbanks on the coast or in rivers, but also to lakes or other stretches of freshwater if they are sufficiently secluded. In general, the other grey geese choose the same sort of country with slight individual preferences. For example, the pink-foot, while visiting the same sort of ground as the grey lag (it is uncommon to find the two actually on the same sort of ground) is fonder of the grain and stubble fields, and has an especial fondness for potato fields. It will also visit fields on hillsides, sometimes, at a considerable elevation, whereas the grey lag is more addicted to low-lying country. The bean goose also chooses the same sort of country as the grey lag, though the two types have rather different habits, the yellow-billed form preferring dry ground in the neighbourhood of hill lochs and roosting for preference on fresh water, while the black orange-banded billed type sticks closer to the sea, roosting on sandbanks. The bean goose is the least addicted of our grey geese to visiting cultivated land, and is very rarely found on the stubble. So, too, with the white-front: in general, it chooses the same sort of ground as the grey lag, but is less inclined to visit cultivated ground, and shows a marked preference for marshy or really wet, even thoroughly flooded, grassland and for the mudflats and saltings.

All the grey geese are birds of the open country and are essentially terrestrial in habit, never perching even on the lowest of objects such as a fallen log or rock. They walk easily and well, with a lithe free movement quite opposed to the ugly waddle of the domestic bird. And they can run with surprising speed, the neck stretched forward and the beak slightly elevated, when they have need to do so, as, for example, during the moult when they are unable to fly. This flightless period is, of course, a time of increased danger, and as it approaches the adult birds, with the young in company, seek the greatest seclusion they can find, resorting to isolated marshes and such like places that provide good cover. During this period the family parties seem to merge, but as the moult passes the family parties come together and even though the birds are in large flocks the individual families are generally recognisable within the whole. Geese are normally gregarious in the breeding season. Odd grey geese or pairs of grey geese are not often seen. Small parties of half-a-dozen birds are more usual, but flocks of a hundred or several hundreds are not uncommon, and abroad I have seen flocks of several thousands. Even in the breeding season flocks occur, and these are made up of immature non-breeding birds. They frequently stick close to the breeding grounds providing by their wariness additional protection to the nesting birds. I do not know for how long the family parties stick together, and I have not come across any data on this point. I do not believe that any of the grey geese breed before they are two or three years old, and it seems to me quite probable that they remain together until the young birds attain sexual maturity. Undoubtedly they migrate in family parties, and I have seen, beyond any measure of doubt, family parties on late spring passage.

All the grey geese are primarily land feeders. They prefer to graze on the grasslands or marshes, resorting to a greater or lesser extent, as individual preference dictates, to cultivation where this is available. But this does not mean that they do not feed other than on land. They will feed in shallow water, up-ending in exactly the same manner as ducks, and I have an idea that they do this more frequently than is generally supposed. They are all diurnal feeders, but if the feeding grounds are much disturbed by day or if the birds are heavily persecuted they will feed at night. Normally, however, they fly into their feeding grounds at daybreak or very shortly after and, unless they are disturbed, they do not leave these grounds until dusk, when they make a return flight to their roosting place. But it must not be thought that they feed throughout the day. In my experience there is invariably a break about midday, and in one district of Scotland that I know well the birds repair during this midday break to a small freshwater loch and rest upon the water. Grey geese are not aquatic in anything like the same degree as ducks, and do not normally sleep on the water—at least when roosting inland on fresh water—but rather on the margin. The birds to which I have referred, however, rest on the water at some distance from the shore. All geese, of course, can swim well and buoyantly, every whit as well as swans or ducks, and they can dive expertly if needs must.

There is an exception to the rule of diurnal feeding. During the period of each month when the nights are brightly moonlit all the geese, or the large majority of them, will fly in to feed as soon as the moon is bright, and will feed so long as the moon is up. It seems evident that they require a good light for their feeding as a protection against enemies. They feed during the day and roost in inaccessible places at night as a protection against foxes and other enemies. On bright moonlit nights they can see their enemies as well as they can during the day, and so the precaution is not needed. They are not, by the way, the only birds that have the habit of turning night into day during the period of full moon. Green plover and curlew will often flight to the shore at dusk, but on bright moonlit nights will remain on their feeding grounds. Occasionally after one of these moonlit nights the grey geese will fly to the shore during the daytime. If they do so it is always at low tide. The flight is not caused, ninety-nine times out of a hundred, by untoward disturbance. It is made in order to secure a supply of sand to help in the digestion of the food taken during the night. Incidentally, the domestic goose is also extremely fond of sand and will take large quantities of it. All grey

Plate XXIII

GOLDEN PLOVER with chicks. Inverness-shire, 1939. ERIC HOSKING

CORNCRAKE on nest. Yorkshire, 1941. W. W. NICHOLAS

Plate XXIV

BUCK RABBIT. Lancashire. May 1940. G. B. KEAREY

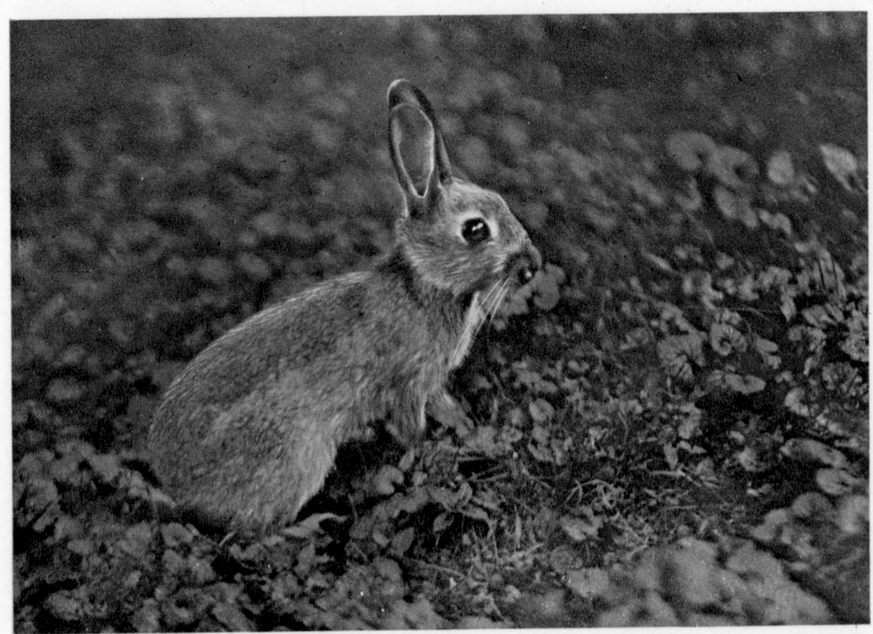

Young RABBIT. Essex, 1933. A. R. THOMPSON

geese are extremely wary and suspicious—it is this that makes them quarry *par excellence* for the wildfowler—and they are generally very hard to approach. When a flock is feeding there are always a few birds with their heads upon the look-out for possible danger. It is said that a flock of feeding geese posts sentinels, and I know experienced wildfowlers who are convinced that they do so. I do not myself believe that they do. I believe that in any feeding flock at any moment there are some birds not feeding—no more than that. In birds so suspicious as grey geese this is but natural. There is not one bird in a feeding flock that is completely at ease. All the birds feed in spasms, raising their heads frequently to make sure that everything is as it should be, and so there are always sentinels. The term " silly goose " may apply truly enough to the domestic bird, it certainly cannot be made to apply to any of the wild geese, but to credit them with the deliberate posting of sentinels is, I think—and I am well aware that in this I run contrary to so great an authority as the late Hesketh Prichard—crediting them with an organisation and a foresight that they do not possess.

I suppose the best known of all the characteristics of grey geese is their habit of flying in formation, this being a favourite subject with bird artists. Geese, when they are migrating or moving any distance, fly in a Λ or, less frequently, an Λ Λ formation, though they will also fly in long trailing lines. Each bird maintains a regular distance from its neighbour, and these formations are always led by an old bird. Regular formations are not always adopted for shorter flights, but on these flights also there is always a leader and it is always an old bird, and each of the other birds in the party maintains an even distance from its neighbour. The flight of all grey geese is direct and powerful, with regular wing beats, and is very much faster than it appears to be. Indeed I do not know of a more deceptive mark than geese on the wing, whether they be grey or black. The birds can rise from the ground very easily (they prefer to do so into the wind, but this is by no means essential), in fact, if pressed they can spring into the air and rise almost vertically to a considerable height. They are by no means so good at rising from the water ; and I have known grey lags beat along the surface for some distance before becoming airborne. Of the grey geese, in my opinion, the white-front is by far the most adept on the wing. It is the only goose that I have seen " whiffle ", though I know that all grey geese whiffle on occasion. " Whiffling " is the wildfowler's name for the astonishing aerial acrobatics occasionally indulged in by the grey geese, and particularly, I think, by white-fronts. The birds come plunging down, sometimes from a great height, in a corkscrew nose-dive with wings half folded. When they have fallen some distance they tilt one or other wing over and sideslip in a manner that would move the stomach of the most reckless test-pilot, recover themselves, and continue the nose-dive, finally flattening out (sometimes within a few feet of the ground), soaring up again in almost the same movement and repeating the performance from a lower elevation. Once, near Swansea, I watched white-fronts disporting themselves thus for as long as twenty minutes. They were well out of range, but I should have been too enthralled to fire even had they been overhead. The white-front, too, has a generally more lively flight, even on the regular journeys to and fro from the feeding grounds, than have the other grey geese, and, as every wildfowler knows, an almost miraculous power of ascending vertically out of gun range. How this is accomplished I do not know. It is a jump in the air more than anything else, and it is undertaken in the midst of headlong flight. Birds that are coming straight over you at, say, thirty feet suddenly see you and in the same instant spring to a height that is out of gun range or so nearly as to make shooting foolish. That has happened to me on more than one occasion, and has never failed to unnerve and intrigue me.

The flighting habits of grey geese are astonishingly regular. At the beginning of winter, that is to say, for a few weeks after their arrival on our shores, the flight is irregular. The birds have not settled down. During this initial period no reliance can be placed upon their movements. For example, pink-feet, when they first come to this country, devote their attention to the upland or inland farms, and do not settle down in their winter quarters, which are the lowland marshes, until some six weeks later, though I have known them to stay on the inland farms until as late as Christmas Day. During this time they will do the most unconventional things, sometimes even returning to the shore at midday. But once this initial period is over and the birds have really settled down they are as regular as may be, always taking into account the essential factors that must govern to some extent their flight movement—light, wind, weather and tide. Of these, light is the most important. In almost all the coastal districts of these islands geese flight by the light, and if, as sometimes happens, their roosting place is covered by the tide at the time of their arrival, they will ride on the water until the ebb gives them the chance to land. The exception is the Severn estuary, where the times of flighting are not controlled by the light so much as by the tides. The tides and currents in this estuary are exceptionally strong, and the geese do not attempt to return unless their roosting places are uncovered and available. They flight when they are available and not otherwise. They know that in view of the exceptional tidal conditions it would be foolish to attempt to ride the water until the ebb uncovered their roosting place. I do not myself believe that any of the grey geese ride the water when the tides are exceptionally strong or the weather really rough (what is rough weather to a human is not necessarily rough weather to a grey goose), and rather than attempt to ride out a gale at sea they will land. Certainly during a stiff gale I have come across both white-fronts and pink-feet sheltering under the lee of a sea wall. But outside the Severn estuary flighting is pretty regular, and the time is governed by the light more than by anything else. But the other factors do play a part. Geese, like all other wildfowl, have certain flight lines and flight times, and the successful wildfowler takes very careful note of these lines and times and of the effect upon them of wind, weather and tide.

Wind, weather and tide all play a part in deciding the line of the morning flight, the height at which the birds come in, and to a less extent the time of the flight. Wind, which has a big effect on the line of flight, is the most important factor. If there is no wind, or just a moderate wind, geese will, as a general rule, fly directly to their feeding grounds. But a strong wind across the normal line of flight will make a great difference, perhaps even to the extent of two miles one side or the other of the usual route. Geese will very rarely fly across a strong wind, preferring to allow themselves to be carried a long way out of the line before turning and beating up into the wind to reach their destination. Again, on a fine clear morning with little wind or only a moderate wind, geese will always come in high, sometimes at a very great height. Against a strong wind they come in low, and against a gale at a height of only a few feet. But if they are flying over ground that is much used by gunners nothing but a gale will keep them down to gun-shot range.

Weather may have much the same effect as wind on the height at which the birds fly. In a snowstorm geese invariably fly low. They do not like snow and are always restless and uneasy while it is falling. Fog they dislike even more than snow, and a thick fog can play the dickens with the time of flight. One November day in Essex I remember well, for the geese did not flight until 12.15 p.m. In fog, too, geese will always fly low. There is also the tide to be considered. An early flood tide may wash the geese off their feet, and this can mean that they will start their flight wide of their roosting place, even perhaps as much as three miles wide. Finally, in fine weather geese come in regularly and generally in big parties, in rough weather irregularly and in small parties ; which is another way of saying that in rough weather the flight lasts longer than in fine.

The evening flight is almost always of short duration. No matter what the weather the birds seem to gather together in large flocks for this flight, and they all take the air at very much the same time. Light plays a very big part in the evening flight, and it is only on those evenings when there is no moon that it is regular and punctual to dusk. As soon as the moon begins to show of an evening it becomes irregular, for if there is any moonlight at all the birds will not fly until it has gone. Bright starlight sometimes has the same effect. Snow on the ground always has. The flight is postponed.

The Canada goose, though a black goose, conforms as far as general habits are concerned with the grey geese. It is a diurnal feeder but without the regular flight times of the grey geese. The flight is that of the grey geese, but it is rarely conducted at any height in this country, and is, I think, a good deal faster than that of any of the grey geese while appearing to be slower. I have several times recently watched a party of Canada geese come in off the sea on the Hampshire coast—apparently from the Isle of Wight—and have been struck by their speed.

The other black geese—the bernicle and the brent—are very different in habit. Both are maritime geese, the brent exclusively so, the bernicle to a much greater extent than any of the grey geese, and this near relation to the sea colours all their habits. The bernicle goose is hardly ever found inland. It needs very exceptional weather indeed to drive it any distance from the sea. It is a bird of the marshes and grasslands close to the shore, and has a particular fondness for the firm springy turf that grows inside sandhills. You will find it often enough on the saltings, but it visits cultivated ground only when driven to do so by a very severe frost. The flight is much the same as that of the grey goose, but it very rarely flies in formation, preferring to advance on a broad front in a rather ragged line, though each bird keeps a pretty even distance from its neighbour. Bernicle generally fly low, except when on migration, and always at a good pace, while

PLATE 13

BERNICLE GEESE WITH SNOW GOOSE

Oil painting by Peter M. Scott 1933

TEAL

GOLDENEYE

Coloured lithographs by John Gould 1865–69 From his BIRDS OF GREAT BRITAIN

they are capable of astonishing bursts of speed. Very gregarious, they gather in large flocks—several hundreds is usual, and I have seen thousands on the Sligo coast, though parties of only a dozen or so also occur—but they are by no means as wary as the grey geese and can with care be approached quite closely. In this country it is exceptional to get within a hundred yards of any of the grey geese on land, and I should not like to say that I have ever done so, but I have approached to within twenty-five yards of a flock of bernicle geese that must have numbered five hundred, and this though they had certainly seen me at about a hundred yards. Bernicle geese are essentially night feeders—the more surprising in view of their confiding disposition—though most of them feed to some extent by day, especially in the early morning. If the weather is at all calm they often go to sea about midday and rest on the water at some distance from land, returning to the shore just before dusk. As they feed close to the sea under normal conditions there is little or no flight movement. I have shot bernicle flighting in from the sea, of course, but I have also on many occasions seen bernicle swim in and then walk solemnly up the beach.

The brent goose is exclusively maritime. It is most exceptional to find it inland. In the very severe weather of early 1940 I saw a party of six by Frensham Great Pond, and another party of fourteen by the Itchen near Itchen Stoke. These are the only brent I have ever seen away from the shore, and they looked thoroughly miserable. Normally the brent is a bird of the estuaries and the tidal flats, occurring in the main only where *Zostera* (the grass-wrack) is abundant. It feeds when the *Zostera* beds are uncovered by the tide or when the water is shallow enough to allow of paddling or of feeding by " up ending " in the manner of ducks. I do not believe that it is correct to describe the brent as a diurnal feeder. It feeds when the state of the tide permits, either by night or day. At high water brents retire some way to sea to rest, and it is quite true that they go to sea at night, but I feel sure that a low tide at night brings them on to the *Zostera* beds again. The plants are for the most part pulled up bodily, for the brent has a strong preference for the roots, but some of the leaves are also eaten, though much is allowed to drift on the tide. This is not wasted in most cases, for you will often as not find wigeon in the company of brents, and the cast-offs of the geese are eagerly taken by the ducks. The brent is the most gregarious of all geese. Abel Chapman, who knew as much about them as any man living or dead, maintained that "a single brent is invariably a pricked bird", and though invariably is a strong word I believe he was right. I have only twice come across single brent geese—both on Fenham Flats—and both were wounded. The flight is much the same as other geese, but noticeably swift. (I do not mean by that that brent fly faster than other geese.) I have never seen any Λ formation flight. Generally the flocks—they may number many hundreds—fly in long lines strung across the line of advance, and these lines at first sight look most haphazard, but you will notice at a second glance that every bird is in time with his neighbour; that the whole flock is perfectly co-ordinated, rising and falling—the line undulates—in a perfect rhythm. I have also seen brent geese fly in a pack, several hundred birds close together, but these birds were at a much higher elevation than is usual and were, I think, undertaking a long journey. It will be seen again that there is no "flight" as the term is used in connection with the grey geese. The brent is, in fact, the punt-gunner's goose.

THE DUCKS

DUCKS are, in general, much smaller birds than geese, with shorter necks and narrower wings. They are also much more aquatic in habit. The flight is similar to that of the geese and swans in that the neck is extended, but the wing-beats, though regular enough, are very much more rapid, and no one could possibly mistake ducks for geese on the wing. Furthermore, in almost all the ducks the sexes are conspicuously different in plumage and usually have very different notes. Ducks may readily be divided into four groups—the shelducks, the surface-feeding ducks, the diving ducks and the saw-bills.

The Shelducks

Shelducks are goose-like in many ways—in flight, in the way they walk, in the similarity of the sexes in plumage, in their largely terrestrial habits—and are often described as links between the geese and the ducks. The bill is rather concave, and the nail is narrow and sharply bent down so that it curves over the lower mandible. Old drakes in the breeding season have a prominent knob at the base of the bill, and there is a conspicuous horny knob at the bend of the wing. The sexes are to all intents and purposes alike.

The Shelduck (*Tadorna tadorna* (Linnaeus))

A very large duck, goose-like in carriage, with boldly contrasted plumage of black, white and chestnut, bright red bill and feet. Head and neck are black with metallic green sheen ; broad chestnut band round fore part of body ; dusky band down the centre of the underparts, the rest of which are white, except under the tail-coverts where they are shaded with chestnut ; primaries and the tips of the tail feathers are black. The female is a little duller in colouring than the male, but this is rarely noticeable in the field. The knob at the base of the bill, conspicuous in the male, is not present in the female. The chestnut band is not really noticeable at any distance, the birds then appearing as large black and white ducks or small black and white geese. It is typically an estuary bird, frequenting low-lying sandy or muddy coasts. Breeds on any rough brambly ground or on heaths, warrens and so forth, but occasionally in ordinary farm land far from water. Occurs occasionally on inland waters but never in any numbers, whereas on suitable stretches of the coast it gathers in large flocks. Has, I think, increased greatly in numbers of recent years. The nest is usually in a rabbit-hole or burrow among sand-dunes, but may be placed almost anywhere (even in a hollow tree), and I have found it more or less in the open by the side of a ploughed field. When in a burrow it may be as much as ten feet from the entrance, and is composed mainly of grey down. Eight to fifteen creamy-white eggs are laid, and incubation, which lasts about a month, is by the duck alone. Only one brood is raised in a season, and the young are fully fledged in about two months. In general a rather silent bird. If frightened the note is a harsh *ark-ark*, but a duck-like quack is used often when feeding or when the duck calls to her young.

The flight is much slower than that of other ducks, and has the regular slow wing-beats of the geese. Flocks usually fly in a rather tight wedge-shaped formation. Shelduck walk and run quite easily, take to wing very easily indeed, and are fond of perching (particularly in the breeding season) on any small vantage point. Though they swim well and buoyantly, and sometimes rest on the water at some distance from the shore, they are much less aquatic than other ducks, and prefer to rest on the shore between tides. The young dive freely, but the adults only when surprised at close quarters or if wounded. Widely distributed and breeds freely in suitable districts.

The Ruddy Shelduck (*Csarca ferruginea* (Pallas))

Properly a rare vagrant to our islands, occurring at intervals in flocks of ten or so; but a great many birds are kept in captivity and some escape, so that it is not possible to say which are escapes and which are genuinely wild. Furthermore, they are hardy and breed freely in captivity, and there is no reason why escapes should not breed in a wild state in this country, wherever they may find suitable conditions. A large orange-brown duck with a paler head. Drake has a narrow black collar, which is absent in the duck, which has an

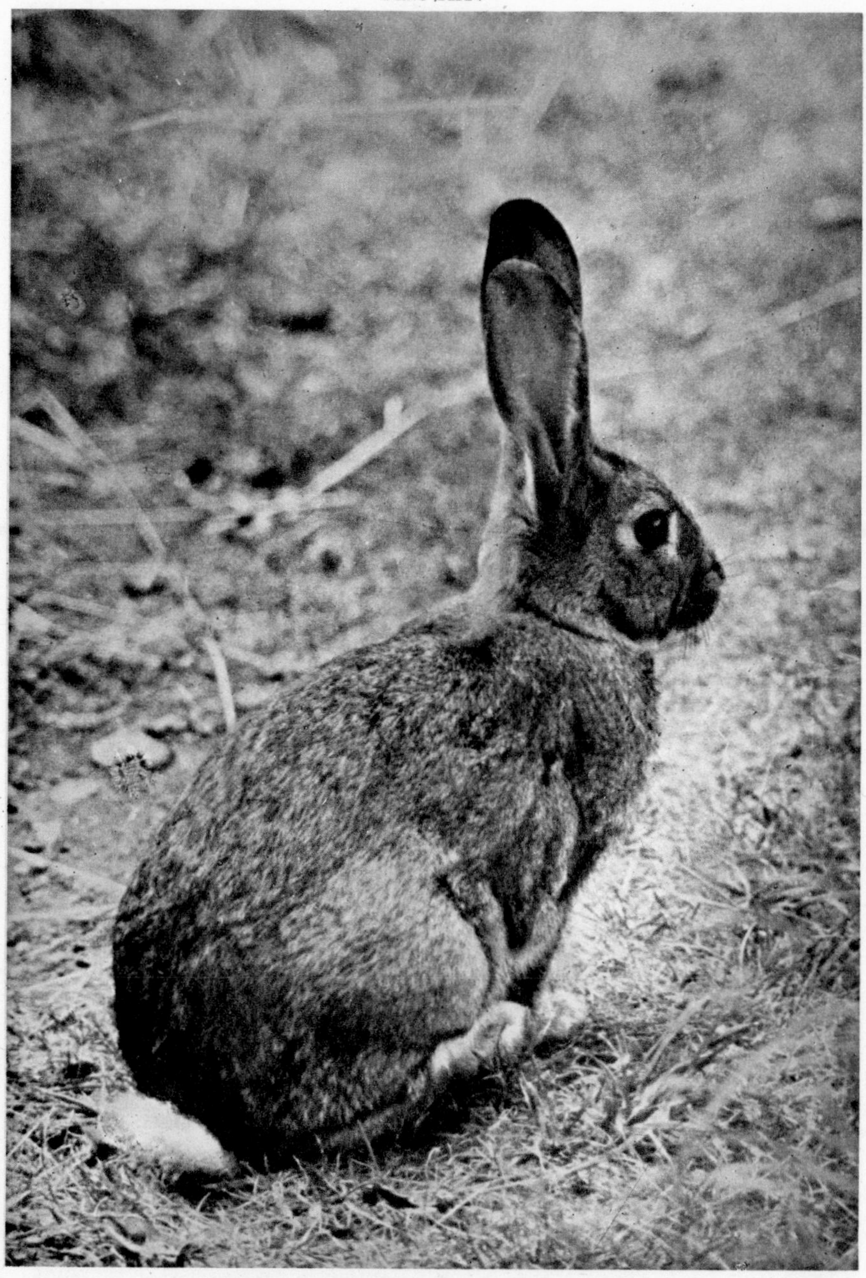

HARE. Bedfordshire, 1941. OLIVER G. PIKE

Plate XXVI

BLUE OR MOUNTAIN HARE. Ross-shire, 1933. M. S. WOOD

almost white head. In flight wing-coverts are very conspicuous. Bill black and legs and feet dark grey. Walks and runs well, swims buoyantly, but prefers to rest on land. Grazes like a goose. The note, uttered on the wing, is a loud honking *ah-honk*, very goose-like. The flight is fast (much faster than that of the shelduck) and the wing-beats are slow and heavy. Wild birds and escapes are very wary. The species is frequently confused with its near relation the Egyptian Goose (*Chenalopex aegyptiacus*), which also turns up as an escape from time to time, and which breeds in Norfolk in a semi-wild condition (I have shot an Egyptian goose in Hampshire), but the resemblance is rather superficial.

Shelduck are almost as wary as curlew and are much disliked on this account by wildfowlers. Undoubtedly many are shot, but I do not think that they can properly be regarded as fair game for the wildfowler, nor do I think that any true wildfowler does regard them as such. I suppose they are eatable. The flesh to my taste resembles childhood memories of a box of cheap paints.

The Surface-Feeding Ducks

Surface-feeding ducks are relatively lightly-built birds. They obtain most of their food in shallow water either by finding it on the surface or by dabbling for it in the mud ; when the water is deeper they " up-end ", paddling with the feet at the same time in order to maintain position. But in varying degree all of them also feed on land. All of them swim well and buoyantly, and all rise easily and directly from the water. Young birds dive easily and not infrequently, but old birds will do so only under the stress of exceptional circumstances, or when wounded. All of them rest on the water, sleeping with the bill tucked under the shoulder feathers (a habit common to all ducks), but most of them also come to the shore to rest. They are all fond of standing on one leg. None of them glide in flight, but when preparing to land they come down in a long glide. Whenever possible they will land into the wind, and they prefer to rise into the wind also, but they do not do so invariably as so many books maintain. They pitch with necks stretched forward and body hanging down so that the water is struck with the feet first. There is generally a conspicuously coloured patch, called the speculum, on the wings, and this is duller in the ducks than in the drakes. In mid-summer the drake adopts an " eclipse " plumage, which is very much the same as the plumage of the duck, but the characteristic male wing-plumage is not lost. The ducks also have an "eclipse" plumage which is adopted some weeks later than the drake's, but in the field this "eclipse" plumage is not noticeably different from the normal dress. Ducks can fly with difficulty or not at all when in eclipse. Full plumage is resumed in the autumn. There are nine surface-feeding ducks on the British list, but only seven of them need concern us here. Their distribution, as is the case with all our ducks, is complicated by the fact that so many are kept in a state of semi-captivity and frequently escape, while the young of pinioned birds are rarely pinioned and so add to the confusion.

The Mallard (*Anas platyrhyncha platyrhyncha* (Linnaeus))

The most common and widespread of our ducks, and the ancestor of our ordinary domestic farmyard ducks. Wild mallard drakes will frequently breed with farmyard ducks. Indeed, apart from the fact that the mallard is a little smaller and somewhat slighter in build it does not differ in any way from the coloured breeds of the domestic duck. The drake has a dark green head and a white collar : the breast is a purplish-brown, and the back (except for the centre which is dark brown and conspicuous in flight) is pale grey and vermiculated, shading into brown above the flanks : the upper and under-tail coverts are black and more or less prominently curled upwards. In strong sunlight the greys of the drake often appear quite white. The female is a mottled buff and brown bird. In both sexes the wings are grey with a black-edged violet-purple speculum bordered with white on both sides. The drake is in complete "eclipse" plumage in July and August, assuming full plumage again in September. The legs in both sexes are orange-red, but the bills differ, that of the drake being greenish-yellow while that of the female is a dark olive.

Breeding almost anywhere in Europe from the Arctic to the Mediterranean and from sea-level to quite high altitudes, the mallard is the least particular of our ducks and may be found almost anywhere provided only that there is water. Thus it occurs on large lakes and small ponds, on rivers and canals, on hillside tarns and ornamental waters in town parks. In winter large numbers visit the sea-coast and estuaries (this is especially true during spells of frost) and will rest on the water some way off shore. It is very fond of visiting flooded land, but will also visit fields far from water to feed. So far as food is concerned, there is remarkably little that comes amiss to the mallard from corn to earthworms. I have shot mallard at the dawn flight that were crammed to bursting with acorns, and others that had been feeding heavily on chestnuts. In hard weather when congregated on the coast they will eat almost any sort of marine weed, and I have watched them dabbling along the groynes. Mallard that have been feeding so are scarcely worth eating.

The nest, which is always made by the duck and lined with dead leaves, grasses, down and feathers, is usually on the ground and in fairly thick cover, at no great distance from water. But the duck will also nest in trees, and will adopt the old nest of a crow or some other bird sometimes at a considerable height from the ground. I once found a mallard and a moorhen nesting in the loft of a barn at least a quarter of a mile from water. Usually about ten or twelve eggs, generally greyish-green but sometimes a clear pale blue, are laid, and they take about a month to incubate. Incubation is undertaken by the duck alone, and does not commence until the last egg of the clutch has been laid. Until incubation commences the eggs are covered with down by the duck. The young take about two months to become fully fledged, but they can look after themselves remarkably well within an hour or so of hatching. The sight of a duck leading her brood to the water is well known, and is photographed almost annually in the neighbourhood of Buckingham Palace by the Press. It is quite usual to find complete clutches early in March, and eggs are frequently found in February. At the other end of the scale they may be found in October and even November, and eggs in September, a month after the commencement of the shooting season, are by no means uncommon. This is probably due to the artificial conditions largely operative in this country, for it is said that the mallard on the Continent is single-brooded, whereas here two broods in the year, though not the rule, are extremely common.

Courtship and display in the mallard have received much attention from the experts, and can be witnessed by anyone who so desires without any trouble almost anywhere in this country. One point about the mallard is of great interest. Pairing takes place early, perhaps as early as November, and normally in December. The breeding season is from February onwards, and as the number of each sex seems to be about equal the species can be taken to be monogamous. But in the late spring the behaviour of ducks and drakes is promiscuous in the extreme, and coition, which as in all ducks invariably takes place on the water, occurs frequently between birds that are not paired and is sometimes solicited by the duck.

The flight is strong and swift, and quite unmistakable, for you can tell the mallard on the wing even on a pitch-black night by the whistling sound produced by the wings. The wing-beats are less rapid than in many ducks (but far more rapid than in any goose), and the wings do not seem to come below the line of the body to any great degree. There is no formation about a flock of mallard on the wing. Though isolated pairs are common the mallard is gregarious in habit—a single mallard is almost as uncommon as a single brent—and very large flocks running into some hundreds are not at all uncommon on the estuaries in the winter. Inland sixty is a large flock, and when such a flock is put up it immediately splits up into smaller parties or even into pairs. The same thing occurs when a large estuarine flock is disturbed. Except in the breeding season mallard rest during the day on as open a bit of water as they can find, and " flight " at dusk to the feeding grounds on flooded fields, marshes, muddy shores, smaller waters or occasionally cultivated fields. There is a return flight at dawn. In this country it is the invariable habit of the mallard to feed at night, but in Denmark I have known them flight to feed by day as well. Flight times are regular and so, in no small measure, are flight lines. These may on occasion take surprising directions. I know of one place on the south coast where the birds rest on inland waters throughout the day and flight to feed on the coast, which is a complete reversal of the generally accepted procedure for wildfowl. The note, of course, is the well-known quack.

The mallard is officially described as a resident, a passage-migrant and a winter visitor. It is said that British mallard are resident and in the main sedentary, moving little, if at all, from the places where they were bred except under stress of hard weather. Even then, though they will move to our coasts and to some extent southward, they are said not to move beyond our coasts. True, a few birds ringed as nestlings have been recovered from the Continent, but so few in comparison with the number ringed as not to affect the official view. No doubt the official view is correct. But where do the mallard go in October? Every wildfowler must have noticed the scarcity that often occurs (I had almost written annually occurs) in some regions round about mid-October compared with the numbers in August and September. This cannot be accounted for by the flapper-shooting of early August. The obvious explanation seems to be migration, the increase in the numbers being accounted for by the arrival of winter visitors and passage-migrants from Scandinavia. Whether our birds migrate or not they are certainly very successful at hiding themselves in most Octobers.

The Gadwall (*Anas strepera* (Linnaeus))

A resident and winter visitor. In general the gadwall is not unlike a small mallard, except that the drake appears at a distance as a grey-brown bird. At close quarters the bold grey half-moon markings on the breast are distinctive. The duck is just like a small mallard duck. But the white speculum, which is common to both sexes, is diagnostic, for though it is often invisible when at rest, it is conspicuous in flight as are the white underparts. The bill is dark grey and the legs and feet are orange-yellow. The drake goes into "eclipse" very early, and this condition is generally complete in early June. Return to the full plumage commences in August, but is rarely completed before mid-October.

The gadwall breeds regularly and in fair numbers in Norfolk and Suffolk, in a number of localities in Scotland, in Essex, Cambridgeshire, Hertfordshire and Surrey, and in several places in northern Ireland. As a breeding species it is extending its range, and appears, too, to be increasing in numbers. There has been a gradual southerly movement of breeding birds in Scotland in the last twenty years; breeding in Ireland has only occurred since 1933, and in counties south of Suffolk since 1921. Breeding was first recorded in Surrey in 1936. In 1943 a pair was in residence on the lake in Warnford Park, Hampshire, throughout the summer, but I could not find a nest and saw no young. Beyond these breeding places the bird is an uncertain winter visitor and is scarce or rare in most parts of the British Isles except Tiree. Indeed, so far as the wildfowl is concerned, it is definitely a very uncommon duck.

The nest is usually close to the water, but in thick vegetation and extremely well hidden. Always on the ground, it is lined with down and grasses. Eight to twelve creamy-buff eggs are laid in May and are incubated by the duck alone for about a month. The young are fully fledged in about two months. Only one brood is raised in a year.

In the breeding season the gadwall likes quiet waters with good cover on their banks—lakes, marshland pools, sluggish streams and so forth. In the winter may turn up anywhere (but probably won't !), but in general seems to prefer fresh to salt water, though it does frequent estuaries when migrating. Flocks over ten are most uncommon in this country, except in Norfolk, where quite large numbers may occasionally be seen together. The note is a quack, not unlike the mallard's, but a good deal less loud.

The flight is similar to that of the wigeon. The wings seem to be more pointed than the mallard's and the wing-beats are much more rapid. The sound made by them is different from that of the mallard, being considerably lower pitched. While giving the appearance of considerable speed the pace is a good deal slower than that of the mallard.

The Teal (*Anas crecca crecca* (Linnaeus))

A resident, passage-migrant and winter visitor. The only British duck with which it is possible to confuse the teal is the garganey, and then only the ducks, for the drakes have most distinctive plumage. From all other ducks it may be distinguished by its small size. Seen at a distance the drake appears a greyish bird with a dark head and with a white band along the side above the wing, the duck as just a brown duck. At close quarters the head of the drake is a rich brown with a buff-edged green band round the eye and running down to the nape of the neck. The breast is speckled grey and black, and the back is almost uncleaned silver. The underparts are white. The duck is mottled brown with the cheeks much paler than the crown of the head. Her underparts are rarely as white as the drake's. The bill is dark grey and the legs and feet are greyish. In both sexes the speculum is half metallic green and half black, but the drake's has a broad bar of buff in front of it and a faint bar of the same colour behind it, and these two bars are replaced in the duck by two narrow, but quite distinct, white bars. The drake is in eclipse in August, and has usually returned to full plumage by the end of September.

As a breeding bird the teal has been recorded from most counties in the British Isles, but it is somewhat less common inland and in the south. Outside the breeding season teal are common almost everywhere. In the breeding season they prefer moorland and bogs or any rough and rather neglected ground, and they will often nest far from any water but a ditch. Moorland and bog is not plentiful everywhere in this country, and so the teal is forced to nest in open fields, woods and even gardens, but it is a conservative bird so far as nesting sites are concerned, and it is most unusual to find a nest in an eccentric position, and I have not yet found one off the ground. The duck makes a hollow in the ground and lines it with dead leaves, bracken, grasses and so on, and also with her very dark down. Eight to ten greeny-buff eggs are laid in late April or early May and are incubated by the duck alone for three weeks. The young are fully fledged in another three weeks, but only one brood is raised in the year. I have, however, found fresh teal's eggs as late as September 7th in the New Forest and September 11th near Frensham Ponds. Unlike the majority of ducks the drake teal does take some interest in his family, and often assists the duck in tending them in their early days. The note is not the usual duck-like quack, but a low and musical *Krit-krit* from the drake normally, but also from the duck when calling her young on the water. This is a note which carries a long way, whether used by duck or drake. The duck has another note, normally used at any time when without young, and I have heard this described as a quack. It does not sound like a quack to me but much more like a short sharp high-pitched bark, not unlike that of a pekinese at a distance.

Outside the breeding season teal gather on lakes and ponds, reservoirs and quiet streams. The size of the water does not matter, but cover does, and you are unlikely to find teal on a pond that does not provide cover in the shape of reeds or something of that sort. Flooded land has an attraction for most duck but particularly for teal—I have known flocks of several hundred come to a small area of flooded land in the Meon Valley—and you can generally be sure of finding them on sewage farms. In fact, you are far more likely to find teal inland than you are on the coast. They do resort to the coast, of course, and to estuaries and mudflats, and sometimes in very large numbers, but whereas large stretches of apparently suitable coast may not harbour a single teal, every suitable piece of inland water will have its population of teal in winter. Teal are gregarious and flocks may number several hundreds, but in the south at anyrate parties of a dozen or so birds are more usual.

On the ground the teal walks rather poorly, much worse than the mallard, and I have never seen one run. On the wing it is a master of flight. If disturbed, whether on land or water, it will spring straight upwards and immediately start swerving and corkscrewing in a most bewildering fashion. In fact the quick wheeling and swerving flight is more akin to that of the waders than the ducks. Flocks of teal fly in no particular formation but usually compactly together in a bunch, and so you may bring down several to one shot, but on the whole teal are difficult shooting. Rarely do they fly at any height, and this helps to give the impression of great speed. I have even heard a great authority mention 150 m.p.h. as the normal speed of teal. Personally, I should doubt very much if it attains 50 m.p.h. under normal circumstances, and I am quite sure that the mallard is a good deal the faster bird. As with mallard and gadwall, you can tell teal in the pitch-black night by the sound of the wings. Like mallard the teal is purely a nocturnal feeder.

The Garganey (*Anas querquedula* (Linnaeus))

A summer resident, sometimes occurring in winter. The garganey appears to be about the same size as the teal when seen at a distance (in point of fact it is a little larger), but the drake can be distinguished at once by the broad white band that extends from the eye to the nape of the neck. At short range the garganey appears as a very beautiful bird, in general colouring mottled brown with fine half-moon pencillings on the breast. The breast is brown and sharply divided from the vermiculated grey flanks and white underparts. The scapulars are blue-grey, black and white. The speculum is metallic green, bordered with white in front and behind, but it is scarcely noticeable in the duck. On the water duck garganey and duck teal are next door to impossible to tell apart. On the wing the pale bluish-grey forewing is conspicuous on occasions, but I do not find myself able to agree with those who say that you can always tell a garganey drake by the colour of the forewing. In my experience you cannot always tell the colour and, in any case, as every wildfowler knows well, light plays funny tricks with colours. The bill is greenish-grey and the legs and feet are grey. The drake goes into " eclipse " at the end of July, but unlike the teal stays in eclipse for a very long time, rarely putting on full plumage before January.

The garganey arrives in these islands towards the end of March and stays until the end of September. It breeds regularly, but in small numbers, in Norfolk, Suffolk, Cambridge, Essex, Kent, Sussex, Hampshire and Dorset. It has bred intermittently in several other counties as far north as Durham and Cumberland (though the latter case may refer to escapes from captivity). In Scotland it has bred in

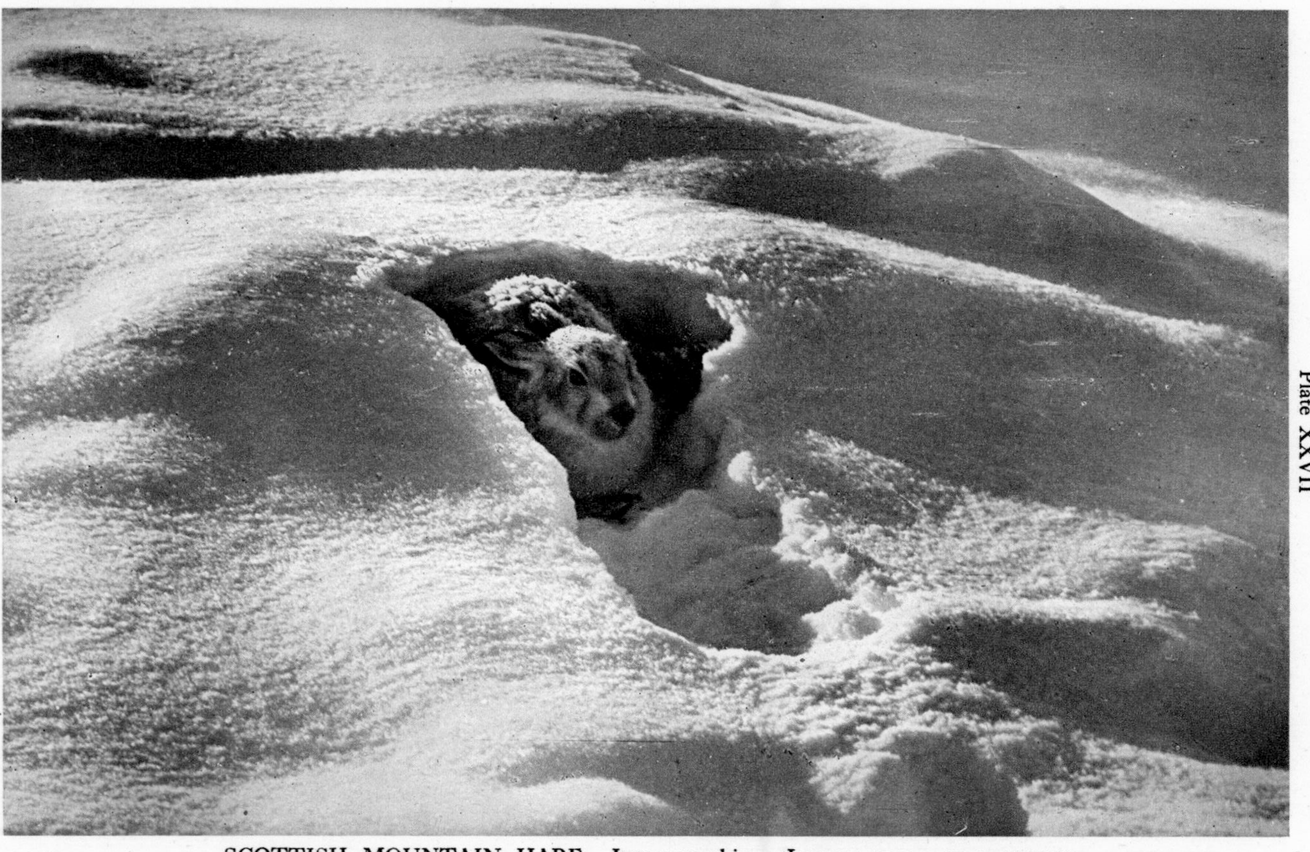

SCOTTISH MOUNTAIN HARE. Inverness-shire. January 1940. G. B. KEAREY

Plate XXVIII

COOT. Hickling Broad, 1943. ERIC HOSKING

COOT and brood. Yorkshire, 1939. W. W. NICHOLAS

the Forth area, but though it has been recorded from many parts, it is an uncommon bird to the north of the border. It has also bred once in Wales, but here, too, it is a rare bird. In Ireland it is very rare indeed. I think that in its regular breeding haunts its numbers are increasing gradually but steadily, and I think, too, that it is showing a tendency to increase its range outwards. It has been staying a good deal in Somerset and Gloucestershire, in both of which counties it has bred recently, and also to southern Wiltshire, though it does not seem to have bred there. Occasionally garganey turn up in winter, and this has been happening more frequently in Hampshire of recent years. I think these winter birds in Hampshire are probably the breeding birds of summer staying on, and I have an idea that one day the garganey will be an all-the-year resident.

The summer teal, as it is often called—the cricket teal is the Hampshire man's name for it, derived, I suppose, from its low chirping note—is a bird of meres and ponds and shallow waters generally. I have never seen it on the coast in this country, nor even on the brackish waters of estuaries. The size of the water does not seem to matter, ditches and mere puddles will suit it very well. What does matter is the richness of the vegetation. Water without rich vegetation will not attract the garganey, for the bird eats a good deal of insects and worms as well as vegetable matter, and you do not find much animal life in waters poor in vegetation. All the nests I have seen have been in long grass and close to water. The nest is a hollow in the ground and is lined with grasses, leaves and down. The down is very dark like the teal's, but you can always tell which is which because the garganey's is white tipped. Seven to a dozen buff eggs are laid at the end of April or in early May, and are incubated for about three weeks by the duck alone. There seems to be no information about the fledging period of young garganey, but I should doubt if it were much longer than that of young teal. Only one brood is reared in the season.

For the wildfowler the garganey is a rare bird, though a number must be shot every September. I suspect this number to be a good deal larger than the wildfowling community knows, for I do not think that most of them trouble to separate immature garganey and teal, and classify the lot as teal from their size.

Large flocks do not occur in England, but birds do show a tendency to pack when on the water and in the air, and parties of a dozen or so are not uncommon in garganey counties in September. The flight is rapid, faster than the teal's, though seemingly not so, because the sudden twists and turns are absent.

THE WIGEON (*Anas penelope* (Linnaeus))

A resident, passage-migrant and winter visitor. At a distance the wigeon is a grey bird with a long white mark on its side and a darker head. Seen facing one in any sort of strong light the forehead and crown seem white. Close at hand the bird is unmistakable. The head is chestnut with golden crown and forehead : the breast is pinkish-brown : the back and flanks are vermiculated silver-grey. The white mark on the side noticeable when the bird is on the water is due to a broad white patch on the wing-coverts, and this, when the drake is in flight, is a most distinctive feature, for it is the only British duck to show a white patch on the front of the wing. The speculum is dark green with a broad black border in the drake, but in the duck the dark green is almost non-existent, though there is a good deal of grey-black which is bordered in front and behind by white bars. The bill is bluish-grey with a black tip. The legs and feet seem to vary a great deal. I have seen birds with grey, blue-grey, olive, olive-brown, grey-green, greenish-yellow, greenish-brown, orange-brown, and brown legs and feet. Eclipse occurs at any time after the beginning of June, full plumage being resumed in some cases in August, in others not until November.

The number of wigeon breeding in the British Isles is increasing rapidly, and the bird is at the same time steadily enlarging its range. It bred first in northern Scotland at the beginning of the 19th century, but did not breed in England until nearly a hundred years later. That was in Cumberland, and it has since bred in Northumberland, Yorkshire, Lincolnshire, Norfolk, Essex, Kent and Sussex. I fancy it must have bred in Durham, but I cannot trace a record. In Wales it has bred in Merionethshire, and in Ireland in Armagh. But in all these counties (except Northumberland) breeding is sporadic, and it may well be that it is due in most cases to escapes from ornamental waters. In Cumberland and Northumberland genuine wild birds seem to breed regularly and in increasing numbers. In the breeding season the wigeon seeks moorland or rough pastures and bracken-covered hillsides. The nest is made by the duck and is placed on the ground, well hidden in heather, bracken or long grass. It is lined with grass, bracken, heather, and also with dark down, which might by the uninitiated be mistaken for garganey down. The tips, however, are not so white, and there is a light and rather ill-defined centre which is missing from the down of garganey. Seven or eight buff eggs are laid usually in late May, and incubation, which is by the duck alone, takes about a month. The young are fully fledged in six weeks and only one brood is raised in a year. The drake wigeon, like the drake teal, sometimes takes an interest in his family, and though it would be an exaggeration to say that he helps the duck to tend them, he not infrequently swims about with them.

Outside the breeding season the wigeon is in the main a maritime duck. It is true that quite large numbers visit the larger inland waters (and like all ducks flooded land attracts them), but these numbers are small in comparison with those that are to be found on the coast. Indeed, though by no means so widely distributed as the mallard and the teal, the wigeon is by far the most numerous of our game ducks. But you will not find them all around our coasts. They favour the areas where *Zostera* grows, and wherever there is *Zostera* there also will you find wigeon in large numbers. The brent geese, as we have seen, are also much addicted to this plant, and so you will often find wigeon and brent in company. This is to the advantage of the duck, for it feeds on the leavings of the larger birds, and brent leave a good deal at each meal. The ducks themselves feed when the tide has left the *Zostera* beds uncovered, or if the tides are unfavourable paddle and wade in the very shallow water, pulling up the grass by the roots. If they cannot do this they will " up-end ", but they are not so adept at this as other ducks. Long stretches of our coast produce no *Zostera* at all, and all these stretches are not ignored by the wigeon though the number visiting them are not nearly so large. On such stretches the ducks will flight inland to the marshes and even to meadow land to graze in the manner of geese. Corn has no attraction for them at all. On land wigeon walk easily and well and run quickly. They are very gregarious and usually gather in parties or flocks (when resting offshore such flocks may run into many hundreds), but single birds do occur every now and again. The wigeon is not by nature a nocturnal feeder. The birds that reach our shores in September and October feed by day. These are mostly immature birds that have not yet learned the ways of man, and for the first two or three weeks of their stay they are almost ridiculously easy to approach. Punt-gunners (the wigeon is the punt-gunner's duck) keep an eager look-out for these early birds. But the wigeon learns quickly. Later in the year they are as nocturnal as the mallard, flighting at dusk and again before dawn. But if undisturbed for any length of time they will return to day feeding and on inland waters are very prone to this.

The flight is rapid (about the same pace as the garganey, I should say), and there is a certain amount of twisting and turning. The duck can rise as easily and directly as any teal. The wings are long and narrow and come down well below the body in flight. Thus again you can tell the flight of wigeon on the darkest night by the sound of their wings. And the call of the wigeon is distinctive too. No suburban quack about it : a loud musical whistling *whee-oo*—a grand thrilling sound coming over the sea to the waiting shore gunner, and a note in keeping with a bird that disdains shelter and seeks always the most open and exposed waters.

The Pintail (*Anas acuta acuta* (Linnaeus))

A resident, a passage-migrant and a winter visitor. No one can mistake a drake pintail. At a distance it appears a grey bird with a dark head and neck ; down the side of the neck runs a white band to join the white breast ; and the end of the bird is black with just in front of the black a patch of pinkish-yellow. Once seen, a drake pintail is unmistakable. At close quarters, of course, the long pointed tail, generally carried slightly raised, is quite distinctive. Head and neck are chocolate-brown, back grey-brown and underparts white. The duck is very much like a duck mallard, but is more slender in bill, has a rather pointed tail, and is without a distinct speculum. The speculum of the drake is green (the sort of green a copper kettle goes if you do not clean it) with a buff bar in front of it and a white bar behind. The duck's speculum is hardly noticeable and the buff bar is very faint, but the white bar behind is bold enough. The bill is pale leaden blue. The legs and feet are grey. Eclipse is from early July to early September. Full plumage is adopted again about the end of October.

The main breeding range of the pintail in the British Isles is in Scotland, where though by no means numerous it is quite widespread. It does not appear to have bred in England before 1917, when a nest was found in Cumberland, but since then has increased its range considerably. It has now been proved to have nested in Westmorland, Yorkshire, Norfolk, Sussex, Kent and Cornwall. In all these cases (except Kent and Sussex) breeding has been sporadic, confined

PLATE 15

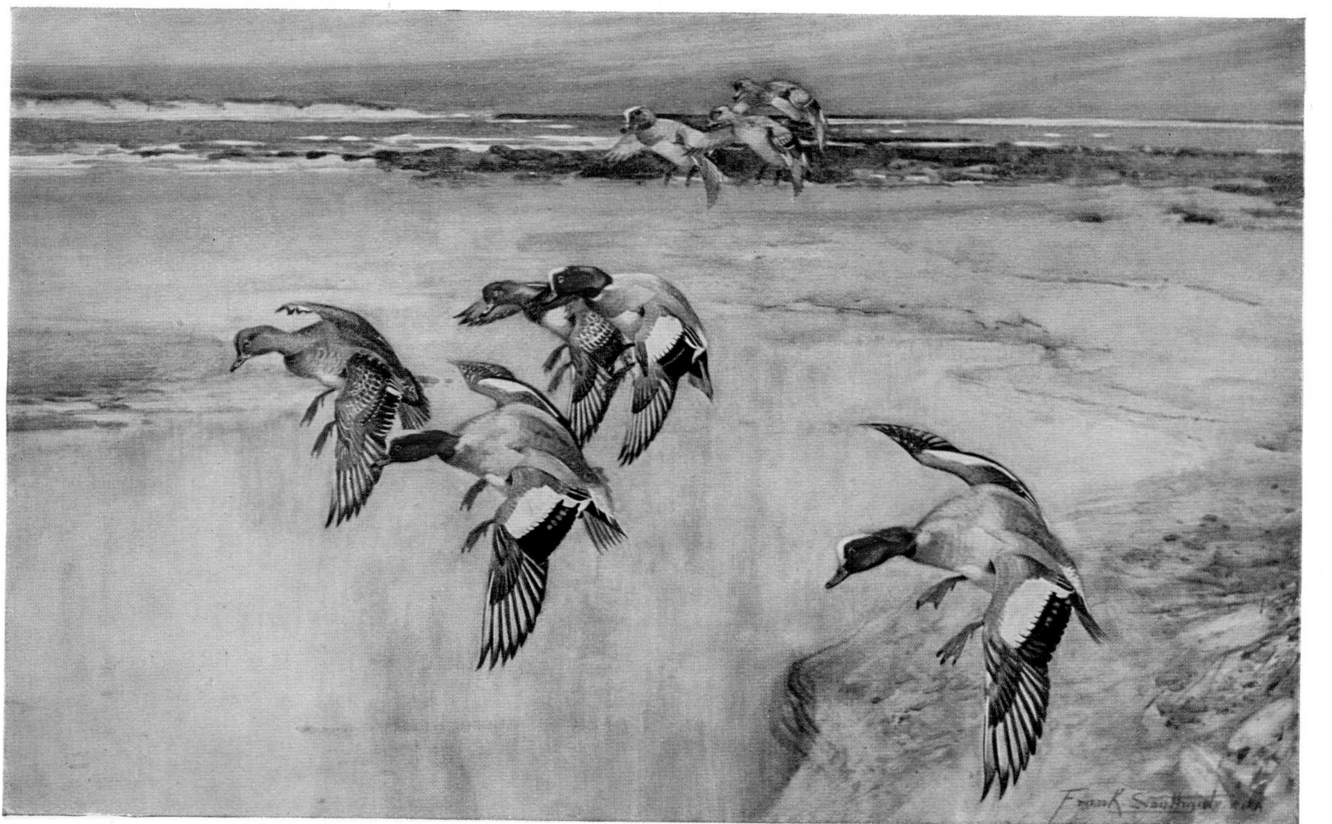

FLYING WIGEON

Water colour by Frank Southgate (recent)

DUCK SHOOTING

to one pair, and from some counties only one record is forthcoming. On the Kent and Sussex border, however, the pintail seems to nest regularly and perhaps does so elsewhere in Sussex. In Ireland it nests regularly in Roscommon, Armagh, Down and Antrim. The pintail is a social breeder (many of the single nests that have been found are probably the work of captive birds that have regained their freedom), and nests in colonies of varying size among the marram grass of sand-dunes or in heather or on islands in lakes, and rarely at any distance from water. The nest is a hollow in the ground and is, as a rule, less carefully concealed than that of most ducks, but may be placed right in the middle of a reed bed. It is generally lined with down but nothing else. Between six and nine eggs are laid in May, and the colour varies enormously from yellow-green through blue to almost white. Incubation takes a little over three weeks. Only one brood is reared in a season.

Outside the breeding season the pintail is almost entirely a maritime duck—even more so than the wigeon, for though it does visit fresh-water lakes it will only do so if they are near the sea. Inland the pintail is distinctly rare, except in Northamptonshire. It is a bird of the seashore and estuary, and is shot more frequently by the punt-gunner than the shore shooter. I think the pintail is a nocturnal feeder by nature, for even undisturbed I have not seen them feed by day. But they are naturally shy and excessively suspicious, and, it may be, need absolutely quiet conditions before they will feed by day. They are quite at home on the land, walk well and even gracefully, and can run with ease, but except in the breeding season they rest offshore in large packs or small parties and flight inshore only after dark, leaving again before dawn. The flight is exceptionally swift with very quick wing-beats. I would put the pintail as by far the fastest of our ducks. The wings make a hissing sound, unlike that of any other duck, and so the pintail is easy to recognise even on the darkest night. I have never, by the way, heard a pintail utter a sound.

The Shoveler (*Spatula clypeata* (Linnaeus))

A summer resident, a passage-migrant and a winter visitor. The shoveler cannot possibly be confused with any other British duck ; the enormous spatulate bill makes that quite impossible. And this bill is conspicuous on the water and in flight. The drake is a strikingly handsome bird with dark green head, white breast and scapulars, chestnut flanks and underparts. The forewing is pale blue, and sometimes this is conspicuous in flight. The duck's plumage is very similar to that of the duck mallard, but the bill is quite sufficient to prevent any confusion between the two. The speculum is bright green with a white bar before and behind it. The bill is black in the drake, brown with a more or less orange base in the duck. The legs and feet are orange, the duck's being as a rule rather dull. Eclipse in the drake is complete from about the middle of July until the end of September, but a very long time is taken to regain full plumage. I do not know that is is ever done before December, and I have known birds not fully plumaged in late January.

Our breeding birds are said to arrive with the passage-migrants at the end of February or in early March, and to leave again in August and September. I am not quite sure how that view is arrived at, and personally I find it very hard to accept. It is quite true that towards the end of August or in September most of the breeding places are deserted, but I cannot see that this must mean that all our breeding birds go abroad for the winter. I feel quite certain that they do not, and that plenty of them are full residents, being joined by large numbers of visitors in the winter. In winter distribution is much wider and numbers far greater. In February and March movement is very noticeable, and after March numbers are far fewer. The shoveler has increased greatly as a breeding species in the last fifty years, and now nests in every county in England regularly every year with the exception of Cornwall, Surrey, Wiltshire, Gloucestershire, Worcestershire, Derby, Northampton and Middlesex, and it has bred sporadically in all of those with the exception of Cornwall, Surrey, Wiltshire, and Worcester. In Wales it breeds in several counties along the coast, in Scotland regularly in the south and east, less regularly in the north and very sparingly in the west. In Ireland it is widespread and common. For breeding purposes the shoveler frequents lakes, reservoirs and large ponds, preferring those with grass banks ; it resorts in numbers to marshy pools, meres and streams, to sewage farms, and to the small pools of swampy country, so long as these provide some cover. Though the largest numbers are usually to be found on meres, I think the shoveler's real preference is for meadowland bordering a lake. The nest is a hollow in the ground lined with grass, down and feathers (and sometimes with such oddments as ribbon, string and silver paper), and is generally placed so that some shelter is afforded against the prevailing wind by a tussock of grass, a gorse bush or some similar bastion. Ten or eleven greenish eggs are usually laid in May and are incubated by the duck alone for nearly a month. The young are fledged in about six weeks and only one brood is reared in a year. The drake shoveler is not always indifferent to his family, and will sometimes rejoin them for brief periods, but does not help the duck in any way.

Outside the breeding season the shoveler is widely distributed, but always on shallow muddy waters, both fresh and brackish. This is because its feeding habits preclude deep water and the sea. The birds feed, as a rule, by paddling rapidly hither and thither with the head held low and the bill constantly dabbling in the water. But it will also stand and dabble about in the mud at the water's edge or in very shallow water. In my experience shovelers " up-end " a good deal and also dive for food a good deal, but these habits are generally regarded as unusual. On land the shoveler is a poor ungainly walker and a shockingly bad runner. Perhaps this accounts for the large amount of time they spend on the wing and on the water. They are powerful fliers, but by no means so fast as the mallard, and I doubt if as fast as the teal, though the very rapid wing-beats give an illusion of speed. They twist and turn about as much as the teal but without that bird's mastery of manœuvre, and they can spring into the air every whit as well as the teal. The flight, however, despite these resemblances, is not teal-like but rather that of the wigeon. When rising there is a rattle of the wings, and in flight the wings make their own distinctive sound. I have seen one or two large flocks of shoveler in the winter, but birds in small parties or even in pairs are more usual. They are silent birds, and I have only once heard them calling, and then the sound was not unlike the mallard's ; indeed, so like the mallard's was it that I was not for some time certain that it came from the shoveler.

Shoveler are comparatively easy to shoot, and in my opinion scarcely worth shooting, for the flesh, though quite eatable, is muddy to taste.

In addition to these seven surface-feeding duck which come regularly to the notice of the wildfowler, the green-winged teal (*Anas crecca carolinensis*, a North American race of our common teal), the blue-winged teal (*Anas discors*) and the American wigeon (*Anas americana*) have been recorded in this country, and will probably be recorded again. The wildfowler may have other surprises from time to time. The mallard drake is a bit of a Lothario and produces some surprising hybrids now and then. The cross with the pintail, though certainly not common, has occurred more than once. And once out of a bunch of mallard I shot a magnificent creature—golden brown but with a mallard drake's head, the product, I fancy, of some farmyard seduction.

The Diving Ducks

The diving ducks are stockier birds than the surface-feeding ducks. They have shorter bodies and their legs are set far back on their bodies; they walk very uncomfortably with the bodies held upright and an exaggerated waddle. They are not at all happy on land, and except in the breeding season come to it as little as possible. The wings are broad and narrow down more abruptly than do the wings of surface-feeding ducks. In flight the wing-beats are more rapid than those of surface-feeding ducks, and the feet stick out beyond the tail. There is no distinct speculum, though most species have white bars or patches on the wings. Eclipse, in most species, is much less marked than in the surface-feeders. Nearly all diving ducks find it difficult to rise from the water and have to patter along the surface for quite a long way before becoming airborne. Most of them pitch on the water awkwardly and with a good deal of splash and fuss. Nearly all the diving ducks like open water and do not bother about cover, and in winter most of them are purely sea-going in habit. All dive for their food—up-ending is uncommon—and all are expert swimmers. Fifteen species figure on the British list, but of these only eight need concern us here.

The Common Pochard (*Aythya ferina* (Linnaeus))

A resident and winter visitor. The drake with its chestnut-red head, light grey back and sides, black breast and black upper and under tail-coverts cannot possibly be confused with any other British diving duck. The duck is dull brown, as Anthony Collett put it, "dark brown fore and aft and a rather lighter brown amidships". The bill is light blue with a black tip and a blackish base, the eyes are red, and the legs and feet slate-grey. Eclipse in the drake lasts roughly from the beginning of July to the end of September, but sometimes it is much later before full plumage is resumed. In eclipse the drakes are very like the ducks but the back is much lighter.

Plate XXIX

WOOD-PIGEON feeding young. Radnorshire, 1937. ERIC HOSKING

WOOD-PIGEONS on stooks. Strath Spey. October 1943. G. B. KEAREY

Plate XXX

STOCK DOVE at mouth of nesting hole. Central Wales, 1926. A. W. P. ROBERTSON

As a resident breeding bird the common pochard has undoubtedly increased in recent years, but it does not seem to have extended its regular breeding range (I am not considering sporadic breeding, which has occurred in many places, in this connection) at all during the last 25 years or so. It prefers ponds or lakes where a large and thick growth of reeds and so forth provides a thick cover for the nest, and such waters are severely limited in this country, which is probably sufficient reason for the lack of spread. While it has bred in many counties its main breeding range is east of a line drawn direct from Dorset to Caithness. West of that line it nests regularly only in Easter Ross, Kirkcudbright, Wigtown and Anglesey. Many of our resident birds and their young leave their breeding quarters in August (sometimes at the end of July) and gather together on reservoirs or other large sheets of water, and this is particularly noticeable in the Thames Valley. There is, too, a general tendency to move south in winter (we have many more common pochards in Hampshire from early September onwards), but there does not seem to be any evidence of migration overseas. Winter visitors in considerable numbers begin to arrive on the east coast in September, the movement reaching its height about the middle of October and ceasing about the middle of November. These visitors leave again about the end of March. In winter, naturally, the bird is much more widely distributed on inland waters and occurs all along our coasts in situations that are not too explored, and some of these winter flocks run into hundreds. The species is, indeed, markedly gregarious, and outside the breeding season it is most uncommon to see one or two pochards : small parties or large flocks are the rule. Generally speaking, these winter congregations show a marked preponderance of drakes—eight or nine drakes to every duck is not at all uncommon, and there are records of flocks in which drakes have outnumbered ducks by fifty to one. In my part of the world six to one seems to be about normal.

Unlike the majority of ducks the nest is usually in or very near the water. Always sheltered by reeds or rushes, it is built up, like the nest of the coot, above water level by a liberal use of flags and rushes. Anything from six to eleven large greenish-grey eggs are laid from the end of April onwards, and are incubated by the duck alone for about twenty-four days. The young leave the nest very soon—always within twenty-four hours—after hatching and are expert swimmers and divers straight away, but they are not fully fledged until about seven weeks old. Only the duck has anything to do with them :

indeed, drake pochards form into flocks again in June. One talks about pochards pairing, but I am extremely doubtful if, using the word in the sense of forming couples, they do do so. It is common to see several drakes displaying around one duck—in point of fact I have never seen anything else—and this, coupled with the known preponderance of drakes—seems to suggest anything but monogamous habit, even monogamous habit for the short period of the breeding season.

The common pochard likes, outside the breeding season, open water of medium depth, and has a fondness for large sheets of water devoid of cover. When disturbed it will, in preference to flying, move farther out. It is, in fact, a very difficult bird to get on the wing. It rises from the water only with difficulty, pattering over the surface for some distance before becoming airborne, but once clear of the water the flight is strong and fast with rapid wing-beats. A flock rising for only a short way does so in a close bunch, but if on a longer flight such as one gets on the Hampshire, Northumberland and Norfolk coasts two formations seem to be usually adopted—long rather irregular lines or rather ragged Λs. Such flights are generally conducted at a pretty fair height and offer very good shooting. Normally, ducks glide in to alight on water, but I have often seen pochards plunge headlong to the water, alighting with much splashing and commotion in a higgledy-piggledy muddle. Except in the breeding season—and to a lesser extent in the late spring—the pochard does not come to land very often. For a short distance it can walk with comparative ease, but like all diving ducks it is not at home anywhere but on the water. It swims low in the water, and in shallow water will sometimes "up-end" like a surface-feeder, but normally it dives—in water of any depth with a distinct jump, in shallow water without any apparent fuss or trouble. Its food is almost entirely vegetable matter, but I have seen pochard take fish, and they are undoubtedly very fond of tadpoles. In my experience pochards prefer to dive in about three feet of water, but they can undoubtedly dive to considerable depths. The longest recorded dive appears to be 30 sec., the average is about 20 sec.

The Tufted Duck (*Aythya fuligula* (Linnaeus))

A resident, winter visitor and passage-migrant. The drake is black with pure white flanks, and the contrast is so distinctive that no one can mistake it. Closer at hand the tuft and the round golden eye are also distinctive, but the head tuft is frequently not noticeable at any distance. The duck and the young are very dark brown birds. In the winter the duck shows some white on the sides above the water-line, but in the breeding season none. The bill is blue with black nail and the legs and feet are bluish-grey. In flight both duck and drake look black with a white belly and broad white wing-bars. Eclipse in the drake begins about the end of June, but is rarely complete before the middle of August, and lasts until November. Full plumage is rarely resumed much before the end of November. In eclipse the drake is very like the duck, and I, at any rate, cannot distinguish between the two at any distance.

As a resident the tufted duck has greatly extended its range in the past twenty-five years or so. For breeding it prefers much the same sort of water as the common pochard, and this restricts spread to some extent, but it is not quite so particular and so is much more widely distributed. Although like the pochard it is not so common as a breeding species in the west of England (and most of Wales and on the north-west coast of Scotland it is rare or unknown), it is widely distributed, and in some districts extremely numerous, in Ireland. As with the pochard our adult birds and their young tend to leave their breeding quarters and gather in flocks on large sheets of water from mid-July onwards, and there is also a tendency to move southwards at this time of year, but there is no evidence that our birds pass beyond our coasts in winter. Winter visitors begin to arrive on our northern and eastern shores until the end of November. Many of these birds, particularly the northern ones, pass on to Ireland, but there does not seem to be any evidence that any of our winter visitors pass through farther to the south. The return movement begins about the end of February, but all such movement does not end much before the end of May. In winter, of course, the distribution is much more general than in summer. Birds, if undisturbed, will visit park waters and town ponds—I have seen many in the heart of Manchester—but the tufted duck is not fond of the sea and is by no means common or even usual along the coast. On migration, of course, they occur on the coast, but they only pause for a rest, beyond this only a severe frost will drive them to the sea. In early 1940 there was a flock of some 800 birds near Lymington for a while, but they were never any distance from the land. The tufted duck is pre-eminently a bird of fresh water. Markedly gregarious, parties of twenty-five or so are normal, but I know a lough in Northern Ireland that in winter is, as a rule, black with birds. There does not seem to be any marked difference in the numbers of the sexes in these flocks. In Hampshire ducks, if anything, outnumber drakes, while in Hertfordshire, I am told, the reverse is the case.

Breeding on islands in large lakes for preference, the tufted duck will also breed happily on very small ponds (it is a bird that takes readily to captivity and becomes very tame), though some cover on the bank is almost essential. There is a decided tendency towards nesting in colonies. The nest is never far from water, and is usually well sheltered. Six or seven green-grey eggs (very large eggs for the size of the bird) are laid towards the end of May—eggs in late June are by no means uncommon—and are incubated by the female alone. The period of incubation may be anything from three to four weeks, and the young, though they can swim and dive well a few hours from birth, are not fully fledged until they are six weeks old. Personally I have never come across more than ten eggs in a nest, but sometimes several ducks will lay together and as many as twenty-eight eggs have been found in one nest. Pairing, so far as the tufted duck is concerned, seems to be the right word, for courtship and display, though very subdued, seems always to be between one bird of each sex. I have seen two drakes chasing a duck on several occasions, but always after duck and drake have paired, the second drake being an intruder. The drake, however, does not take the slightest notice of his offspring.

So far as general habits are concerned, the tufted duck behaves in much the same manner as the pochard, but is rather more easy to get on the wing and is less inclined to " up-end ". The favourite diving depth is rather greater than in the pochard, and both duck and drake like turning over stones at the bottom. The food is much more largely composed of animal than vegetable matter, and frog-spawn, tadpoles and small fish are greedily taken. I can find no record of the longest dive. Millais gives fifty seconds as typical, forty seconds is the longest I have timed, and I should say that thirty seconds is about average. Dives to a depth of twenty feet have been recorded.

The Scaup Duck (*Aythya marila marila* (Linnaeus))

A winter visitor and passage-migrant. Seen at close range the drake has black head, shoulders and breast, grey back and white flanks, and the black head has green gloss. At a distance it is easy to confuse the drake scaup with either drake tufted or drake pochard, and particularly so in the case of individual birds. Happily individual scaup are uncommon, and the duck scaup with a broad white band round the base of the bill is distinctive. Furthermore, scaup have rather different habits from the tufted and the pochard and frequent rather different waters, and, provided that one has some general acquaintance with ducks and their habits, confusion should be avoided. In the scaup the round eye is a rich golden-yellow, and the bill, legs and feet bluish-grey. The above applies to mature birds. It is by no means easy to distinguish between an immature drake scaup and a duck tufted, and quite impossible to tell an immature duck scaup from a duck tufted at any distance, and by no means easy in the hand. So far as living birds are concerned, however, the difference in habits outweigh any similarity in appearance.

As a winter visitor the scaup reaches our northern coasts about the middle of September and continues to come in until the end of November. Many pass through to Ireland, but there does not seem to be any evidence that birds coming to us pass beyond our shores. The return movement commences early in March and continues until about the middle of May. Occasionally, however, some birds stay through the summer but without breeding. The scaup has, however, bred in Scotland on a number of occasions.

Outside the breeding season—and that is all that need concern us—the scaup is thoroughly gregarious and thoroughly marine. It is very uncommon on reservoirs or other large sheets of water inland (the common resort of tufted and pochard), and is uncommon on fresh water anywhere, though it will visit fresh water when it is near the coast. Beyond this it prefers estuaries and bays. Very hardy, it does not in the least mind cold, and the stormiest weather will not drive it inland. I have noticed flocks resting on the shore just above high-water mark in March, but generally speaking the scaup rest on the water. Flight is high and fast with rapid wing-beats, and flocks, in my experience, fly in bunches. Flocks of hundreds are common, but on the water they stretch out in long lines. Being sea-going birds feeding times are governed by the tides, but on stretches of coast that are much shot over the birds fly largely by night. Rough water does not appear to impede feeding to any great exteent, and I think they normally feed in deeper water than either the pochard or the tufted, though they also feed in the shallow pools left by the retreating tide on mudflats. The longest recorded dive seems to be 60 seconds and the greatest depth 21 feet. The average dive is short, say 15 to 20 seconds, and the usual feeding depth is round about 10 feet.

The Goldeneye (*Bucephala clangula clangula* (Linnaeus))

A winter visitor and passage-migrant. The drake is a boldly contrasted black and white bird, mainly black above and white below, with a black head and a white neck. There is a round white patch between the eye and the bill which is conspicuous even at long range. Seen very close at hand or dead the black head has a green and purple gloss. The duck is a mottled-grey bird with a chocolate-brown head and a white patch on the wings. In flight goldeneye look very short-necked, and the broad white patch on the wings is very noticeable. But I think that the chief characteristic of this species, the one by which it may at once be recognised anywhere, is the triangular shape of the head. The head is not, of course, triangular, but the crown feathers are so arranged that they give one that impression. The name comes from the bright yellow eye. The bill is blackish with a yellowish tip in the ducks. The legs and feet are bright orange in the drake, noticeably less bright in the ducks. The drake is in complete eclipse through August and September, but full plumage is not resumed until late October and sometimes not much before Christmas.

As a winter visitor goldeneye reach our shores about the middle of September and the movement, which reaches its peak towards the end of October, continues until the middle of November. The return movement commences about the middle of March and continues into May. But goldeneye are frequently seen in summer and have nested in England (in Cheshire in 1931 and 1932), and it seems probable that the species is in the process of extending its breeding range. While there is no evidence that our birds pass south beyond our shores in winter, there is in early April an appreciable increase in numbers along the south coast, and I think these are birds returning to the north from farther south. Breeding birds prefer lakes and rivers in wooded country. Normally they nest in holes in trees, and they will take over suitable nesting boxes, but in Cheshire they nested in rabbit-burrows. Six to a dozen blue-green eggs are laid—they are very bright blue when newly laid but fade quickly—from the middle of April onwards. Incubation is by the duck alone and lasts about four weeks, and the drake, though it has nothing to do with tending the young and seems to lose all interest in the matter once the young are hatched, does stay about in the vicinity of the nest while the duck is sitting. The ducklings get themselves out of the nest and can swim and dive immediately, but are not fully fledged until about eight weeks old.

Outside the breeding season the goldeneye is chiefly a sea-going duck, preferring the sea coast and the tidal estuaries, but it does also occur in small parties on large sheets of fresh water far inland. Like the scaup it is hardy and does not mind severe cold or rough weather. Unlike all our other regular diving ducks it rises very easily from the water, almost as easily as a surface-feeder. In flight, which is strong and fast, the wing-beats are very rapid, much more than is the case with any other British duck, and they make a distinctive ringing sound. Most diving ducks are hard to get on the wing ; the goldeneye spends a good deal of time on the wing, and is altogether a restless creature, rarely remaining still or in one place for long. It does not come to land often, but when it does is certainly much more at home, walking quite gracefully and quickly, than other diving ducks. In the breeding season ducks will perch on the branches of trees, but I have not heard of drakes doing so. It is much less gregarious than most ducks, and solitary individuals are by no means uncommon, but while parties of ten or so are usual very large flocks are sometimes seen on migration. The largest I have ever seen in the British Isles has been forty-nine off the east coast of Scotland, but in Denmark I have seen flocks of several hundred in March. It is exceptional to see goldeneye in the company of other duck, and if they are on the same inland water as other duck you will almost always see all the goldeneye together. There seems to be a definite preponderance of ducks in the parties around our coasts in winter, certainly along the south coast it is by no means uncommon to find parties entirely composed of brown heads. Millais says that goldeneye flight at night to feed in brackish water or freshwater lakes. My personal experience is exactly the reverse. The goldeneye, I know, are day-feeders. The food taken is almost entirely animal. The bird is an expert diver, and will often dive to reach a particular place in preference to swimming to it. The usual depth for diving is about six feet (goldeneye always feed near the shore), and the average dive lasts about twenty seconds. The longest recorded dive appears to be fifty-five seconds.

The Long-tailed Duck (*Clangula hyemalis* (Linnaeus))

A winter visitor. This is a most distinctive bird on or off the water. In winter both sexes have the head mainly white and the flanks and underparts white, and the drake, with his bold pattern of brown and white and his very long and pointed tail, is quite unmistakable at any distance. But, even more than the colouring, the shape of the head is, I think, sufficient to ensure correct identification. It is a small and rather delicate head, with a short bill and a noticeably steep, almost abrupt, forehead. Added to this there is a distinctive call, and this is a noisy species which calls frequently. Beginning about the end of February the drake takes on breeding plumage in which the sides of the head are white, but the rest of the head, the neck and the breast is dark brown and the back is reddish-brown. This plumage is complete by the beginning of May and lasts until about the middle of June. The eclipse plumage, which is complete in July and August, is very much the same, but the long tail feathers are shed. Winter plumage is generally complete by the middle of October, but I have shot a bird in full winter plumage late in November. The bill of the drake is pink with a black tip and a blackish base, the bill of the duck is blackish. The legs and feet of both sexes are slate-grey.

As a winter visitor the long-tailed duck reaches our shores about the end of September, and the movement continues until the end of October. Return movement commences early in March and continues until May. It is a regular visitor to our eastern coasts as far south as the Essex marshes, on the south coast it is scarce and occasional, and the west coast can best be described as rare. Inland it is altogether exceptional. It has bred in both Shetland and Orkney, and a few birds seem to stay throughout the summer in northern Scotland.

Outside the breeding season this is a thoroughly sea-going duck, preferring the open sea and resting and feeding as a rule well away from the shore. It is, therefore, a punt-gunner's duck rather than a shore-gunner's, but it will sometimes feed inshore, and even flight in to fresh water near the coast on rare occasions and so sometimes falls to the shoulder gun. It is a restless and noisy bird, calling continually both on the water and on the wing. The call is loud and resonant, and I have not yet seen it translated satisfactorily into words. To my ear it resembles the bagpipes, but whatever it resembles, once heard it can never be confused with the call of any other bird, nor can it ever be forgotten. The flight, too, is distinctive—low and fast, with a pronounced swing from side to side (the long-tailed duck is an astonishingly difficult mark), and with a peculiar un-ducklike wing action. If you see a bird that is now white, now black, as first the white under-

Plate XXXI

SCOTTISH RED DEER. Inverness-shire, 1927. SETON GORDON

SCOTTISH RED DEER. Inner Hebrides. July 1938. G. B. KEAREY

Plate XXXII

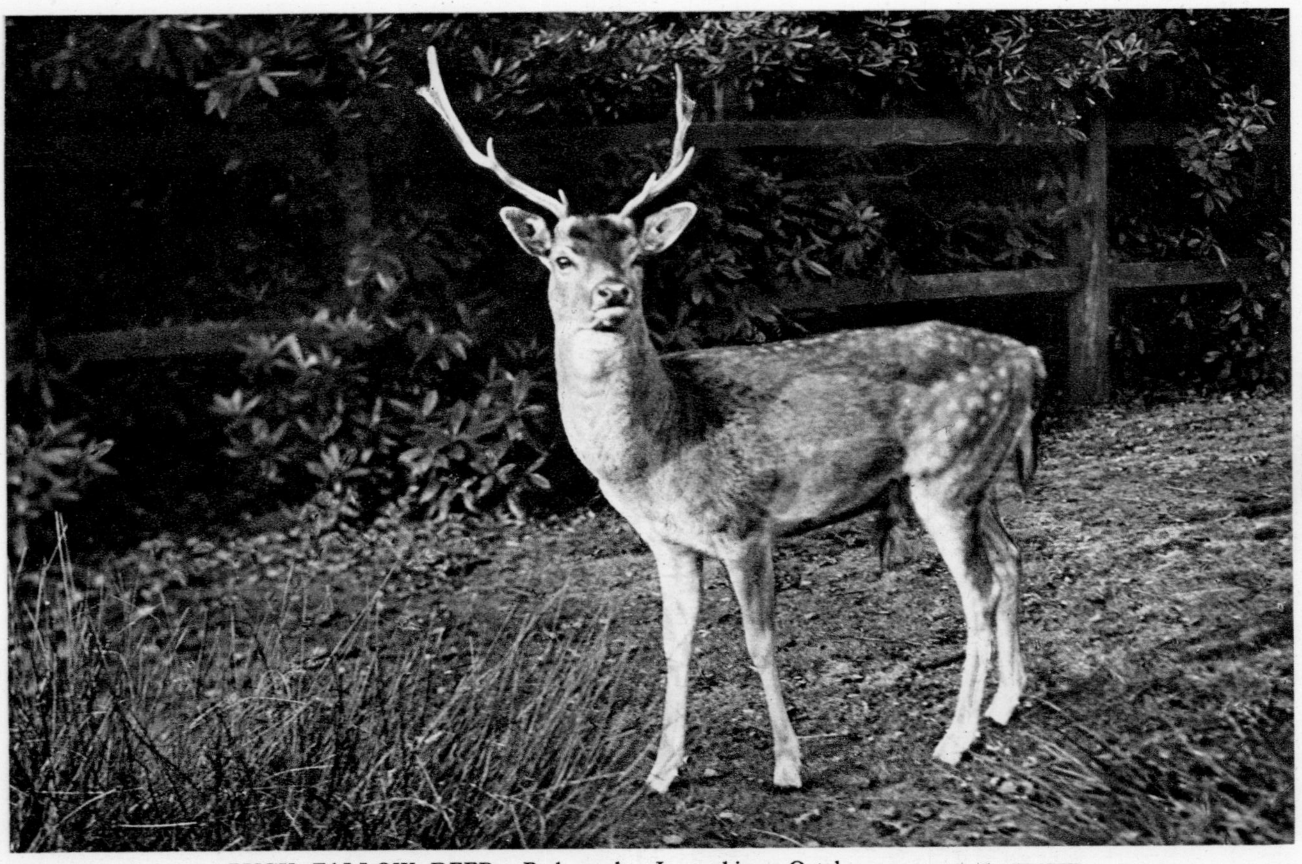

BUCK FALLOW DEER. Park stock. Lancashire. October 1939. G. B. KEAREY

parts then the brown upperparts are visible in the swinging action, and the wings do not seem to be above the body at all ; a long-tailed duck.

Like the goldeneye the long-tailed hardly ever associates with other ducks, but unlike the goldeneye it is markedly gregarious, flying in loose flocks strung out in irregular lines. Those birds that I have seen alight on the water have not glided at all but have just dropped down abruptly, landing with a big splash. I have never seen a long-tailed duck on land, but it is said to walk gracefully. An expert diver, it will go to depths of fifty feet and more, and I have seen it dive from the wing. Normally the duration of the dive is about 30 seconds. The longest recorded is 90 seconds.

Most of the birds round the English coats are immature, and on the south coast in particular an adult drake is a prize indeed for the shore-gunner.

The Eider Duck (*Somateria mollissima mollissima* (Linnaeus))

A resident. The drake, with his black crown, black flanks and underparts, and black tail boldly contrasted with the white of the rest of the body, is unmistakable. The duck is warm brown mottled and streaked with black. Quite apart from the colouring, both sexes may be recognised at once by their heavy build and the flat shape of the head. In flight the whole forewing of the drake is white. The drake is in full plumage from about the end of November until the end of June. The eclipse plumage is blackish, giving the bird a dingy appearance, rather as if it had been dipped in soot. The bill is yellowish-green at the base and bluish-green at the tip with a greyish-white nail. The legs and feet are yellowish-green.

In England the eider breeds only along the coast of Northumberland, on the Farne and Coquet Islands, and on Holy Island. In Scotland it breeds along the east coast from Berwick to Aberdeen, along the north Sutherland coast, along the west coast in suitable places down to Wigtownshire. In Ireland it breeds only on islands off the Donegal coast. It is common in Orkney and Shetland. In winter it can only be regarded as uncommon south of its breeding range, but it does occur in small numbers at irregular intervals all around our coasts from October to March, and I have seen a drake in full plumage off the Isle of Wight in May.

For breeding purposes it likes low-lying coasts and islands with sandy shores and plenty of rocks. In most of its British breeding range it nests close to the sea, but in the Outer Hebrides and Shetland it nests also on hills and lochs inland. It is a social nester, and where undisturbed or protected these colonies sometimes attain great numbers. The nest, made of grass and seaweed or any other handy vegetation, is lined with down and feathers in a most liberal manner, and is built by the duck. The usual number of eggs is about six, but numbers far in excess of this, probably due to the layings of two females, are not uncommon. Nests are often very close together, and the eider duck is not over particular about laying in her own nest. The colour of the eggs is very variable. Pale olive is probably the most common, but I have seen green, greenish-grey, buff, buffish-yellow, and bright blue eggs. In Northumberland they are laid from mid-May onwards, in Scotland rarely before June, and incubation, which lasts four weeks, is by the duck alone. The young are taken to the water by the duck as soon as they are dry, but they take little notice of their mother after that, attaching themselves to any duck that happens to be about and being tended by her. They form, in fact, nurseries under the charge of one female.

Outside the breeding season the eider is exclusively marine. Generally it stays well out to sea, but it also comes close inshore—especially off rocky coasts—where reefs afford good feeding. It comes to shore much more commonly than other diving ducks. Indeed, in spring and autumn it spends a good deal of time on land resting and preening, and though it walks with an exaggerated roll and very slowly, it is obviously not ill at ease. The flight is strong and direct and a good deal faster than it appears. The bulky body, short thick neck, and the fact that the birds generally fly only a foot or so above the water make confusion with other species on the wing impossible. Furthermore, eiders almost invariably fly in single file with but a short distance between birds. Gregarious flocks running into hundreds are not uncommon off suitable stretches of coast, but these big bodies tend to split up into small parties without, however, losing touch with each other. The usual depth for diving is about 12 feet, but there is no doubt they can dive to much greater depths without any inconvenience. The longest recorded dive seems to be 47 seconds. In my experience dives are usually of short duration, and I should put the average length at under twenty seconds.

It is, perhaps, unnecessary to state that comparatively few modern eiderdowns contain eider down. But there is still a big trade in the down, and the eider is a bird much more valuable alive than dead. It should not be shot.

The Common Scoter (*Melanitta nigra nigra* (Linnaeus))

A resident, winter visitor and passage-migrant. The drake is an entirely black bird with a patch of pinkish-yellow on its black bill. The duck is a dark brown bird with a patch of dirty white on the side of the head. This patch is very noticeable at some considerable distance. Eclipse in the drake is scarcely noticeable and seems to mean little more than a brownish tinge to some of the black. The bill of the duck is black without the yellow patch (incidentally, the patch in the drake is not noticeable at any distance), and the legs and feet are black in the drake, dark brown in the duck.

The common scoter nests in the British Isles only in Scotland and Ireland. In Scotland it has bred in several places, but does so regularly in Caithness, north Sutherland, Easter Ross, east Inverness and Orkney. In Ireland it breeds on only one lough, but is doing so in slightly increased numbers. This Irish breeding-place is a large sheet of water with wooded islands and is different from the usual breeding haunts of the species, which are lochs in hilly country or moorland. The nest, a hollow lined with grasses and down and usually well sheltered, is never far from water. Five or six buff-coloured eggs are laid as a rule in June and incubated by the duck alone for about four weeks. The young, very well able to care for themselves a few hours after birth, are fully fledged at six weeks old.

Outside the breeding season the common scoter is exclusively marine—birds turning up on inland waters, as they occasionally do, are generally storm-driven—preferring open sea near the coast but avoiding water over reefs. It is a common winter visitor along our east and south coasts, but is less common along the west coast. Some birds are usually to be seen along the south coast throughout the year.

A heavily built bird, the common scoter does not rise very easily from the water (though more easily than the next species), and so far as my own experience goes is unable to do so unless facing up-wind. Once on the wing, however, the flight is direct and very fast (I fancy this is the fastest of all the ducks that visit Britain), with rapid wing-beats that make a high whistling sound. Generally it flies, like the eider, close to the water but not in single file. If it flies in formation at all it flies in a wedge-shaped bunch, but more usually there is no formation at all, the birds being strung out in long irregular lines. Outside the breeding season it comes to land very rarely, for though it does not relish rough water it is a good and buoyant swimmer and quite capable of riding out all but the worst storms. On the south coast, at anyrate, it seems to be a day feeder, choosing water about six feet deep and diving frequently for periods of about 15 seconds. On the Hampshire coast drakes are comparatively uncommon.

The Velvet Scoter (*Melanitta fusca fusca* (Linnaeus))

A winter visitor and passage-migrant. The drake velvet scoter, though rather larger than the common, is very difficult to identify correctly at any distance when at rest on the water, for the white wing patch, which is its chief characteristic, is then very often concealed. In flight this patch is conspicuous. At close quarters a small white patch is visible just below the eye and the side of the bill is yellow. Duck velvet scoters have two dirty white patches on the face, one before the eye and one behind it, and these are visible at a good distance. The ducks have black bills. The legs and feet in both sexes are red, but much brighter in the drake than in the duck. Eclipse in the drake is as inconspicuous as it is in the common scoter.

As a winter visitor and passage-migrant the velvet scoter reaches our shores about the middle of September and the movement continues until the end of November. Return movement commences in April and continues until the end of May. The species is regular all along the east coast of Britain and along the south coast as far as about Selsey Bill. West of Selsey Bill and right round the west coast as far as Anglesey it is very scarce indeed. I have seen considerable numbers in the Firth of Forth, but along the east coast of England and the eastern half of the south coast it never occurs in large numbers, parties of four or five being much more usual, and single birds being not uncommon. It is very common in Orkney in summer.

It is said to be a tamer bird than the common scoter, but I have not noticed this myself on the few occasions on which I have come in contact with it. It swims in single file, but flies in no sort of formation. Like the common scoter it rises from the water only with great difficulty, but once on the wing is fast, flying low over the water. Wholly marine in winter, it does not have the common scoter's dislike of rough water, and will feed and dive comfortably in choppy water over reefs, but will also come in to estuaries to feed in the shallow

PLATE 17

SNIPE

Coloured etching by Winifred Austen (recent)

PLATE 18

WOODCOCK

Coloured lithograph by Joseph Wolf 1866 From John Gould's BIRDS OF GREAT BRITAIN

water over mudbanks. Here it dives in depths of about four feet, but I have also seen it diving on the reefs outside Bognor Regis where the depth is certainly in excess of 30 feet. The maximum depth recorded seems to be about 60 feet, and the longest recorded dive is 180 seconds. Normally dives average about 30 seconds, and in shallow water about 10 seconds.

There is no sound reason why either the common scoter or the velvet scoter should be shot.

In addition to these eight diving duck, which come more or less regularly to the notice of the wildfowler, the red-crested pochard (*Netta rufina*), the ferruginous duck (*Aythya nyroca nyroca*), the buffel-headed duck (*Bucephala albeola*), the harlequin duck (*Histrionicus histrionicus histrionicus*), Steller's eider (*Polysticta stelleri*), the King-eider (*Somateria spectabilis*), and the surf scoter (*Melanitta perspicillata*) are included in the British list All of them are too rare to warrant consideration here, though the red-crested pochard occasionally turns up in some numbers on the east coast.

The Saw-bills

The saw-bills, with the exception of the smew, can be recognised at once by their slender build, long slender bills, and the crest of feathers at the back of the head. The smew is more generally duck-like but has also the crest. The flight of all of them is characteristic, with the head and neck held in a straight line with the body. In flight flocks are strung out in oblique lines, though occasionally a Λ formation may be adopted. They are diving birds and almost entirely fish eaters. They are not birds that should interest the wildfowler, for they are quite uneatable, and I do not propose, therefore, to give any detailed description of them. The drake smew, by reason of its outstanding appearance, makes a handsome trophy for the gunner and is undoubtedly shot for that, exceedingly inadequate, reason. The others are generally shot by those people who cannot resist firing at anything that flies. Four saw-bills figure on the British list. The goosander (*Mergus merganser merganser*), which breeds locally in Scotland and is elsewhere a winter visitor ; the red-breasted merganser (*Mergus serrator*), which breeds widely in Scotland and Ireland and is elsewhere a winter visitor ; the smew (*Mergus albellus*), which is a winter visitor chiefly to the eastern and southern coasts of England ;

and the hooded merganser (*Merganser cucullatus*), which has been reliably recorded only four times. The goosander is but partially marine in winter, and has a fondness for rivers and reservoirs. The smew is rather more addicted to fresh than salt water and rarely goes to open sea. The red-breasted merganser is almost entirely marine, but is rarely at any distance from the coast.

THE NUMBERS OF WILDFOWL

I HAVE heard wildfowlers who live by a particularly favoured stretch of coast declare that there are to-day as many duck as ever there were. Such men take a peculiarly parochial, and perhaps also a peculiarly selfish, view of wildfowl and wildfowling, though it is, I admit, hard to believe that numbers are decreasing when one sees a flock of many thousands resting on the water. But, as a matter of fact, there has been for the last fifty years or so a steady diminution in the world's stock of wildfowl. This steady decrease in numbers is world-wide—the numbers of particularly favoured winter resorts and the number of birds visiting them is steadily declining not only here but abroad—and has given rise to concern in many countries.

It was Canada that first drew attention to this state of affairs. Canada was continually complaining that she bred the duck and the geese and that the United States shot them in the most wholesale and thoughtless manner. It was a long time before any definite action was taken, but in 1936 the United States, as a temporary measure, limited the shooting of wild duck to about one month in the year. That was a drastic step and it pointed to a very drastic state of affairs. A very similar state of affairs exists in the Old World. Here, too, the duck and geese breed in the north and are destroyed in a remarkably reckless manner in the south. But in the Old World, despite international conferences and committees, nothing very definite on an international scale has been done. There has been much shortsighted opposition to any measure of protection from commercial interests. Sweden shortly before the war prohibited the shooting of wildfowl in three of her provinces : it was Sweden that first drew attention to the serious decline in wildfowl numbers in Europe, and this step on the part of her government shows clearly how seriously she views the situation. In contrast, France has done nothing at all. Her wildfowl have almost ceased to exist, and shortly before the war a million and a half shooting licences were issued annually. The average French "sportsman" ignores close season and all species come alike to him. Again, in Hungary, on the great marshland of Hortobagy, it is the common ambition of "sportsmen" to shoot hundreds of geese a day—and there are quite a few sportsmen. In Holland shooting gives place to decoying, and up to the outbreak of war approximately one million wild duck were taken in decoys annually. Decoys in other countries accounted for large numbers as well. It will be seen that "wholesale destruction" is not too strong a term. This wholesale destruction has, of course, been going on for many years and is not in itself entirely responsible for the decrease. It is the fact that it has continued, and perhaps increased, while other and dominant factors have altered that has brought about a situation so serious, both from the commercial and the sporting point of view, that it can only be rectified by international action over a period of years. This, in Europe, has proved impossible to accomplish in the past owing to the obstructive attitude of certain countries and certain vested interests, and it is to be hoped that when international action is again possible a saner attitude will prevail.

In the meanwhile let us consider the position in the British Isles. This is, of course, affected by conditions farther north, conditions on the breeding grounds, and over there we have no control at all. The grounds that chiefly matter so far as we are concerned are Iceland, eastern Greenland and Spitsbergen. Natural conditions in Greenland and Spitsbergen have altered very little since man first visited them, and in the last fifty years have altered not at all. I have heard at different times a good deal about the depredations of vermin —arctic foxes, ermine, and so forth—on these grounds, but these animals have always been there, and I know of no evidence to suggest that their depredations have increased. Their numbers are in any case subject to the most violent fluctuations, and while in one year they may levy a very heavy toll on nesting birds and their eggs, in another the birds will remain almost unmolested. The depredations of humans, however, is quite another matter. In Greenland, Spitsbergen and the smaller islands the eggs of ducks and geese are systematically plundered by hunters in the most wholesale and ruthless manner. This is a comparatively new feature, and is a purely commercial and profit-making enterprise on a large scale. In Iceland, too, eggs are taken by the inhabitants on an enormous scale. This is not a new feature. The eggs of wild birds have always been highly valued as food by the islanders, and the practice is certainly as old as the island's history. So long as enormous numbers of birds returned annually to breed it had little or no effect, but to-day, when the numbers of birds returning to breed decrease year by year, this systematic plundering of nests is quite another matter. Several breeding grounds formerly tenanted each year by enormous numbers of wildfowl are now wholly deserted, and the Icelanders themselves are perturbed. But the mere prohibition of egg-collecting for food—even were it possible—would not restore the situation. Conditions farther south must be altered also. The problem is an international one, but each country can do something to solve its own local problem.

Here, in Britain, the shooting man and in particular the punt-gunner is blamed for the decrease in numbers. Shooting is rather an obvious business, involving a certain amount of paraphernalia and a certain amount of noise, and a dead bird is evidence for all to see. Very few people trouble to look beyond the obvious, but the obvious is by no means always the most important. And so far as the British Isles are concerned, I would put shooting quite low down on the list of factors affecting the decrease of wildfowl. In my opinion these factors in the order of their importance are :

(1) Increased facilities of transport and the consequent spread of building.
(2) Reclamation of swamp lands, fens and marshes.
(3) Silting up of estuaries, inlets and harbours.
(4) Shooting.
(5) Decoys.

Of these the first is by far the most important. The internal-combustion engine has revolutionised life in these islands. It is now possible to reach places very quickly which formerly could be reached only with considerable difficulty, and often discomfort, and at the expenditure of a good deal of time and money. The centre of England is within a few hours' travel by road of the coast. As a result there has been much building around our coasts and much disturbance of wildfowl. Many examples could be given, but the Sussex coast will suffice. This has been ruined by the jerry-builder, and one formerly famous haunt of wildfowl has to all intents and purposes been destroyed. Pagham Harbour is still visited by duck and geese, but by fewer and fewer each year. Indeed, it is only in an exceptionally severe winter that wildfowl come in any numbers, and then they are obviously ill at ease. Examples could be multiplied for all our coasts. Easy travel has, of course, meant more shooting, and consequently greater disturbance of the birds.

The reclamation of swamp lands, fens and marshes, of course, destroys much animal life. It destroys the nesting haunts of many birds, it destroys much insect life, and it destroys large areas of breeding ground. Frequently it does much more than that: it destroys the general level of the water-table of the country. In the United States there has been a good deal of very ill-considered reclamation with disastrous results to the surrounding fertile land, and examples could be given for Europe also. In Britain we have been rather more fortunate, but some of our own reclamation has certainly not been wise. Coupled with such reclamation as we have done, there was for twenty years a neglect of agriculture that very nearly had disastrous results for all of us, and which affected wildfowl no less than it did the rural population. The neglect of drainage and the cessation of irrigation in water meadows did agriculture no good at all, and undoubtedly had an adverse effect on wildfowl. It is an entirely erroneous and ignorant view that good farming and wildfowl do not go together.

Decoys are regarded by many people with horror. In point of fact, they cut both ways. They can be very very destructive—abroad and particularly in Holland, where at the outbreak of war some 150 were working full time, they are very often destructive indeed—but they also offer daytime sanctuary to birds subject to fairly incessant persecution. In England and Wales—there have never been any decoys in Scotland, and they are now illegal in Eire, and there are none in Northern Ireland—there were at the outbreak of war only five decoys in full use, and one of these was used only for the ringing of duck and was therefore a sanctuary. In addition, six decoys were in partial use. These partially used decoys are of the greatest benefit to duck, for they offer sanctuary in return for a very small toll of numbers. These ten decoys in the ten years 1924–1935 accounted for an annual catch of some 11,500 duck, of which the four in full use accounted for more than 10,000. Decoying in England is dying out rapidly, and the number of duck destroyed by this means is certain to decrease. Decoys are expensive to maintain—the cost is something between £150–£250 per annum—but it would, in my opinion, be a great pity if the partially used decoy disappeared.

The shooting man, whether he be wildfowler or not, has many sins laid at his door by those who do not shoot. I would not say that he is blameless. In the past, at any rate, there have been shooting men who, in their eagerness to amass a huge bag, have done the sport little good, and there is always the man who will shoot anything just for the "fun" of it. There is also—happily he is becoming rarer every year—the man who will shoot any rare bird he comes across or any bird he does not know, either to find out what it is or in the hope that it is a rare bird. There are others—fortunately their number is insignificant—whose ignorance of wild life and of the ethics of shooting is as profound as the depths of their pockets. It would be foolish, and grossly unfair, to lay such sins as these men commit at the door of the shooting community in general. And certainly it would be most unfair to lay such sins at the door of the wildfowling community. Wildfowling is a hard sport. It carries with it little or no social kudos and a great deal of discomfort. In wildfowling you will find only those who count the game far above the prize. The man who will bear all the labours, discomforts and dangers of wildfowling, who will get out of bed long before dawn on a bitter morning, who will trudge miles over treacherous marshes in pitch darkness and icy cold carrying a heavy gun, who will stay out after dark has fallen in cold that leaves no feeling in fingers or feet on the off-chance of a shot or two that may well be unsuccessful, the man who will do all these things day after day maybe for weeks with but poor reward in the way of a bag—such a man is a wildfowler because he loves wildfowling and the solitary places, and such a man must inevitably be a sound naturalist with knowledge of and love for the birds against which he pits his wits.

It can safely be said that shore and marsh shooting for sport with the shoulder gun does no harm, and the total annual bag in the British Isles is so small as to be a negligible factor. Wildfowling with the shoulder gun is not a matter of big bags but of a few birds gathered here and there with much difficulty after a long time. It is true that modern travel has brought an increase in shore shooting. A lot of young men leave the cities nowadays—or did so until the outbreak of war—to blaze away on the shore. It is true that they did no good. They killed very few birds, pricked a few more, but they did create a lot of noise and a lot of disturbance. However, with very few exceptions they did not stay long. It is a hard business wildfowling, and wildfowlers in general are in my experience rather hard-bitten, morose and solitary men: the best companions on earth when you know them, but they take some time to know. Those young men who stayed became wildfowlers. The rest did not stay long enough to do much harm.

Punt-gunning is regarded by most Continental sportsmen as thoroughly unsportsmanlike, and British punt-gunners are widely credited with slaying thousands of birds every winter. In Britain, too, punt-gunning is regarded with disgust by many people and with contempt by quite a few shooting men who have never tried it. Possibly in the olden days very large bags were obtained : that is most certainly not the case nowadays. And the fact that many people believe that hundreds of birds are killed or wounded at every shot is very largely the fault of the punt-gunner. Punt-gunners in general are a little inclined to exaggerate. It is rarely safe to take a punt-gunner's word for his bag. Simple pride plays old Harry with figures. Actually there are to-day very few punt-gunners working in England. I should doubt if in 1939 there were 100, and probably there were not more than 20 in Scotland. Of these 120 punts, probably 40 were not used more than twice in a season, and the numbers of punt-gunners who live on the seashore (the fisherman-fowler type) and who are prepared to go out on every possible occasion is very small indeed, not more, I should say, than 50 in England and Scotland combined. Furthermore, the professional wildfowler has to all intents and purposes ceased to exist. I very much doubt if there were five alive, much less working, in 1938. The modern "professional" is really no more than a guide to wealthy amateurs. In addition to these punts there are a number of power-driven boats mounting punt-guns. The number is, I believe, fourteen. These boats are looked upon with contempt by all true punt-gunners, and their owners are usually regarded with disgust. I do not know that they kill many more birds—they may do so, but I should think it unlikely—but they do undoubtedly cause a great deal of disturbance, and I feel quite sure that they wound many more birds than they kill. It would be an excellent thing if all power-driven boats mounting punt-guns were barred by law.

Now what is the average annual bag of a punt-gunner going out regularly? Sir Ralph Payne-Gallwey, writing at the end of the last century, maintained that anybody using a double-handed punt did very well indeed to get 700 ducks and geese in a season. He was right. Inquiries made by the Wildfowl Inquiry Committee show that the average annual bag of a good punt-gunner working regularly in a good locality is about 400 ducks and geese. The average of twenty-six punts going out regularly, taken over a series of years and from all the coasts of England, worked out at 287 ducks and geese. The average bag per annum, taking in all the punts working in Great Britain, is only just over 100 ducks and geese. Large bags are altogether exceptional. The largest bag made in one season during the present century is 1,500 ducks and geese, and this was made by four men using the same double punt. The largest bag made by a single-handed punter was in the winter of 1917–1918 (an altogether exceptional winter) and amounted to over 1,000 birds, but this same man's annual average is only 152 birds. I think I have said enough to show that the punt-gunner does not slaughter myriads of wildfowl every time he fires his gun. As a matter of fact, he does not fire his gun very often—on an average through the season about once a day—and if he averages 15 birds to a shot he has done extremely well. He is much more likely to average something less than 10 per shot.

It is often held against the punt-gunner that his methods are unsporting and that he wounds a great many birds. An experienced punt-gunner wounds and loses very few birds in daylight, and at night practically none, for at night he fires from close range. It is true that novices do wound and lose a fair proportion of birds, because they usually fire at much too long a range. Novices make mistakes at other sports too. But the novice wildfowler has to learn pretty quickly or give up, and I should doubt very much if the number of birds wounded and lost by punt-gunners is in excess of the number wounded and lost by men using the shoulder gun.

The " unsporting " cry comes, of course, from those who have not tried punt-gunning. I am never quite sure what is meant by " unsporting ". If by it is meant that the birds have no chance, the accusation is pure and unadulterated nonsense. If by it is meant that no skill on the part of the gunner is required, then again it is pure nonsense. Handling a punt-gun is not easy. It requires great skill to bring a punt within range—at the very most 100 yards, preferably not more than 60 yards—of wildfowl in the open. Not only has the punter to get within range, he has got to choose the moment to shoot and he has got to shoot straight. A miss may well mean the end of the day, and every good punter is at great pains to cause as little disturbance as possible to the fowl. Disturbed fowl means no shooting. All this is not at all easy. It requires great skill and it requires great knowledge of the birds and their habits—not only of the birds that are being stalked but of any others that may happen to be about. It requires a very fair knowledge of water and weather and of seamanship. It requires considerable physical strength and complete physical fitness, and it requires quick judgment and the ability to shoot straight. In many waters it is, finally, not altogether devoid of the element of danger. All that is required is to fire on the average one shot a day on perhaps thirty days in a season if one is prepared to go out on every possible occasion.

It will be seen that I do not regard either shooting with the shoulder gun or punt-gunning as having a very serious effect on the numbers of wildfowl in this country. I may well be accused of bias. I have done a good deal of wildfowling, and I was initiated by one whose favourite sport it was—Abel Chapman. My shooting days are over. I derive, as I have always done and as did Abel, immense pleasure from watching birds. I can at least say that I know both sides of the picture. And my view of punt-gunning has not altered.

But I would not pretend that in conjunction with other factors shooting has not some effect. I know perfectly well that it has. I would very much like to see the close time under the Wild Birds (Ducks and Geese) Protection Act extended. At present the *minimum* close time extends from February 1st to August 11th, but there is a clause granting power to the County Councils to make application, should they think fit, to allow shooting on the "parts contiguous to the low-water mark of ordinary tides" up to a date not later than February 21st. County Councils have the power to extend the time of the close season but not to shorten it. I should very much like to see the powers under the Act removed from the County Councils altogether. The question is a national not a local one. And I should like to see the close-time period extended *as a minimum* to September 1st. The few days lost to the shooting man would not matter in the least (and few of them are so selfish as to think it would), and the gain to the birds would be immense. And I should like to see the clause giving extension on "parts contiguous to the low-water mark of ordinary tides" (a clause inserted to cover the shooting of wigeon and brent geese, but which opens the door to all sorts of abuses) removed altogether for a period of years. These things would help. But they would not be enough. What is so sorely needed is one or more areas in which all shooting of wildfowl is prohibited. The setting up of one or two such sanctuaries would be of immense value to the stock of wildfowl and would undoubtedly be of great benefit to the sport of wildfowling.

Part Three

THE WADERS

CHAPTER I

The Great Snipe (*Capella media* (Latham))
The Common Snipe (*Capella gallinago gallinago* (Linnaeus))
The Jack Snipe (*Lymnocryptes minimus* (Brünnich))

ALTOGETHER there are six snipes on the British list, the three listed above and the Faeroe snipe (which is a sub-species of the Common Snipe), the American snipe and the red-breasted snipe. The last three can be ignored. The American snipe has been recorded only once, the red-breasted snipe only six times, and the Faeroe snipe in the field is quite indistinguishable in appearance from the common snipe and has exactly the same habits.

The great snipe is a passage-migrant and a scarce one at that. Personally I have never seen a great snipe on the wing in this country, though I have seen a few in the poulterers' shops. The bird does visit us regularly in the autumn (mainly our east and west coasts) and probably regularly in the spring also, but it does not stop, and so is generally missed. Inland it is very uncommon indeed, but I am by no means sure that it is so uncommon on the coast. It sits astonishingly close, and I know experienced shore-gunners who maintain that without a dog you are much more likely to walk over them than to put them up. As I say, I have never seen one on the wing in England, but I have seen them in Norway and Denmark. There is no possibility of confusion with the common snipe, for the great snipe rises silently, flies directly and for no great distance, and is altogether a larger and darker bird with a noticeable amount of white on the sides of the tail.

Every countryman knows the common snipe, if only because of its drumming or bleating. It is a dark striped bird with a very long straight bill. The upperparts are richly mottled and barred with black, reddish-brown and buff, and it is the buff edgings to the feathers that give the effect of the longitudinal stripes on the back. The crown of the head is black with a central buff stripe, and the sides of the head are brown with buff stripes above and below the eye. The neck and the breast are buff with brown markings and the flanks are light buff, or dirty white, with more or less distinct white bars. There are narrow white tips to the secondaries, and the tail, which is barred somewhat irregularly with black and red, also shows a little white at the sides. The legs are pale green. "Sabine's snipe" is merely a melanistic variety of the common snipe. The great snipe has sixteen tail feathers, the common snipe fourteen, and the jack snipe twelve. The number of the tail feathers is commonly regarded as diagnostic, but the number in the common snipe is by no means constant. I have shot common snipe with sixteen tail feathers, and I have shot common snipe (all, by the way, melanistic, the so-called "Sabine's snipe") with twelve feathers. On the other hand, I have never seen a great snipe that had not sixteen feathers, nor a jack snipe that had not twelve.

One of the best-known sounds of the countryside in spring—in damp country at any rate—is the drumming or bleating of snipe. This is not the love-song of the bird, but is part of the display commonly associated with territory. Most birds have very definite love-songs (though some are only noises), and the snipe's is a montonous *chicka-chickarr* (that at least is how it sounds to me, though most of the bird books describe it as *jick-jack*), which is uttered on the wing or on the ground or when perched on a rail or post or the dead branch of a tree (I have never seen a snipe perch on a branch bearing leaves), and besides being the love-song it is also used frequently as a note of alarm. The drumming sound is exactly like the bleating of a goat—in Gaelic the bird is called *Gabhar-athair* (goat of the air), *Meann-an-athair* (kid of the air), *Gabhar-reodhtha* (goat of the frost) or *Gabhar-oidhche* (goat of the night), and in Welsh *Gafr-wanwyn* (goat of the spring), *Gafr-y-gors* (goat of the marshes) or *Dafad-y-gors* (sheep of the marshes)—and how it is produced has been the cause of much argument; still is the cause of much argument. There are three theories: that the sound caused by the air passing through the funnel-shaped wings strikes the two stiff outer tail feathers, causing the drumming: that the sound is vocal: that the quivering wings cause the sound.

This is what happens. The bird takes wing, rises to a considerable height, turns on its side and swoops downwards. As it swoops it produces the bleating or drumming. It flies up again and swoops again, flies up, swoops down, keeping a rough circle, generally, but not always, with the breast turned towards the centre of that circle. And each time it swoops it drums.

For a long time it was thought that the sound was made by the bird's wings rapidly beating on the downward swoop. But careful observers could see no movement of the wings. Yet, they argued, as the noise is made on the downward swoop it must be produced in some way by passage through the air. In 1856, Meves, a Swedish naturalist, noticed in the downward swoop that the two outer feathers stood out at right angles to the rest. He fastened a pair of those feathers to wire on the end of a stick, swished the stick through the air, and found that he could reproduce the sound of the drumming. Sir Philip Manson-Bahr, in 1907, experimented in the same manner, but with feathers stuck in a cork which he whirled round his head on the end of a string. He, too, produced the drumming sound. His conclusions were generally accepted, and later still—round about 1920—Mr. Eric Parker corroborated his evidence when he fitted the tail feathers to an arrow, shot the arrow up into the air and produced the drumming sound as it fell. That the two outer tail feathers produce the drumming is the generally accepted theory.

But you will find many men who do not accept it, and among these men many competent ornithologists who know the common snipe well. I do not think you can dismiss the views of these men by merely saying (as does the *Handbook*) that they are imperfectly acquainted with the facts. I was until very recently quite convinced that the sound was not produced by the outer tail feathers, and I was certainly well enough acquainted with the facts and well enough acquainted since boyhood with the snipe. I have spent hours watching snipe, and more than once I have detected the drumming *before* the bird has turned for the downward swoop. I, too, have tried the accepted experiment with the tail feathers, all three of them. And though I, too, produced a sound something like that of a snipe drumming, it was not—to my ears—exactly like a snipe drumming. Of course, no two men hear the same sound exactly the same, but I found the result unsettling to say the least of it. And there were other factors that prevented me from accepting the evidence brought forward by Meves, Bahr, Rohweder and Parker. If the drumming is instrumental, would not other snipe produce the sound in the same way? The great snipe drums: and the great snipe has no outer tail feathers capable of producing such a sound in flight. Furthermore, the great snipe has been observed to drum on the ground. The jack snipe drums, producing a loud noise like a horse galloping on hard ground, and the jack-snipe, though he soars to a great height and swoops downwards, has no tail feathers capable of producing such a sound. And finally, the common snipe has been observed apparently to drum on the ground, not once but several times. In view of all these matters—and I do not think you can dismiss them lightly as being due to faulty observation—I found it impossible to accept the tail-feather theory and in a book I wrote, published as recently as 1939, I plumped for the vocal theory. I have since changed my mind. I now believe that the sound is instrumental. I have changed my mind because since the publication of that book I observed three different snipe drumming on three different occasions in three different places, and all three in the course of their downward swoop, and while producing the bleating sound, uttered the *chicka-chickarr* love-song. I do not believe that any living creature can produce two utterly different vocal sounds at the same moment. One of them must be instrumental, and I know that the *chicka-ckickarr* is not.

The drumming flight is not the only aerial evolution performed by the snipe during courtship. All sorts of other stunts are performed, the most remarkable of which is that of turning over on the back and gliding with open wings for some little distance either in ordinary rapid flight or during the course of a drumming display. The usual zigzag sexual chases common to many birds are also performed, and there are many variations in flight. On the ground males display before females with drooped wings and spread tail, and I have watched males circling round a crouched female alternating their walk with stiff little sideways jumps. Drumming, however, is not confined to the breeding season. I have more than once heard and seen snipe drumming in August, and the latest date on which I have heard and seen the performance is November 6th—that was in 1938. The earliest date on which I have seen and heard it is February 18th, 1927.

Snipe are early breeders. Eggs in late March are by no means uncommon, though early April is more usual. Eggs have also been found in August, so in some cases at any rate the bird is double brooded. The nest is almost always situated on damp or marshy ground. It is no more than a hollow in a tussock of grass or a clump of rushes—and is lined with grasses. I have, however, found snipe's nests most artfully concealed, the actual nest, in fact, being completely hidden from view, with an entrance at one side over which the rushes (I have never found this sort of nest except in rushes) form a sort of curtain which is most carefully adjusted by the bird every time she enters or leaves the nest. From a snipe's nest you will almost always find a well-beaten path leading away on one side for a distance of three yards or so. This is the route taken by the bird when approaching or leaving the nest, and in my experience there is never any variation in the route from the day the bird begins to sit until the chicks leave the nest. No snipe ever drops directly on to her eggs, and no snipe, given any warning of approaching danger, ever flies directly off her eggs. Always she alights two or three yards from the nest and walks up the pathway, and always when leaving she steals down the pathway before taking wing. The result is that the track before incubation has proceeded very far is plainly visible to an observant eye. The eggs, usually four in number and olive-grey to olive-brown in ground colour boldly blotched with sepia, are very large for the size of the bird. They are incubated by the female alone for about three weeks. The young leave the nest as soon as they dry, and it is said that they are tended by both parents and fed from the bill at first. I have never seen this happen myself. Indeed I am not at all certain that the snipe is not polyandrous. Snipe breed regularly on ground near my home, and it is not at all difficult to arrive at an approximate estimate of the number of nests on the ground. Snipe, in the breeding season, are not gregarious, and it is commonly said that each pair keeps a definite territory to themselves. You can form a rough idea of the territory and the position of the nest by the drumming of the males, and it is certainly true that on the ground I have in mind the nests are well spaced out. This ground usually carries about eight nests—twelve is the most I have ever found—and that would mean sixteen birds. But I have often noticed more birds drumming than I have reason to suppose there are nests, and regularly every year I flush birds in places where I am pretty sure there are no nests, and at a time when if there were a nest they should either be sitting or with young. Possibly these are non-breeding birds, but I am not convinced that they are. If they are, then there must be a pretty big population of non-breeding snipe in this country every year.

Snipe are much less frequently seen in the open than most waders. They are largely crepuscular in habit (they may be nocturnal), and they spend most of the day resting or sleeping in the cover of thick grass, rushes and so forth. But they do also feed in the daytime, for

I have often watched single birds doing so in the mud by the streams and ponds near my home, and more than once I have watched parties of half a dozen or so feeding unconcernedly on the saltings in broad daylight. The food is mainly composed of worms, water-snails of various kinds, and insects. They also take in a certain amount of grit in order to aid the digestion. Snipe are birds of ravenous appetite, and they lose condition rapidly if the food supply falls short. Snipe in a period of prolonged hard frost are very skinny creatures, and at the beginning of the shooting season they make remarkably poor eating. An August snipe is proverbially a rotten table-bird, ill-flavoured and thin. This, I feel sure, is because during the summer months insects form the greater part of their diet. Snipe prosper on a diet of worms and water-snails.

Snipe feed by probing the mud with their long bills. They are particularly fond of feeding in the wet mud at the edge of ponds and streams and in the thick ooze of bogs and sewage-farms, but they will also wade in shallow water, and I have seen them feeding in water so deep that at each probe the whole head was submerged. It is, however, very unusual for snipe to submerge their eyes, which are set very far back on the head, when feeding. The reason for this—and it is even more noticeable in the woodcock—is obvious enough. If you watch a feeding snipe you will notice that the bill is driven right into the mud and buried as far as the frontal feathers. If the eyes were placed in the normal position they would stand a very good chance of being buried, and even if they were not they would not be much good for seeing. As it is, the bird can make the most of its long bill and still see all that is going on around it. But the search for food is carried on out of sight. Food has to be found by touch, and the snipe's bill is admirably fitted for the purpose. It is extremely long—sometimes between 2½ and 3 inches in a bird that measures only 10 inches in all—and it is very pliable and very sensitive. If you examine the bill of a freshly killed snipe you will see that the end is bulbous and swollen and quite smooth. A bill dries and shrinks very quickly, and you will then see that it is pitted with a number of tiny depressions. If you were to take away the outer skin—an easy job—you would find that it is honeycombed with a multitude of little cells. You can see these cells (they are hexagonal) quite easily with an ordinary magnifying glass. These little cells are nerve containers, and they are joined up with the great sensory nerve of the face. It is by these nerves contained in the elongated bill that the snipe finds its

"THE MONARCH OF THE GLEN", RED DEER
Oil painting by Edwin Landseer 1851

PLATE 20

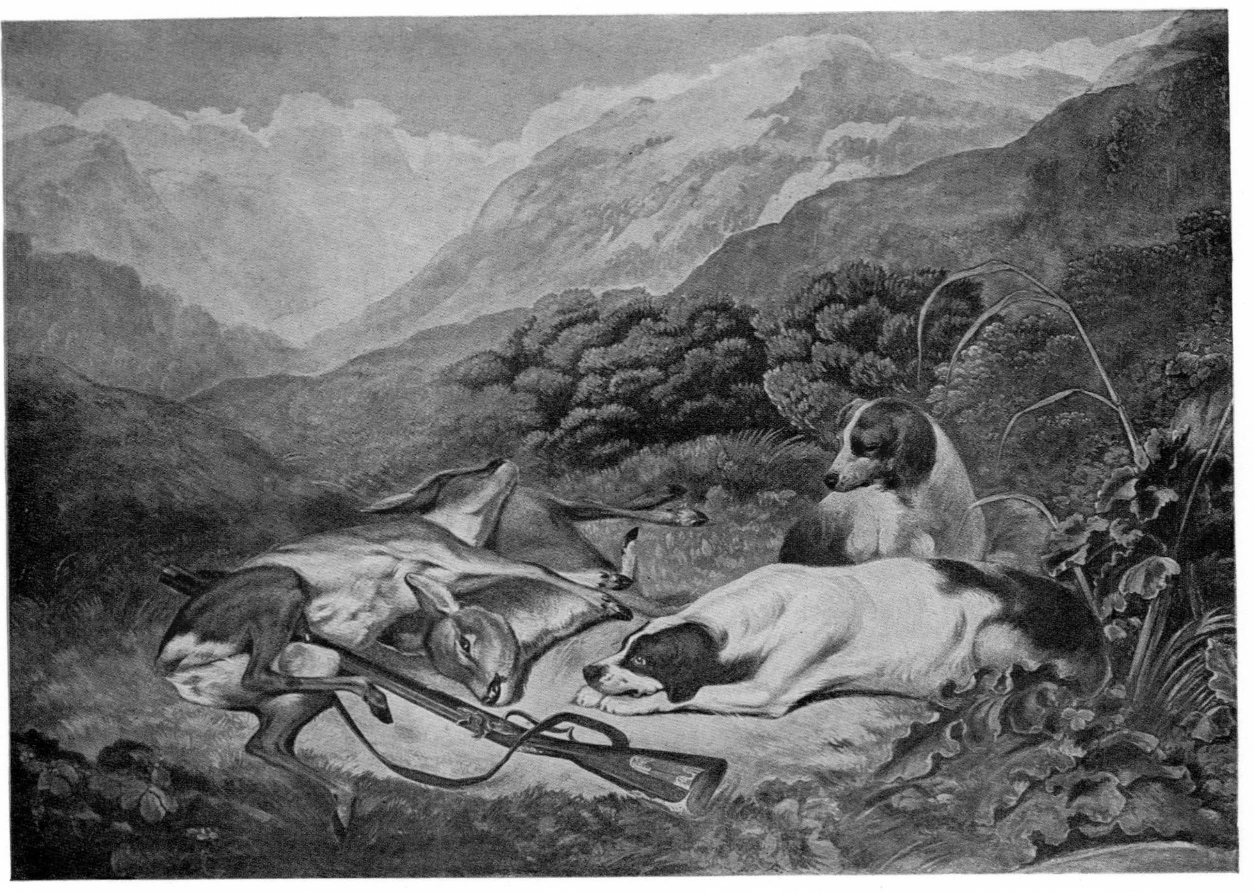

ROEBUCK

food in the thick mud and ooze. All the snipe that I have seen feeding have been remarkably unconcerned, moving in a slow, even stately manner, and probing the mud around them in a most methodical manner. I have, personally, never seen any of the jerky movements of the head so often described, and the movements are quite different from those of a feeding sandpiper. Sometimes the bill is buried only a little way, say to half its length, sometimes right up to the frontal feathers, but always it is slanted away from the bird. Sometimes it is in the mud only for a moment and is then withdrawn and immediately thrust into it again, but often it is thrust right into the mud and held there for a second or so, the bird remaining motionless the while. I have never seen a snipe bring food to the surface, and I imagine that almost all the food is sucked up in the mud.

A flushed snipe rises with a hoarse grating cry, very properly described in all the bird books as *scaap*. It springs into the air and then zigzags in rapid twisting flight close to the ground for some distance before rising to some considerable height and making off in direct and yet more rapid flight. A common snipe, once flushed, usually puts a good distance between itself and the cause of the disturbance. If taken unawares, not by any means a common occurrence, it will as a rule crouch and refuse to fly until the last possible moment, but snipe have remarkably good eyesight and remarkedly good hearing, and they are generally on the wing while danger is yet some way off. The flight is extremely fast, with very rapid wing-beats, but I do not for one moment agree with the estimates of 120 m.p.h. and more. I would content myself with saying that the sportsman is not likely to fire at many faster birds. In alighting the snipe is fond of dropping from a height—alighting by gradual descent is, I think, uncommon—and at the last moment it raises its wings high above the back in the attitude common to many waders. On the ground it walks deliberately with the typical horizontal carriage of waders and with neck drawn in and bill pointed downwards. In spring and summer at any rate it is fond of perching on rails, fences, bare branches of trees, walls, gates and so on. The habit is a common one, but seems, judging by the number of letters I receive every spring describing it as something most unusual, to be little known. Generally speaking, the snipe is rather a solitary bird. When shooting it is much more usual to flush snipe singly than in pairs or parties, but during migrations the birds move in parties or " wisps " of half a dozen or so. Larger parties are uncommon but do occur, and I have once put up a large party of snipe. This was in Galway. I flushed one bird which went off *scaaping* for all it was worth, and suddenly there were snipe everywhere, all *scaaping* like billy-ho. I estimated that there must have been fifty or more (it is just about impossible to count snipe under these circumstances), and they all broke away to my left. About a hundred yards farther on I flushed another bird, and again snipe rose all around me, *scaaping* hard. And this party I estimated at twenty or more. The date was September 15th, and I had not got a gun with me.

The common snipe is described in the *Handbook* as a resident, a passage-migrant and a winter visitor. If the word resident just meant that snipe are with us every month of the year I would be in entire agreement: but it does not. Resident means that the snipe that breed with us remain with us throughout the year. There is, says the *Handbook*, no evidence that British or Irish birds migrate abroad: in most nesting areas snipe are summer residents dispersing more or less locally as soon as the young can fly, by the middle or end of July: recoveries of ringed birds show movements of only a few miles before the end of September and almost complete sedentariness from October until March. This view, despite the recoveries, is quite contrary to my own experience.

I have observed snipe year by year on a marsh very close to my home for some twenty years now. And this is what happens. Very few birds breed in the marsh: there are perhaps eight to a dozen nests each year. If you walk the marsh carefully in the first half of July you will find plenty of birds: in the latter half of July comparatively few. In the first ten days or so of August you will be lucky if you put up two or three birds, but after that one day may find many birds in the marsh, the next none or only a few. This sort of thing goes on into early September when the marsh fills up and most days will find a few birds in residence (remembering always that the snipe outside the breeding season is a chancy bird), but from mid-September until the beginning of October, generally towards the end of the first week in that month, the odds are that you will draw a blank day after day. A snipe on this marsh is a rarity indeed in the latter half of September. The foreign migrants begin to come in October, and from then onwards the marsh is subject to the usual vicissitudes of snipe ground anywhere, but the latter half of September is blank. What I believe happens is this. The snipe that breed with us are at the northern limit of their range, and breeding accomplished they migrate in a southerly and south-westerly direction. That movement is, I believe, common to the whole country. But before this migration proper commences there is a good deal of purely nomadic movement, which may be local or may not. This movement is undertaken by the birds of the year, who do not wait for the adults to complete their moult, but set off on their own in small wisps towards the end of July, moving from feeding ground to feeding ground. The young birds of my marsh move off at the end of July, and for the first ten days or so of August I am left only with a few adult birds. After that I am visited by wandering parties of young birds, perhaps even by my own home young ones returning. In September the migratory movement proper commences, and the marsh fills up with birds that are moving steadily south or south-west. By the middle of September they have passed through, and there is a blank until the foreigners come in. Where do these resident birds go? If their movement were a local one of only a few miles one would expect suitable snipe country in the neighbourhood to receive additional birds at this time—for that matter one would expect to receive birds from neighbouring snipe country oneself. I certainly receive none, and so far as I know, and I am pretty certain that I would know, my neighbours do not receive mine. Perhaps the birds move on down towards Devon and Cornwall: I believe myself that most of them go overseas.

You may find the common snipe almost anywhere in this country provided only that the ground is wet. They like swamps and open grassy marshes, they like the boggy patches on hillsides, they like the peat moors, badly drained rushy fields, the borders of lakes, pools, streams and reservoirs, they like sewage-farms. They are to be found on the salt marshes of the coast, even occasionally on the shore itself, feeding right out to the limit of the ebb. That is a wide enough range of habitat, and you might think that any boggy ground would hold its snipe. But that is not so. If a marsh does carry a breeding population then you can be almost certain that birds will breed there year after year—birds born on the marsh returning to breed on it, as I think—and you will, in my experience, find the nests in very much the same position year after year. But that is just about all that is moderately certain about the snipe. Outside the breeding season there is nothing certain about them at all. I know excellent damp grounds, truly deserving the name marsh, which never hold a bird; I know many small damp bits of ground that hold snipe if there are any snipe about; but I do not know any ground in England of which

I could say that I would be certain to find snipe there on any winter day I chose to visit it. In Ireland you may take your boggy acres of shooting purely for the snipe : you do not, if you are wise, do that in England.

Nobody knows why snipe are so uncertain. We talk about certain aspects of the moon, and in this we are not altogether foolish, for it is known (though I doubt if many of us when we talk about the moon are aware of it) that lunar rhythm does affect worms in some degree : we talk about north-east winds—but we do not know. And it is quite certain, in my part of the world, that a nice soft southerly wind, warm and friendly, is just as likely to make the snipe leave as a hard north-easter : that is, if the wind has anything to do with it at all, which I doubt. Snipe are night feeders in the main, or at any rate feeders in the late evening and very early morning. Often you will know that there are snipe on the marsh in the evening, and when you go out in the morning they are gone. There may be frost in the air, there may be a bitter north-easter or a gentle southerly breeze, the moon may be full or new, the fact is that they have gone, and we were not about in the night to see what made them go. And had we been about in the night it is long odds that we would be any wiser.

And why is it that one bit of boggy ground will hold snipe if there are any about, while another, apparently just as suitable, will never hold any ? I think that the explanation of this lies in the sort of food the marsh provides. The major portion of the snipe's diet is made up of worms, and worms are to be found everywhere, so that at first sight this theory does not appear very sound. But I fancy that snipe eat more water-snails than is generally realised, and I believe that they do not go to ground that is devoid of water-snails if they can possibly help it. I do not know that any full ecological study of water-snails has ever been made, but it is well known that their distribution is very variable. It is well known also that certain sorts of water-snails occur only in certain sorts of water, so it seems to me that it is the water in the marsh and not the marsh that controls the presence or absence of snipe. If this is so, it should, with a little care and a lot of study, be possible to make snipe grounds attractive to snipe, and so within reasonable limits ensure a constant supply of the birds.

The jack snipe is a much smaller bird than the common snipe and with a relatively shorter bill, and unlike the larger bird it rises silently. It does not twist and turn so sharply after rising, and rarely flies more than a short distance before pitching again. Altogether it is not unlike

Plate XXXIII

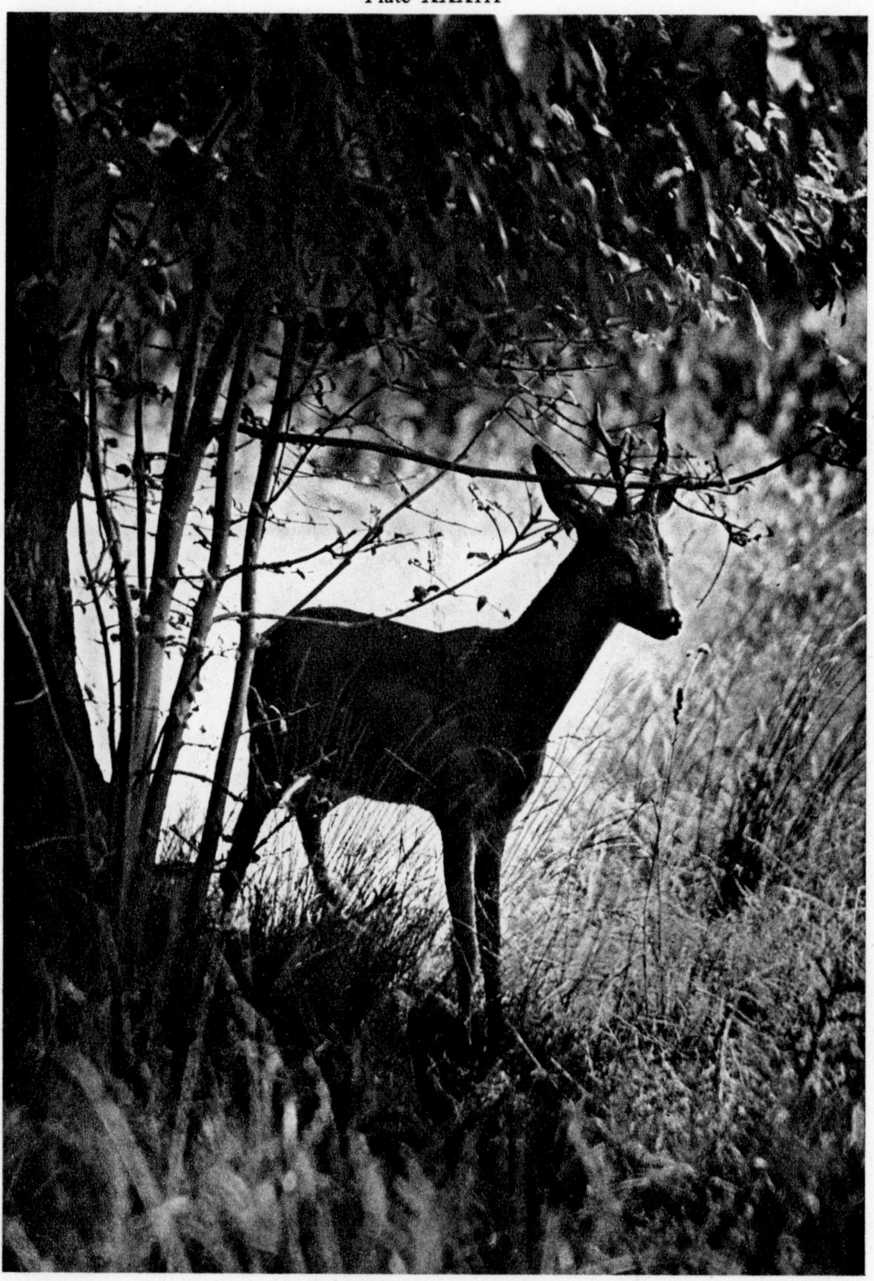

ROEBUCK. H. GORNY

Plate XXXIV

GOLDEN EAGLE and chick. Scottish Highlands, 1939. ERIC HOSKING

the landrail in habits, for though it possesses great powers of flight it will not fly unless it must. When flushed the flight is not unlike that of a butterfly, but I did once put up a jack snipe that immediately rose to a great height and set off in the general direction of France at a very great speed, an exceptional occurrence. Generally it is so reluctant to fly that it will crouch motionless until it is almost trodden upon, when it gets up with a breath-taking suddenness right under one's feet. On more than one occasion I have come upon jack snipe at my feet, and they have shown no alarm but remained there with bills pressed along the ground, and tail feathers, dark with lovely pale edges, fanned out, quite immobile, until having gazed my fill I have bent down to touch those shining feathers. Then they have got up and flitted rather than flown away, and dropped down again within fifty yards. Seen thus at one's feet the jack snipe is a very beautiful bird with its upper parts glossed with green and purple, and the longitudinal buff and chestnut streaks distinct upon its back and wings, and a broad buff stripe over its eyes. Incidentally, the central buff streak is missing from the dark brown head, and this, if you see the bird on the ground (which is not always easy as it loves thick cover), is sufficient to distinguish it from the common snipe.

The jack snipe is a winter visitor and passage-migrant. The birds reach our northern and eastern coasts about the second week in September, and the movement, which reaches its peak about the middle of October, continues until the end of November. They generally reach the Hampshire coast early in October (my earliest Hampshire record is September 4th and my latest April 7th), and emigration from this coast continues until late December. The return movement commences in March, and the passage north continues until late in May. There have been many records of jack snipe in summer and many suspected instances of breeding, but no authentic record of breeding has yet been reported.

Widely distributed, but decidedly local, the jack snipe is much more common than is generally realised. It is usually a solitary bird and it likes thick cover, and this coupled with its great reluctance to get on the wing means that it is less often seen than, from its numbers, it might be. I would be inclined to call it common in Hampshire even though it is comparatively rarely seen, and I have known numbers on my own particular marsh. Even when numbers are on the ground at the same time it is still the rule to put up one bird at a time, and I have only once seen a wisp of jack snipe. They are hard-weather birds and mind severe frost much less than the common snipe, and I think they secure a good deal of their food in the form of seed from the ground.

It is generally said the jack is an easy bird to shoot. It is also an extremely easy bird to miss, and I think this is because one always expects it to act like a common snipe and it never does. The common snipe, of course, is a difficult bird to shoot, and I think my advice to anyone going out for a day after snipe would be " take plenty of cartridges ".

There is always much difference of opinion as to the best way to walk up snipe. Most people seem to be of the opinion that it is best to walk down wind because the snipe, like most other birds, will get up against the wind if it possibly can, and so just possibly may fly past the gun. Personally I have never had any success walking down wind. Snipe are very wary and have excellent hearing. Also I have found that birds walked down wind are very wild, and even if they begin their flight into the wind they turn round quickly enough and go away down wind at a tremendous pace. Approach against the wind almost invariably means closer approach, but it does not mean easier shooting. However, nine times out of ten the nature of the ground governs the means of approach, and it is probably best to ignore the wind altogether. Personally I like to approach cross wind if possible (preferably, of course, with the wind on my left-hand side), because if the bird does start off into the wind he will be flying across the gun, and his acrobatics are then not quite so disconcerting, though disconcerting enough.

THE WOODCOCK

(*Scolopax rusticola* (Linnaeus))

USUALLY the woodcock is seen as, having been flushed from cover, it twists away among the trees, and then it appears a medium-sized reddy-brown bird with rounded wings and a long bill. The only bird with which confusion is at all possible is the common snipe, and, quite apart from the obvious difference in habits and flight, the much larger size and stouter build and the black transverse bars on the back of the crown are sufficient to distinguish the woodcock.

Woodcock vary tremendously in the range of their colouring. Pure white birds have been recorded on several occasions, and birds with some white feathers are quite common. Cinnamon blended with darker markings and cream and brown birds are also not uncommon. I have seen a completely buff bird, and Mr. Eric Parker records one in which all the lighter markings were almost lilac. But in general there appear to be two types of plumage : the one a rich rufous brown with a wonderful combination of black, buff, chestnut and grey in bars and mottles and vermiculations, and the other darker and greyer but with a similar though less definite combination. It is held by some that the grey birds (which tend on the whole to be larger) are English and the others foreigners. My friend, Major J. W. Seigne, who lives in Ireland and knows a good deal more about woodcock than most people, holds exactly the reverse opinion. The *Handbook* maintains that variations in colour are purely individual and not in any way connected with locality, sex or age. I imagine that very few Irish shooting men would agree with that. For myself, I can only say that I have not yet found in Hampshire a grey bird at the nest.

The woodcock is officially described as a resident, a summer visitor, a winter visitor and a passage-migrant—a description wide enough to cover all eventualities. It has bred in every county in the British Isles, but does so only locally in some and irregularly in many others. Generally speaking—and with the exception of Kent, Surrey, Sussex, Hampshire, Dorset and south-eastern Wiltshire—it nests most freely in the west midland, north and north-western counties of England, in Scotland (excluding the far north), and throughout Ireland except for the treeless districts of the west. As a winter visitor it is universally distributed. The majority of our resident birds are sedentary. There is a certain amount of dispersal movement, but in this the direction taken is haphazard and the distances covered small. This, at any rate, holds good for southern England and I think for Ireland, but northern birds do show more of a tendency to move southwards in the winter. Some of our breeding birds undoubtedly go abroad for the winter, but the vast majority of these are, I imagine, summer residents. Immigrants from the Continent begin to arrive on the east coast about the beginning of September, and the movement continues until the end of November, reaching its peak at the end of October and the beginning of November. At the height of the movement the birds come in in waves, often just in two very large ones, and these waves are remarkably punctual. One, on the Norfolk coast, is due about the 10th of November and is rarely more than a day or so out. The passage-migrants travel south and west. Many go to Ireland and there is no evidence that they go farther. The birds that reach the Hampshire coast about the third week in October (and it always seems to me that a large proportion of them are the grey type) begin to leave the coast at the end of the month, and the movement continues until about the beginning of December. From December until about the end of February there is also a good deal of movement related to the weather, but resident birds, if they move at all, do so only for a short distance. The return migration begins about the middle of March and continues until the end of April, the movement reaching its peak at the end of March.

The woodcock is a bird of the open woodlands. It does not like old woods that have become too big and thick, and it dislikes cold and draughty woods, as, for example, woods composed of tall beech trees. It likes moist oak woods, birch, larch, spruce and Scots pine, and woods with open glades and rides and a good cover of bracken and bramble and evergreen bushes such as holly, rhododendron and laurel. It likes plantations of young conifers, and also frequents rough ground that carries a scrubby growth of oak or birch or hazel and plenty of good cover in the form of bracken and bramble. But its particular liking, so it seems to me, is for larch woods, and especially for those larch woods that have patches of scrub oak and hazel or holly and an undergrowth of bracken and bramble. If there are some boggy bits or an overgrown ditch in such a wood so much the better, but the main essential is that there should be some good dry ground in cover, for the woodcock requires dry ground to rest upon by day. Whatever sort of wood is chosen it is never very far from marshy or boggy ground, to which the birds flight regularly at dusk to feed. So far as the breeding season is concerned, the same requirements hold good with the proviso that seclusion and freedom from disturbance are essential. In very severe weather woodcock will go to the coast and feed on the saltings. In at least one place in Hampshire birds flight regularly to the coast at dusk, and I know of another in western Ireland, but this is, I think, exceptional. In the very severe winter of 1940 the resident birds in my wood left—the only time I have known the wood deserted—and I suspect they went to the coast. In that winter large numbers of woodcock frequented the marshes of Lymington, and there were equally large numbers by the sheltered waters north of Hayling Island. In normal weather, however, woodcock are less inclined to go to the coast than any other wader.

Crepuscular in habit, the woodcock spends the day lying up in cover. It is very unusual to see a woodcock feeding in the daytime, but I have watched them feeding at midday in very frosty weather. The method of feeding is very much the same as that of the snipe, but considerably less stately, and I have several times seen food brought to the surface before being swallowed. Woodcock walk like snipe with the neck drawn in and the bill inclined downwards, but the walk is not nearly so easy and they seldom walk very far. When flushed from cover during the day they rise with a great swish of wings, but generally they do no more than dodge through the trees at a low elevation to come down again at a safe distance. But the flight varies a good deal. When undisturbed it is usually slow and rather wavery. I have often watched woodcock flying up and down the rides in the wood in which they nest by my home, and the flight reminds me of nothing so much as a large bat. It is a slow, muffled, undecided flight. But woodcock can fly high and very fast indeed, and I have seen birds flighting to feed moving directly and at a great pace. When thoroughly alarmed they can dodge between trees at a great pace too, displaying a marvellous mastery of distance and timing. The woodcock is the least sociable of all the waders. Except during courtship display it is exceptional indeed to see woodcock other than singly, and even when there are many birds in the same wood they behave quite independently of each other. Yet they have certain habits that can only be described as communal. The birds in my wood all use the same feeding grounds, and they all fly to these grounds by the same route and return by the same route, but they fly independently. They come flying down the ride—usually at a height of about five feet—one behind the other with an interval of a minute or so between each. At the end of a ride is a gate leading into a field and at the farther side of the field, about 350 yards away from the gate, is boggy ground bordering a pond which is connected with the river by a small stream some 60 yards long. This boggy ground, covering in all $3\frac{1}{2}$ acres, is their feeding ground ; they have others, but this is the main one. The birds come flying down the ride, but they never fly over the gate. Ten yards short of it they leave the ride, turning abruptly left-handed, dodging between two oaks (and always the same two oaks), and coming out of the wood between an oak and a holly exactly eight yards east of the gate. Bird after bird does exactly the same thing, and bird after bird has done exactly the same thing evening after evening for all the twenty and more years that I have known them in the wood. I do not, of course, by that mean that I have watched them every evening for twenty odd years, for I have not. But I have watched them many many times and have not seen one variation from the routine. Once clear of the wood they fly very fast low to the ground, maybe only two or three feet above the earth, direct to the marsh. The return flight is exactly the same, and entrance to the wood is made in exactly the same place, and a similar flighting movement takes place at dawn. During the daytime woodcock habitually rest upon the ground. There have been a number of records of them perching, but it is obviously an uncommon habit, and I have not personally seen a woodcock perching in the daytime. But some woodcock at any rate roost in trees. At least two of the birds in my wood have done so. Foxes are rather too common in my neighbourhood, and I imagine that these birds took to the trees to avoid disturbance. I have not seen any reference to roosting in trees in any of the books, so presumably it is not a common habit. Or is it one that has escaped attention ?

" Roding " is quite another sort of flight. It is a display flight and occurs only during the breeding season. It takes place normally in the evening, at or just after sunset (though as the season advances it tends to become earlier), and it lasts anything from a quarter of an hour up to about an hour. There is another " roding " at dawn, but this is usually very short, and I have once observed " roding " in the early afternoon. A " roding " cock travels a regular circuit, so regular a circuit that it is easy to plot an almost exact course, and I have done this many times for the birds in my wood. The flight during " roding " has a special wing action all of its own, a slow wing action something between that of an owl and a serotine bat, but the actual flight is pretty fast. In my wood it is always conducted just above the tree tops, but I know that in some woods 'cock will " rode " between the tree trunks. In the open it is rarely conducted at a height of more than 30 feet. Major Seigne believes that both sexes join in the " roding " : but my own experience has convinced me that it is confined to the males. Sexual chases of female by male, of course, occur frequently, but they are not in any way connected with " roding ". Occasionally the courses of two " roding " males cross (as a matter of fact they usually do so in my wood), and this sometimes (if the two males happen to meet) leads to fast erratic chases during which both birds croak a good deal. The croaking is very like the croaking of a frog. The other note uttered by a " roding " male is *chiswick*, a rather thin sound but one which carries a very fair distance. " Roding " in my wood usually commences in the first week in March and continues (rather irregularly after the end of April) until the end of June, but I have witnessed " roding " in the last week in February and in the first week of August. Long before " roding " proper commences there are aerial games above the tree tops of the wood. These may commence as early as the last week in December, but generally speaking the second week in January is about the earliest. I have seen as many as eight birds in the air at once twisting and turning and diving, croaking every now and then, obviously at play, but eight is exceptional and two or three is usual. I am sure that the females join in this performance, and certainly it is altogether wrong to say that the females cannot croak. These playful flights are of short duration and do not follow any regular course as in " roding ". Those that I have watched have begun with one bird flying just above the tree tops, another comes up to it, and the intricate evolutions commence and continue for perhaps five minutes, when the birds drop down into their own parts of the wood.

It is said by many sportsmen that males are more numerous than females, and this does appear to be the case in Sweden, where the woodcock is said by Zedlitz, a great authority, to be polyandrous.

Male and female are indistinguishable except by dissection, and so I presume this theory is based upon dissection of birds shot. If the theory is not so founded it is worthless : and I cannot imagine the average sportsman having the patience to dissect the day's bag. No doubt some have done so (I hesitate to think that the theory is founded on mere guesswork), and no doubt they found more males than females. But I cannot regard that as proof that there are more males than females. Personally I believe that females outnumber males, and that the woodcock is either promiscuous in his sexual affairs or, more probably, polygamous. I believe that the ratio is about one male to three females. (Major Seigne from his experience in Ireland believes the woodcock to be monogamous and that there is a large population of non-breeding birds in each season. Conditions in Ireland, however, are quite different from those in Hampshire.) In my wood there are usually four or five nests in each year, but it is altogether exceptional to see more than two woodcock " roding ". Now " roding " is undertaken very regularly each evening, and I am quite sure that I could not have missed " roding " flights by other males in the area. I am, therefore, forced to the conclusion that there are, as a rule, two males to four or five females. " Roding " is very rarely, if ever, undertaken by the female and is a sexual business of the male. The word is derived from the old Scandinavian word " rode ", which means " foray " or " excursion ". I do not think that it is at all a bad word when applied to this flight of the male woodcock. It has been suggested that the flight is a method of keeping territory, a sort of " beating the bounds " ; if this be so the bounds are not, in my experience, very rigid. The lines of flight of roding woodcock in my wood frequently intersect, and the circuits of both about one night in six become considerably enlarged. All this, of course, does not prove that the shooting men who have found more males than females in the day's bag were wrong. There is the foreign population to consider, and, if it is true that males predominate in Scandinavia, it is by no means unlikely that we get more males than females over here in the winter. In Hampshire " roding " usually commences well before the end of February and continues, with varying intensity, until the end of July or the beginning of August. I have, however, seen woodcock " roding " early in January and late in September. From the sporting point of view it is unwise to shoot woodcock after the end of December.

There is also a certain amount of display on the ground. I have

Plate XXXV

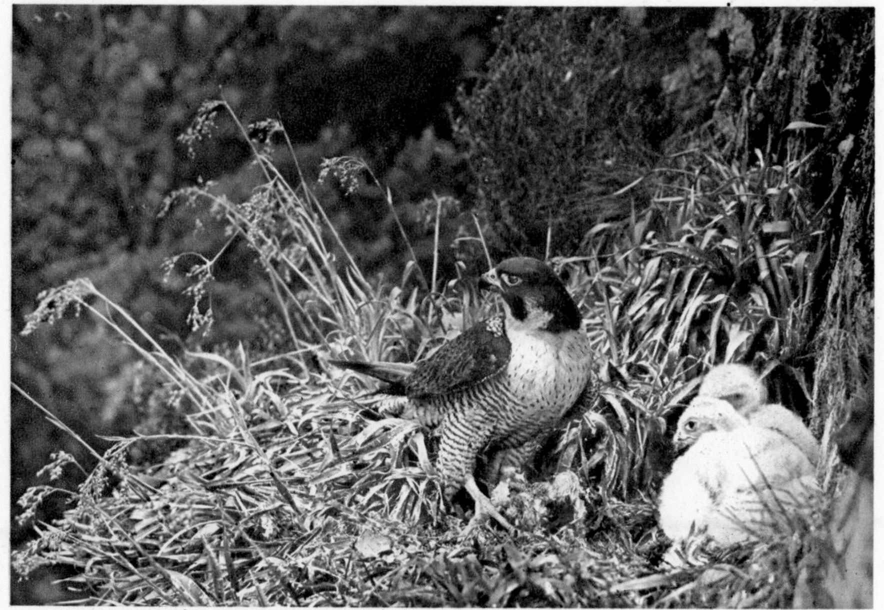

PEREGRINE, tiercel and chicks. Merionethshire, 1941. H. PLATT

HEN MERLIN and young. Inverness-shire, 1940. ERIC HOSKING

Plate XXXVI

HEN SPARROW-HAWK and family. Dorset, 1940. G. K. YEATES

HEN SPARROW-HAWK with young. Norfolk, 1942. ERIC HOSKING

not been fortunate enough to watch this at all frequently, and have only once witnessed actual coition. Such ground display as I have watched has always been the same, the male strutting round the female with drooped wings and the tail raised and fanned out. The feathers of the head and neck are also puffed out. Every now and again the male would make a queer little stilted run at the female, who took very little notice of the whole performance. In all these cases the birds sooner or later moved into thicker undergrowth and I was unable to see what happened. In the one case in which I did witness coition the procedure was rather different, for the female also walked around, half turned away from the male, and then suddenly crouched with bill touching the ground, when coition immediately followed.

In Hampshire every nest that I have found has been close to the foot of a large tree, some being sheltered by undergrowth while others have been quite open. In the north, I believe, woodcock will nest far away from trees on occasion. "Nest" is rather a grand word to apply to the woodcock's home. It is never any more than a hollow scraped in the ground and lined with the dead leaves that lie around. Suitable nesting sites are apparently hard to find. At any rate the nests in my wood have always been in roughly the same place, almost always within a few feet of the site of the previous year. Once one understands this—and in no small degree I have found it to be true of most game birds and the common snipe—the difficulty of finding the nest (and woodcock nests are by no means easy to find) is considerably lessened. The eggs, usually four in number, are bluntly oval in shape and vary a great deal in colour, ranging from dirty white to reddish-brown liberally spotted and blotched, with varying shades of violet, chestnut and ash-grey. In Hampshire they are laid from mid-March onwards. I have found eggs as early as March 2nd and as late as August 4th. Two broods are raised in a year, but generally speaking July is late to find the eggs of the second brood. In my experience the eggs are laid at considerable intervals. I have known four days to pass between the laying of the second and third eggs, and I think that there is usually an interval of 48 hours or more between layings. Incubation takes about three weeks, and all the work is done by the female, and she alone tends the young.

Despite the brilliance of its plumage a woodcock is wonderfully difficult to see on the nest. The markings so brilliant when seen at close quarters form one of the very best examples of camouflage in the world of nature, and a sitting woodcock is to all intents and purposes invisible at a distance of only a few feet. She knows it, too, and generally sits so closely that you can pass her day after day and be unaware of her presence. I remember well a bird that nested within a few feet of a path down which I used to walk every day. She nested out of cover, and yet I was unaware of her presence (and I am at least moderately observant) until one day I took a dog and he put her up. That was in 1924, and there has been a nest within a few feet of the place every year since : an example, as I believe, of an hereditary nest. And on the nest they are very tame. They will sit tightly while you watch them from a distance of only a few feet, and I have even stroked a sitting bird. She did not seem to mind in the least and was sitting when I left, but she deserted and I have never approached a nest so closely since. During incubation she sits very closely. I do not think that, unless disturbed, a sitting woodcock leaves the nest during the day. But regularly at dusk she will leave to go and feed, and sometimes she may be away for a long time. Sometimes, too, but not, I think, invariably, she will feed at dawn. A woodcock returning to her nest is very careful and very suspicious, and will spend a long time circling round before finally walking quickly to the nest and settling on the eggs. So wonderful is the protective colouring that, though I have heard a woodcock moving about around her nest and known quite well that she has been within a few feet of me, I have been unable to see her until she has been actually straddled over her eggs.

There is sometimes a considerable delay in the hatching of the eggs. Once they are hatched the mother leaves the nest and the young quite frequently, and she is less inclined to sit closely after the hatching of the first chick. The chicks, it seems to me, take rather longer than most ground-nesting birds to dry off. But once they are dry they grow in strength rapidly and are generally able to run to meet their mother on her return to the nest by the evening of the day on which they emerge from the shell. I have seen this happen on several occasions, and each time the parent bird has brooded the chick or chicks for a short while at the place where they met, sometimes a few feet, sometimes a few yards from the nest, before going on to the nest to incubate the remaining eggs. Once safely settled on the eggs she calls the chicks back to her and broods them also. I have handled woodcock chicks several times, but only twice has the mother displayed. Injury-feigning appears to be of common occurrence among woodcock, but I have never witnessed it. Most of the parents whose chicks I have handled have appeared remarkably unconcerned. One displayed before me, by drooping the tail, half opening the wings and running round and round me (within two feet or so) the while I had the chick in my hand. As soon as I put it down it ran to its mother and she promptly brooded it. The other bird demonstrated rather than displayed, placing the tip of its bill on the ground, erecting and fanning out its tail, ruffling its neck feathers and spreading its wings, and generally giving the appearance that it was standing on its bill and about to topple forwards.

Another thing I have never seen is a woodcock carrying its young. That this does occur is beyond question. It has been observed too many times by thoroughly reliable naturalists for there to be any doubt about it. What is not certain is how the chick is carried. Most of the records suggest that it is carried between the thighs, some that it is carried in the feet (personally I doubt whether the woodcock's claws are really strong enough for this), some that it is carried pressed to the breast by the bill, some that it is carried on the back. The first of these seems the most likely, but probably all of them (except the feet) are used. The carrying of the young seems to be done in the main to remove them from danger, though there are well-authenticated cases of their being lifted over obstacles. I do not think it can be a common practice. I have lived cheek by jowl with woodcock for a good many years now, and I feel sure that if it were at all usual I would have witnessed it. There is, however, much to do with the young which I have not seen. I do not know, for example, how they are fed, for I have never seen a young woodcock fed, though I have seen chicks only a day or two old pecking about among leaves. Again, I do not know how they reach their feeding grounds. I have many times watched adult woodcock at the time when the young are about flighting in the normal way by the normal route to their feeding grounds, and I have seen young woodcock, about three weeks old, on the feeding ground. But I have never seen a young woodcock on the way to the feeding grounds.

Many shooting men would rather bag one woodcock in a day than half a dozen brace of pheasants. But woodcock, even in those districts (Ireland excepted) which can properly be regarded as woodcock country, do not form a noticeable proportion of the average shooting man's bag. The woodcock is generally an item, an interesting and exciting item, in the " various ", an incident rather than the main object of the day's sport. There is always an element of surprise and uncertainty about 'cock. You can never be quite certain if they are in or if they have gone. Certainly you can never fix up a party for woodcock shooting well in advance and be certain of shooting woodcock. They are capricious birds, capricious in their movements and with pronounced likes and dislikes. If you study these likes and dislikes carefully—which remarkably few men trouble to do—you may increase the holding capacity of your coverts and so increase the size of your bag in a season.

I have already said that the woodcock is a bird of the open woodlands. It likes moist oak woods, birch, larch, spruce and Scots pine. It likes woods with open glades and rides and a good cover of bracken and bramble. It likes evergreen bushes such as holly, laurel and rhododendron. It does not like old woods that are big and thick, and it dislikes cold and draughty woods. And though it likes moist woods, it dislikes dripping trees and wet cover. There are many exceptions, of course—have I not said that the woodcock is capricious ?—and you may flush a woodcock from all sorts of unlikely places (but I have never yet flushed one from a wood solely composed of beeches) and from the wettest and most draughty of places, I know that well. There are exceptions to every rule : they do not invalidate the rule. In the main woodcock do prefer the sort of country I have described. And if you have that sort of country and improve upon it, then if the woodcock visit you at all you should be able to increase the number of visitors. I would stress that : the number of visitors. You will not increase the number of nesting birds. That number is controlled in the long run by factors over which we have no control. In the wood I know best the number of nesting birds has remained constant over many years, but careful attention to the amenities has undoubtedly increased the number of visitors.

Woodcock and soft wood forestry do not go together. Tall trees close together provide little or no undergrowth and are cold and draughty and uninviting. The Forestry Commission's plantations, once they have grown above a certain height, hold no woodcock. If you want woodcock you must eschew growing timber for profit if it involves afforestation of this type. You want a wood with open spaces and scrub growth, with both sun and shade, with plenty of laurel or rhododendron dotted here and there, and either plenty of food within its boundaries or plenty of food within reach. And, I am quite sure, you want plenty of oak, for woodcock love

HOODED CROW AND GROUSE EGGS

Coloured lithograph by Joseph Wolf 1870

From John Gould's BIRDS OF GREAT BRITAIN

SPARROWHAWK
Coloured lithograph by Joseph Wolf 1864
From John Gould's BIRDS OF GREAT BRITAIN

poking about amongst fallen oak-leaves for insect food and frequently choose places with lots of fallen oak-leaves as resting places, knowing well that the leaves harmonise closely with their plumage. We were fortunate in having oak and one or two open spaces with coarse grass. In these spaces we planted rhododendrons and a few holly bushes. We cleared some of the saleable timber and planted two small clumps of Japanese larch (Japanese larch from the 'cock point of view is better than common larch : it gives better shade and it bears a bigger crop of needles), and we clipped a big laurel hedge that some forgotten ancestor had for some reason planted along one of the rides. In two of the damp places we planted a few Sitka spruce. Sitka spruce is more or less immune from rabbits and does well on damp soils, and I know that in Ireland it is attractive to 'cock. We had no success with them so far as 'cock were concerned, and in due course they were removed. But in winter the Japanese larch and the laurel were, when 'cock were in, always sure finding places. And we did something else, perhaps the most important thing of all. We cut two shallow trenches under the oaks, so that they formed a right angle with the extremities facing south and west. Along them we planted brambles. The brambles ramped and the trenches collected leaves. They were so placed that they remained dry or dryish in all but really wet weather, and they were popular with 'cock throughout the year. We had one further problem—rabbits. Rabbit-infested ground will never hold woodcock. It will never, for that matter, hold any reasonable population of ground-nesting birds. And it is an unfortunate fact that the more you open up a wood the more rabbits you will breed. We never succeeded in ridding ourselves of rabbits, but constant and expert ferreting had a most beneficial effect.

The boggy places also received attention. Boggy places are essential to woodcock, and though we were fortunate in having a marsh which performed the function of communal feeding ground we devoted some care to the boggy patches in the wood. We planted dogwood, partly because it is a pleasant shrub but mainly because its fallen leaves attracts insects galore, and we planted some bog sedges because these provide dry resting places. You will often flush a woodcock from boggy ground, but woodcock never rest on boggy ground, and examination of the spot from which the bird sprang will invariably show a dry spot or two.

The result of all this was a marked increase in the number of 'cock on the autumn and spring passage, and a definite increase in numbers throughout the winter. There was no increase in the breeding population. The increase was not, of course, apparent all at once, it was gradual, and was not really noticeable for some five years or so. Nor was there any marked increase in the season's bag, though days on which a number of 'cock were shot did become more numerous. We did not, however, beat the wood at all frequently—on the average only four times a season—being more interested in the birds and the experiment.

Work such as this will always be effective. Of that I feel confident. But the work must be continued year after year. There must be some planting and some felling every year (not a good thing from the forestry point of view !), to ensure that there will always be a variety of wood of all ages and a good undergrowth. The boggy patches will always need some attention. Indeed the work never ends. But the rewards can be magnificent.

CURLEW AND PLOVER

CURLEW and plover belong to the realm of shore shooting. When we come to the consideration of the innumerable birds that throng the shore we are immediately faced with the question as to what is and what is not legitimate quarry. I suppose it depends a good deal on how you regard shooting. If you are one of those who shoot just for the fun of hearing a bang, just for the fun of killing something no matter what, you will probably regard the gull as fair game. This book is not written for you. But if you shoot with something more in mind you will certainly give the gulls a miss. I have eaten gull, and I strongly advise you not to do so. Which then of the thousands of birds that haunt our shores in autumn and winter can be regarded as fair game for the sportsman? My own view is that all gulls, terns, herons (I have eaten heron and found it a loathsome experience), oyster-catchers, turnstones, grey plovers, and all the little birds—the stints and the sanderlings—should be regarded as quite outside the limit. The curlew and whimbrel and the plovers, the golden plover, the lapwing, the knot and the dunlin I regard as legitimate quarry.

I am aware that many people regard the shooting of curlew with horror. Many of the people who so regard the shooting of curlew are blessed with a fair amount of the world's goods and as many meals a week as they desire to pay for. In the coastal cottages "th'ole curloo" is more or less a staple dish. And the old rhyme,

> "The curloo be she white, be she black
> She carries twelve pence on her back",

has not lost its truth. The curlew is a good substantial bird with plenty of meat on it, and in September it is really good eating. September birds should not be skinned, but merely drawn. Winter birds—they taste a bit kippery—should be skinned. But whether in autumn or winter the curlew provides good nourishing fare for the humble folk of the shore cottages. Furthermore, it is available in the winter months in vast herds, and these show no signs of decreasing. The curlew, particularly when in company with its kind (individual birds are sometimes astonishingly careless), is very well able to look after itself, and it needs a quick shot who is thoroughly familiar with the ground to do well at curlew. Even so, it may well take him hours to secure his bird, and the days with no success are many. The curlew shooter must be tough and inured to damp and cold. Shore shooting has its own incomparable pleasures, but they are far removed from the well-organised and comfortable pleasures of pheasant and partridge shooting.

Both green and golden plover occur inland as well as on the shore. The lapwing is one of the farmer's very best friends and should not be, and broadly speaking is not, shot when away from the shore. Actually the question as to whether it can be shot or not is determined by the various county councils, and there is no general rule for the country as a whole. Our bird protection laws are for the most part quite inadequate—the police have not the time to enforce them, and in any case they presume a knowledge of birds which is largely wanting—and the protection of such a bird as the lapwing, which is subject to sudden and quite inexplicable local movements, in one county and not in another is in itself farcical. The bird should be protected throughout the year inland. On the shore protection would be impossible without prohibiting shore shooting entirely, which is unthinkable. But the shooting of lapwings on the shore does no harm. It is a wary bird, and once shot at it is every whit as wary as the curlew and every whit as difficult to shoot.

Golden plover also breed with us but not in anything like the same quantity. So far as shore shooting is concerned, I would rank the golden plover right at the top. They are fast—but not so fast as a bar-tailed godwit coming in on the wind, when it is about the fastest thing that flies—and they are excellent eating, for though they do feed on the saltings they are in the main feeders in fresh marshes. But they are erratic in their movements, and you can never be sure of finding them. Many fowlers maintain that golden plover move off before a frost and that their departure foretells hard weather. My own notes, I must admit, do not bear this out, but Abel Chapman always maintained that it was so.

Of the smaller birds the knot and the dunlin are the most important, and the former is really excellent eating. You cannot fire at individual knot or dunlin (you hardly ever see one anyhow), and from the semi-professional gunner's point of view it would be incredibly wasteful to do so. These men shoot for food more than for anything else, and they are after quantity not individuals. You cannot blame them : cartridges are costly. And if you have ever shot at knot or dunlin you will blame them still less. The gunner likes a flock, and he likes a shot which makes a gap in the flock. It sounds wasteful and cruel, but in practice it does no harm—I have noticed no diminution in numbers, and the practice is as old as shore shooting—and the amount of harm it does to rare birds is negligible. It is quite true that a fair proportion of rare shore birds on the British list have acquired British nationality in this way—you have shot at a flock of dunlin, you are lucky, but you do not know what you have got until you examine your bag—but the number is very small.

The curlew has rightly been labelled the wariest of shore birds. They are certainly every whit as wary as the grey geese, and just as much knowledge of local conditions is required to encompass their downfall. Shore shooting is never a matter of wandering along a beach with a gun ! But though the curlew is excessively wary it is still a conservative bird. It feeds, as do all waders, by day or night as the tide serves. Knowledge of the tides is, therefore, of the utmost importance to the shore shooter. When they are feeding at low water they scatter over the mud-banks in small parties. When the tide turns and begins to flow these small parties draw together on the higher ground, and when they are finally pushed off they flight, in good-sized herds, either well inland or to some higher ground well out of reach of the water. If on flighting inland they start from some mud-bank well off shore they rise as they cross the shore line, and this is a point the waiting gunner should never forget. If he is visible on the skyline he will never get a shot. At the same time, if his pit is so constructed that the birds as they rise can see into it, and curlew have uncanny eyesight, he will never get a shot. As a general rule the best shooting is obtained with the flowing tide, and the best time is an hour or so before high water. Shooting with the tide ebbing, that is at birds coming off the fields to feed, is a much more chancy business, though, heaven knows, the other is chancy enough. Curlews are very susceptible to decoying, and I have known many men put out decoys and secure good bags. Personally—with the exception of pigeons—I dislike shooting over decoys. But curlew can be lured within range by other means. Though so intensely wary they are intensely curious. This inquisitiveness does not outweigh, does not even balance, their wariness, but it does sometimes lead to their undoing. They will always swoop down at a dog running on the beach—not so much curiosity as indignation is the prompter here, I think—and they are apt to swoop at any strange object, a handkerchief left lying about or something like that. And they can be attracted by calls. I do not know if an instrument for imitating their calls is on the English market (there used to be one on the French), but quite a number of the semi-professional gunners can imitate them very well with the aid of two fingers, something after the manner of a small boy calling up his friends. I have seen this trick worked very successfully. But it does not always work by any means. And usually it works only with young birds, which is rather a pity, though young curlew make better eating than do old ones.

In some places there is a regular flight of lapwings and golden plover at morning and evening, the birds coming inland soon after dawn and returning to the sea marshes shortly after dusk. This evening flight, by the way, does not, as is the case with the grey geese, occur during nights of moonlight. On such nights the birds stay inland. This evening flight proffers the most difficult shooting to be obtained anywhere in the British Isles. The birds seem to fall out of the sky and skim along only a foot or so above ground level. Under such conditions the golden plover is pretty well invisible and the green plover as near so as makes little difference. The local gunners in such places go out for the birds, lying in deep ditches to await their coming, but the evening flight cannot be recommended to the ordinary amateur. In the presence of the locals it is often dangerous, and it is hardly ever worth while from the point of view of the bag. The morning flight offers far better chances and far better shooting. But it is not easy shooting. The lapwing looks a slow and cumbersome bird with its flapping flight and rounded wings. But taken all round they are as hard to hit as any bird of the shore, with their turns and twists and dips and the way the wind seems to blow them about. You can drive most birds but you cannot drive lapwings. And lapwings are extraordinarily difficult to stalk. Once they have been shot at they become extraordinarily wary and are almost impossible to approach. The bird living in an area where shooting is prohibited will allow of quite close approach. The bird on the shore or the coastal marsh is a very different proposition, taking care to keep well out in the open and always flying over or past any place that might contain a gunner well out of range. Lapwings much prefer a marsh that is flooded : they like to feed in water a few inches deep, and such places are the best to wait for them in the daytime. You can get them down to decoys on the marshes, but the battle of wits is the greater, and the satisfaction brought by success in the battle much greater if decoys are not used. In the open or on the shore the only possible chance of getting within range of lapwings is in a strong gale. The birds are then most strongly inclined to fly, will not take off with the wind behind them, and can sometimes be approached up wind to quite close range. But when they do rise they do not lose their heads, and in a very high wind the green plover is not an easy mark.

Golden plover, fast as they are, are, I think, easier from the gunner's point of view, for they are much less inclined to be erratic. The golden plover is a wonderful bird combining the very best of both game bird and wader, and making excellent eating withal. In this it differs from the grey plover, a bird with a distinctly tasteless taste (if such a contradiction may be allowed), and in comparison a dull bird on the wing. Incidentally the golden plover has only three toes, a point often overlooked by hotels that put golden plover on the menu.

The knot is the smallest bird that is worth the attention of the shore gunner and by far the best eating of the lot. They are present on some of our coasts in enormous numbers at times, and for some while after they first arrive are extremely unsuspicious and can be walked up to within easy range. Later they become wild, keep well out in the open, and are to all intents and purposes unapproachable. Every now and again they do give the gunner a chance shot at longish range, but then so compactly do they fly that anything may happen. I believe that the record bag to a single shot from a shoulder-gun (an old 4-bore, I think) is eighty birds. You can walk up to knot on an open beach if there are three or four guns in line and a stop, but I do not know that any great success has been obtained in this manner, and again shots have to be taken at extreme range.

Normal range seems to be regarded by most people, and particularly by the experts who write in the papers and in books, as anything from forty to sixty yards. That is probably not inaccurate for game-bird shooting ; it is all wrong for shore shooting. Sixty yards on the shore is a very long way indeed, and forty yards is a good deal too far for most people. On the shore twenty-five to thirty yards may be considered normal range. Distance on the shore is very deceptive, and a bird must appear very close before it can be considered within range.

GROUND GAME AND VARIOUS

RABBITS and hares have each been awarded the honour of a column in the game book. It is true that both are good to eat. It is true that the rabbit can provide excellent sport, and the hare a good deal of amusement. But both are very destructive indeed to agriculture, and the rabbit is also destructive to genuine game interests. Neither, under any circumstances, should be preserved. Certainly neither deserves the honour of a column in the game book.

The rabbit is a menace. It is a menace to agriculture. Up to the outbreak of war it was costing this country some millions of pounds annually. Since the outbreak of war it has been the target for a concentrated offensive which has happily done something to reduce its numbers. It is a menace to forestry and it is a menace to the interests of the game preserver, though comparatively few game preservers seem to realise that. Its value as a cheap (in peacetime !) and wholesome, if not very nutritious, food and the value of its fur for clothing (four rabbits, by the way, make one felt hat) cannot be weighed against the damage it does. It remains a menace.

Almost every predatory creature preys upon the rabbit. Foxes, stoats, weasels, badgers, rats, cats and a large number of birds of prey attack it, and man is also an inveterate enemy. The rabbit, in fact, lives in a hostile world, and to balance this extreme hostility it has been granted by nature extreme fecundity. It breeds with indecent haste and regularity. Were nature left to herself the numbers of its enemies would undoubtedly keep the rabbit population within bounds, but man, in addition to attacking the rabbit, wages a ceaseless war upon some of the most important of its enemies, with the inevitable result that the number of rabbits is always too great.

The rabbit is promiscuous. It can and does breed at six months old. The period of gestation is twenty-eight days, and it has between four and eight litters in the year with three to nine in each litter. Thus rabbits born in February will have litters of their own in September.

The possibilities for rapid increase in the population are almost limitless. The doe before breeding usually leaves the bury and digs a new breeding hole about two feet long in which she makes her nest, lining it with leaves, bracken fronds, and fur from her own body. Sometimes, though rarely, a nest is made in the open. (I have found a nest in a flower bed within six feet of the house.) The young are born naked and blind and with closed ears, and are completely helpless. They are left in the nest by the doe, and in the case of an underground nest the mother upon leaving usually covers up the entrance. Only the doe tends the young, and timid as she is, she will fight fiercely—even attacking a stoat in defence of the litter. The eyes of young rabbits open on the eleventh day, the ears on the twelfth. On the fourteenth day they can run about, and by the end of a month they are self-supporting and rejoin the main bury. The main breeding season is from the end of January to the beginning of October, but young are born in every month of the year. The largest litters are produced in summer and the smallest in winter, but in a mild winter large litters are not uncommon, and I have more than once found litters of six or seven in December.

Very gregarious, the rabbit digs large burrows. In most of these the main entrance dips sharply down for four or five feet, sometimes as deep as eight feet, and then rises to a central chamber from which a large number of bolt holes lead to the surface. One rabbit warren may contain several such buries, and on occasion these buries will connect. As a general rule most of the day is spent underground or in very thick cover, but in really fine warm weather rabbits will lie out in forms in the open. At nightfall and in the early morning they come out to feed. It is always a big buck that comes out first. He comes out very cautiously and usually spends some moments in or at the entrance before venturing into the open. He is usually followed by at least two other bucks before the does begin to appear. Well-trodden paths lead from the buries, and these are always used when coming out to feed. The rabbit in this way is a conservative creature, a fact which helps a great deal in trapping and snaring them. Normally excessively timid, there have been records of bucks turning upon and routing stoats. The kick of a big buck rabbit is powerful, and I have known a large tom-cat put to flight by a doe in defence of her young. But this sort of thing is exceptional. It is much more usual for a rabbit hunted by a stoat to run only a few yards and then sit down and wait for death, screaming piteously the while. A " stoated " rabbit, indeed, seems to be hypnotised, and it is noteworthy that other rabbits seem to know that they are not in danger. I well remember hearing a rabbit scream very close to me in Dorset once, and on looking over a bank I saw plenty of rabbits playing about unconcernedly and one moving very slowly screaming loudly. In due course a stoat appeared, the playful rabbits made way (giving it a wide berth and showing no signs of fear), and killed the screaming rabbit. It seemed quite evident that those rabbits knew they were in no danger.

The rabbit is always hungry and will eat almost anything that is vegetable. The chief food is grass, and where rabbits abound weeds very soon replace grass and grain. There is no farm crop that they will not attack, and there are few trees that they will not bark. When eating turnip they do not strip the vegetable, but starting at the side eat right through. As for trees, they are specially fond of young birch, and they will gnaw the end of branches of scrub oak and hazel, and play the dickens with plantations of young conifers. They will gnaw at gorse bushes, and they are equally fond of the flowers in a garden. Crocuses, wallflowers, lupins, carnations, canterbury bells, lavender, pinks, roses—I have known them all destroyed by rabbits. Laurel is sometimes said to be rabbit-proof, but that has not been my experience, and rhododendron, which appears in some lists of rabbit-proof plants, is most certainly not rabbit-proof. The following plants are supposed to be rabbit-proof: common barberry, holly-leaved barberry, Japanese rose, sea blackthorn, common lilac, Japanese lilac, single guelder rose, Japanese snow flower, Japanese wine-berry, shrubby St. John's wort, box and dogwood. It must depend a good deal, I suppose, upon what other plants are in the immediate neighbourhood, for rabbits have their preferences. For myself I have never found lilac to be rabbit-roof. But I have never known a box or dogwood to be attacked.

In addition to the damage done to agriculture and forestry the rabbit is harmful to true game preservation. Wherever rabbits abound partridges decrease, and in country that is riddled with rabbits partridges are non-existent. This is partly because wherever rabbits abound grass and grain give place to weeds, and partly because in addition to what they eat they foul much land and destroy much top soil, destroying at the same time much insect life. Moreover, wherever you have rabbits there sooner or later you will have rats. The rat is the enemy of the rabbit: it is a much more deadly enemy of the partridge, the pheasant and the game preserver. I hate to see hedgerow banks holed by rabbits. As nesting-sites for partridges they are entirely spoiled, and they provide excellent homes for rats.

The means by which rabbits can be kept down are many. They may be shot, be snared, trapped, netted, and gassed. When bolted by ferrets they do provide excellent and sometimes difficult shooting, but I confess that I prefer to ferret with purse nets and no gun. Snaring is useful also, and gassing can be very effective in certain buries. I have even drowned them. The only way in which I could clear one very large bury was by flooding it, but this, of course, is not always possible. Experiments have also been conducted with diseases—infecting several rabbits and then letting them loose—but this has not proved as effective as was hoped. Shooting, netting, snaring—all are good, but in themselves not sufficient. Shooting alone is most certainly not sufficient to keep numbers down. Trapping is essential. The gin trap is a wicked instrument and every humane person must wish to see it abolished. But in the absence of any equally effective and more humane trap (and I have not met with one yet) it is impossible to do away with it. There is not the slightest doubt that on any given area by systematic trapping rabbits can be exterminated. Unfortunately an area cleared of rabbits (as I know well from experience) is rapidly filled again with the surplus from neighbouring areas. A skilful trapper trapping for the market is not going to exterminate his stock and so put himself out of business. The gin trap can clear an area of rabbits, but in the hands of a skilful man it can also maintain a steady population. To exterminate the rabbit by trapping would mean a national campaign organised and directed by one person. It could be done, and done fairly quickly. But it will not be done, for this is Britain and in rural Britain we are strongly individualistic. In any case, I do not know that I would like to see the rabbit utterly exterminated. I would like to see its numbers greatly reduced.

The hare is also a menace to agriculture. A much larger animal than the rabbit and also promiscuous, it is fortunately not gregarious—in fact it is distinctly unsocial—and not quite so prolific. The main courting season is in February and March, when the bucks run about all day fighting, kicking and jumping in pursuit of the does. But leverets may be born in any month of the year. The period of gestation is thirty days, and three to four litters in a year with two to six young in a litter is normal. Young leverets—they are among the most beautiful creatures in the world—are born covered with their hair, open-eyed and able to run. They are born in the open, and shortly after birth the doe finds a separate form for each leveret, carrying them there in her mouth (after the manner of a cat carrying kittens), and visits them during the night to suckle them. The does are very good mothers and fight fiercely in defence of their young. The young at a month old are independent and begin to breed at about a year old, possibly at nine months.

Hares prefer low rolling ground. They spend all their life in the open (I bolted a hare from a rabbit burrow on one occasion while ferreting, and I have seen a hunted hare go down a rabbit burrow, but these are exceptions), living in forms. These forms are very carefully selected. They are invariably chosen to give a view (this is the most important factor), but they are also situated so as to give shelter from the prevailing wind, and in winter to catch as much sun as possible and in summer as much shade. Most of the day is spent couched in the form. If alarmed when in the form it crouches to the ground, leaping up and moving off rapidly when danger presses. The senses of hearing and of smell are very acute, but the sight straight ahead is not good at all, owing to the position of the eyes.

They are creatures of habit. They have their particular exits and entrances to fields (a fact which makes them easy to poach), and they stick to these under all circumstances. A hare leaving its form takes no precautions, but goes straight to the particular exit of the field. Returning to the form is another matter, and the greatest precautions —doubling and turning and finally making two very long jumps— anything up to eighteen feet—to baffle the scent are taken. When hunted it has at least as much cunning as the fox and quite a few tricks that the fox has not got, and added to this it has remarkable speed which, unlike the rabbit who tires easily after about fifty yards, it can maintain for miles. Up-hill particularly, where its long hind legs are an aid, it is very fast, and it is noticeable that a hunted hare will always start off up-hill if it can. It has a reputation for being excessively timid, but I do not think that it is. It will fight fiercely in defence of its young, it will drive off cattle from its form, it is more than a match for a small terrier and can deliver a very telling kick with its hind legs, and it is altogether a strong, even a powerful animal. I have had a full-grown wild hare in my arms, and though I am by no means small, I had all my work cut out to get it under control and was severely scratched and bitten. Hares are said never to drink. I do not know if that is true or not. They can swim well and will do so apparently for pleasure. They can jump extraordinarily well also. One has been known to clear a Grand National jump easily, and they think nothing of hopping over a five-foot fence into a kitchen garden.

As they do not burrow and as they are in themselves cleanly animals, they do not do as much damage as rabbits. But they are very destructive and very much too common. They are wholly vegetarian and chiefly eat grasses and roots. When eating turnips, unlike the rabbit, they tear down and leave the outside, and when eating wheat they leave the ears and take the stalks and leaves. The damage they can do to a field of grain has to be seen to be believed. In a garden they can wreak havoc. They will take any flower (wallflowers and primulas are special favourites), and in the kitchen garden like lettuces and broccoli in particular. Part of the food passing from the bowel is re-swallowed and passed again.

The blue hare lives on high ground in Scotland and changes to a white coat (except for black ear tips) in winter. It will breed with the common brown hare, but it is a separate species. The Irish hare is another distinct species and is noticeably gregarious, sometimes occurring in herds of two or three hundred.

The hare, too, is attacked, especially as a leveret, by every sort of predatory animal. But the adult hare is fairly well able, on account of its speed and the open country in which it lives, to look after itself. Man is the chief enemy of the hare, but man also, despite the inalienable right granted to farmers under the Ground Game Act to kill hares (a right which also extends to rabbits), protects the hare for sport. As a result there are far too many hares. Hares are hunted with beagles and harriers, coursed with greyhounds, shot and netted. They are because of their conservatism in the matter of routes remarkably easy to net or snare, and so are poached fairly extensively. At a hare drive they are quite easy to shoot. All you have to do is to stand quite still and they come lolloping up, stopping when they realise that there is danger ahead (and they always stop too late), and sitting up and staring about in a foolish manner. They are easy marks. But hares if not killed outright scream in an almost human manner, like small children that have been hurt. And so I hate shooting hares. But they have to be shot, and so I prefer to shoot them when they come through a hedge when being driven. A hare that is not hunted or pressed always stops and sits up when it passes through a hedge—and that way there is less chance of screaming. Beagling is a good sport. The hare has a chance, and appears to know perfectly well that it has a chance. Indeed I am sure that the hare when first put up by the beagles is confident that it is going to get away. Coursing is another matter. I dislike the huge meeting, when the hare is forced to run between lanes of shouting people. I can see no sport in that at all. And even the course in open country finds all my sympathies on the side of the hare, much as I like and admire greyhounds.

I can find no argument for the preservation of ground game, particularly in agricultural country. They can only be preserved at the cost, often the extreme cost, of the farmer. They are vermin, not game, and they should be treated as such. There is no reason to believe that either would be exterminated, but their numbers should be kept under control.

The " various " column in the game books can cover a multitude of entries and a multitude of sins. I have myself seen a green woodpecker shot at a pheasant drive, and I have heard of a bittern suffering the same fate. The list of birds that might quite legitimately fall to the gun during a day's driving or rough shooting would be a long one, ranging from the corncrake to any one of the waders. Two birds, however, do merit serious consideration under the heading of various—the woodpigeon and the coot.

The coot does not figure in the average man's expectations for an ordinary day and is not in any case shot so frequently nowadays as it used to be. From the sporting point of view the coot is much neglected, for though it is its habit to fly low over the water it can be made to fly high and then it does fly fast. It is a large heavily-built bird, and personally I find it good eating. Young moorhen are very good eating, but I would infinitely rather have a coot. In years gone by there used to be an annual coot drive on Hickling Broad. It was a public shoot and everyone was welcome. It was indeed regarded as something in the nature of a public holiday. The guns were divided into two parties. One party manned the boats, and it was their duty to sweep the water in line. The rest lined the shore of some bay or whatever stretch of the Broad it had been decided to drive the birds into. The coot will not rise from the water (which it can only do with difficulty after the manner of a diving-duck) unless it is forced to do so, and the birds would come swimming along in front of the boats. Then finding themselves trapped between two lines, they would rise and fly wildly round in all directions. The shooting, I understand, was inclined to be dangerous. But the bags were enormous. The record for a public shoot at Hickling seems to be 910 coot in 1901, but on 25th February,

1927, 1,175 coot were killed by twenty guns. On Slapton Ley in Devonshire similar public shoots were held, and Slapton Ley holds the English record for coot driving. In January, 1891, some 1,700 coots fell to about twenty guns. This sounds like massacre, but the numbers of coots has not diminished. Public shooting is a thing of the past. All coot shooting—except shore shooting, and the bird is quite common in estuaries in winter—is now in private hands. But the same method is employed to-day as in the old days.

The woodpigeon can only be regarded as vermin. It is good eating, and it stands high in the estimation of shooting men because it is extremely wary, flies high and flies fast. These are the characteristics most highly praised in game birds. But the woodpigeon is not game in law, and is vermin in fact. It is present in enormous numbers, it has an enormous appetite, it will eat almost any plant apparently for the sake of eating. It should have no close season. It should be destroyed, at least until its numbers are within reasonable limits.

There cannot be many places in the British Isles—except mountain tops—where the woodpigeon does not occur, and in too many of them it is excessively common. Normally it frequents more or less wooded districts or country with plenty of trees, but it is also common in town parks and suburban gardens with trees. It occurs also on the downs and on the seacoast, and will even feed on the saltings and the shingle. Those that frequent woods, copses, plantations and thick hedgerows feed in the open fields and have a marked preference for cultivated land. It breeds freely. The nest is merely an untidy, but surprisingly strong, platform of sticks, and it may be put up anywhere and even made on the ground. Hedgerows, any sort of tree, walls, fences and the roofs of buildings are used, and nests are also built on the top of the old nests of crows, hawks, magpies and jays, and on the top of old squirrel dreys. The most normal time for laying is from April to September, but in southern England eggs may be found in any month of the year (I have found them in December and January), and young are raised then as expertly as in summer. Usually two eggs, white and rather glossy, are laid, and incubation is by both male and female, the male chiefly by day and the female by night. Incubation takes only seventeen days, and the young may be fully fledged in three weeks, though a month is, I think, more usual. Three broods are reared every year, and I fancy this number may be exceeded at times.

Our English birds are resident and do not usually move far from

PLATE 23

BADGER AND BULLDOGS

Coloured aquatint by Charles Towns 1807

PLATE 24

COURSING

Coloured aquatint by Richard Reeves 1807

their breeding haunts. In the autumn immigrants, sometimes in enormous numbers (these huge immigrations occur about every five years), begin to arrive on the east coast from the Tay southwards, and the movement lasts from January to September, reaching its peak about the end of November. The return movement commences about the middle of February and lasts well into June, though the peak is attained about the end of March. It is not certain that these immigrants necessarily come from abroad, though in south-east England they probably do. From the midlands northwards the visitors may well be from Scotland. It is this large immigration that does most of the damage. I do not mean that our resident birds are blameless, far from it, for they join up with the immigrants, nor do I mean that our own birds are blameless in summer. Again far from it, for the woodpigeon is apparently always hungry and is omnivorous by nature. But the summer woodpigeon does do a little good to offset some of the great harm. It does eat quite a few destructive insects. When there are really immense numbers of pigeons in this country disease breaks out. Gamekeepers sometimes call it " acorn disease ". It is not, of course, anything to do with over-eating, but rather with overcrowding. The most common form is that in which the bird's mouth and throat fill with a thick yellow mucus so that they cannot feed, and die. In a year when the disease is rampant—and pigeons then will be roosting in thousands in the woods—birds fall dead from their perches. A wise gamekeeper burns the bodies. A wise employer sees that he does.

The woodpigeon is a wary and suspicious bird gifted with remarkably long and keen sight. And it is worth stressing as emphatically as possible that it relies almost entirely on its sight. It is much more likely to be put off by the sight of a man or the glint of light from a gun barrel than by the noise of shooting. There is one more point about pigeon shooting that cannot be stressed too strongly. That is patience. If you are not patient you will not, no matter how good a shot you are, do very well at pigeon shooting.

Now there are a number of ways of shooting pigeons. Some, but they will be few, may be got by beating a wood. In this case the guns must be placed well before the beaters enter the wood, and they must be placed on the normal line of flight. Pigeons usually take the shortest route out of a wood, and they usually fly from covert to covert. It is most unusual for pigeons leaving a covert to fly against the wind, but returning to covert they almost invariably come in against the wind. If these points are remembered, if the guns are well concealed and dressed soberly and if they have patience, they may secure a small bag. Personally, I hardly think it is worth while beating the wood. There are other methods. These are : (1) shooting to decoys, (2) stalking feeding birds, (3) shooting birds in recently sown fields of corn or clover or roots, (4) shooting them when they visit drinking places, (5) when they are feeding in woods or on food put down for pheasants, (6) when the crops are big, (7) in tall grass, and (8) by waiting behind shelter on a known line of flight in to roost. To these may be added shooting birds from trees in woods, a method that is sometimes startlingly successful, for pigeons have favourite trees.

Lord Walsingham once said that "it will be found useful to be prepared beforehand with several short sticks, pointed at both ends, and when ten or twelve birds are down, to gather them quickly and set them up on open spaces beneath the trees as assistant decoys. With wings closed to their sides, resting on their breatbones, they can be fixed with heads erect or craning forwards, as if in search of food, by passing the upper end of the stick through the lower portion of the beak, the opposite end being stuck into the ground beneath the crop of the bird." It is a good idea. In any case, decoys may be used if any large bag of pigeons is desired. These may be wooden ones, stuffed birds or birds just shot. I prefer a combination of the last two. The placing of the decoys is, of course, a matter of importance, but I do not think that it matters in the least if they all face up-wind (the invariable instruction in all the books) or not. More important is the concealment of the gunners. A hut is as good as anything, but a hut is not always possible. However the gunner is concealed he should, if possible, be so placed that the decoys are down-wind. Pigeons usually enter a field down-wind and turn up-wind to settle. They will pass over the decoy, turn and beat up-wind either to settle slowly or to see what it is all about. If a hut can be built so much the better. Birds are not shy of huts as a general rule, and a hut does offer some comfort—all huts should have a seat—to a man who may have to wait for hours.

Provided that one has an effective shelter and a sound knowledge of the habits of the birds, shooting pigeons from trees is a very good method. Pigeons have favourite trees which they use as look-out posts as well as resting places. If these trees are found—and that is not at all difficult for an observant man—good shooting may be had, and it takes a great deal of shooting before the favoured tree is given up. Shooting pigeons coming in to roost is also a successful method, but it is better to wait for the dull days with a strongish wind and a threat of bad weather to come. On such days pigeons come in to roost an hour or so earlier than on calm days, and as they will return again and again to the roost despite the gunfire and general disturbance there is the greater chance of killing a respectable number. Decoys for this sort of shooting should not be used : they will put the birds back to the fields just as surely as will sight of the gunners. Big flocks coming in to roost always have an old bird or two reconnoitring in advance. These birds will fly round several times to make sure that there is no danger, and they should never be shot at. When the main flock comes in it will do so at a great height, and will then glide down over the trees to windward, having a good look round for danger. Then they will beat up-wind flying very much lower and very much slower, and so, eventually, settle. It is obvious that the gunner must wait until they come up-wind.

Except during the long days of high summer, pigeons usually feed three times a day—at dawn, about midday and in the late afternoon. During the spring seeding and autumn ploughing there is a certain amount of casual feeding at other times, but the three main feeds are adhered to. In the long daylight hours of summer there is a fourth feed in the late evening. Normally pigeons do not feed after sunset. But for about a month in the middle of winter, when it gets dark early and there is a long night to face, they will continue the afternoon feed until some little while after dark.

There is one other point about pigeon shooting. The crops of birds should always be opened in order to find out on what food they have been feeding. If you are anything of a countryman you will have a pretty accurate knowledge of the cropping within an area of two or three miles. And this coupled with knowledge of the birds' feeding times and their roosting places should save you a lot of trouble and, if you can shoot reasonably well, bring you many more birds.

THE DEER

CHAPTER I

THE RED DEER

(*Cervus elaphus* (Linnaeus))

THE RED deer (*Cervus elaphus*) as a species is subject to extreme variation in size, weight, antler and general appearance. Some naturalists, struck by these differences, have divided the species up into subspecies and have given to the red deer of Scotland the name *Cervus elaphus scoticus*. Personally, I regard all red deer, whether they be continental or park, warrantable stags from Exmoor or Highland stags from the Black Mount, as one species within which it is not very useful to try to identify subspecies. It is true that in general the face of the park deer is long with a short and rather narrow forehead and eyes set rather close together, while the Highland deer has a shorter face and a blunter muzzle with a wide, deep forehead and eyes set wide apart. It is true that a shootable Highland stag may weigh twelve to twenty stone " clean ", while an English park stag may weigh thirty stone or more, and a continental stag, even double that weight. But all that this means is that red deer vary in size as much as human beings, and I do not know that anyone has yet suggested that an Englishman of sixteen stone with a long nose is a different subspecies from an Englishman of eight stone with a short nose. In any case, good feeding has a lot to do with the size of park deer. Lord Arthur Cecil put his finger on the chief difference when he said that it lay in the hindquarters. The Highland deer has a " blue-hare-like appearance astern " which the semi-wild deer of the parks lack altogether. It is to these hindquarters that the red stag of the Highlands owes its ease and grace of movement. If the antlers cannot

Plate XXXVII

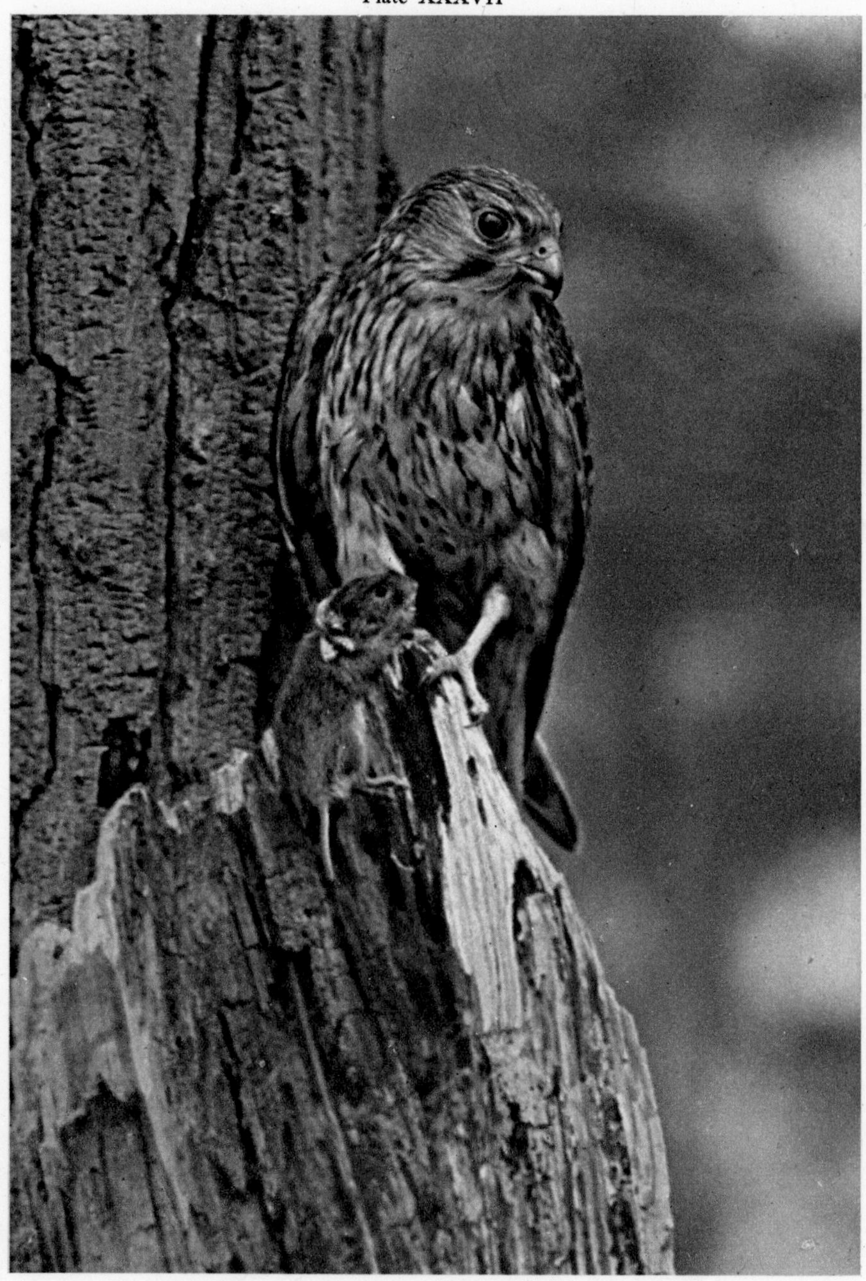

KESTREL with field-vole. Suffolk, 1934. ERIC HOSKING

Plate XXXVIII

COCK MARSH-HARRIER and young. Norfolk, 1942. ERIC HOSKING

compare with those of the parks, of Exmoor, Donegal and Kerry, the Highland stag is yet, in my view, the most noble of them all. The difference is one of atmosphere.

The sexes in red deer (as I suppose everyone knows) differ. The male (the stag or hart, *never* the buck) stands about four feet at the withers, extreme measurements being 42 and 55 inches, and the average weight " clean " of modern Highland stags is about fourteen stone. Seventeen stone in these days is a heavy beast, and twenty stone is a newspaper item, but there have been Highland stags of thirty stone. The female (the hind, *never* the doe) is a smaller, more lightly built animal and without antlers. The average hind stands about 3 feet 5 inches at the withers.

The young (calves, *never* fawns) are dropped about the end of May or early in June after a gestation period of seven or eight months. Only one calf is born to a hind in a year. It is one of the many arguments of the forest as to whether or not twins are ever born. Mr. Allan Gordon Cameron mentions that twins do very rarely occur, and his opinion is worth a dozen of anybody else's, but I do not think that twin-birth has ever been proved, and have never heard that the gralloch of winter hinds has revealed twin foeti. The parturition of the hind is very quick and easy, and she drops her calf while standing. The new-born calf is about the size of a hare and is born with hair dappled with white spots, which disappear when the first winter coat begins to grow. The calves are hidden in high heather or bracken or among boulders and left, the hind returning only to suckle them. For about a week or two they are unable to stand and lie motionless if approached. If handled during this first week they will scream rather like a hare that has been shot. The calf lies like a hare too, chin on the ground and ears laid back along the neck, though sometimes you may come across one curled up like a dog. If it can move it will jump and bound away, and before doing so it will move its head from side to side three or four times. After a week the calf will try to follow its mother, but the hind will not have it and will always push it down into the nest again. But before a month has passed the calves are following well, though they are a great cause for anxiety to their mothers, who fuss about them a great deal and are continually talking to them with a nasal, rather nagging bleat, to which the calves reply with a soft plaintive, much higher-pitched bleating. Young calves have only two enemies—foxes and eagles. The fox is by far the more dangerous, for Highland foxes will hunt in couples, one being unable (as is the eagle) to carry more than a newly born calf. Calves are very active and playful by the time they are two months old, and at three months are pretty well able to look after themselves as far as danger is concerned. They frequently remain with the mothers for two years, and it is a common sight to see hinds with two calves at foot, the yearling (who can now eat grass) taking its share of the new calf's milk even though the mother will generally try to prevent it.

Male calves in their second year grow in May a little knob under dark brown velvet on each side of the head. They are then (if they are Highland calves) called " knobbers ", but if they are Exmoor calves or park calves they are called " prickets ". These knobs in their velvet continue into the third year, when they become antlers. The calf is then called a " brocket " by the particular, but a " staggie " by everyone else. A " staggie " he will remain until he is six years when, by courtesy, he becomes a stag. He will by then be full grown so far as stature is concerned, but his antlers will still be light. At eight years old he should be a seven-pointer and shootable if there is nothing better, and at twelve years old he should be in his prime and a " royal " if he is ever going to be one. At eighteen years of age he will begin to deteriorate and lose points, but he may live to be thirty, though the limit of life is probably somewhere around twenty-five as a rule.

The antlers on a stag grow yearly from the knobs in the skull. They are covered with a substance called " velvet ", which is made of skin, hair and bloodvessels. This is very sensitive until the antlers harden and are fully grown, when the bloodvessels close, the velvet dries, and the stag rubs it off on heather or trees, leaving the antlers clean. The whole process takes only four or five months, an astonishingly short time. As a general rule stags cast their antlers in late April, and the new antlers are grown and clear of velvet by the end of August. Folk-lore says that stags cast their antlers on the same day each year, and as a general rule there is a lapse of from one to four hours or so between the shedding of one and the other. Antlers are divided into the " coronet " or " burr " at the root, the " beam ", which is the main shaft, and the " tines " or points, which from the " burr " upwards are named the " brow ", " bez " and " trez ". Points branching from the beam above the trez are known as " points on top ".

A " royal " is a stag with twelve points including three on each top. And the shooting of a royal by fair stalking means (or should mean) a bottle of whisky to the stalker. Up to a royal a stag is known by the number of points—a ten-pointer and so on—and after a royal he should be known again by the number of his points—a thirteen-pointer, a fourteen-pointer and so on. An " imperial " is a fourteen-pointer, and a very fine trophy indeed. But imperial is a word you use on Fleet Street and not on the forest. A " wilson "—and heaven knows where that word came from—is also a fourteen-pointer. You do not use the word wilson at all—you leave it to the novelists. Park deer often show eighteen points and more, and as many as forty-seven have been known on the Continent among beasts fed on sessame-cake.

There are other stags on the forest. A " switch " (Gaelic *caber-slach*) is a stag with, above the brow tines, the straight up and down of an antelope. It is a dangerous opponent for any normal stag to fight, and most of the deaths caused by Highland stags fighting during the rut (they are few and far between) are caused by the switch stags. A " hummel " (or humble) stag is an animal born without the ability to grow horns. Humble is quite the wrong word. A hummel is invariably a master stag, and no antlered beast, not even a noble royal, dare dispute the ground with him. Having no antlers to support all that it eats goes to bone and muscle, and a hummel is invariably a great heavy beast of twenty stone or so when full grown, built like a bull in front. Folk-lore says that a hummel cannot produce a hummel. A " heavier " is a stag that cannot reproduce its kind at all. A " heavier " is a perfectly normal antlered stag, normal in every way, except that it is born impotent or has become impotent as a result of a wound. I think that almost always heaviers are born impotent, because their habits are so very different from those of normal stags, and I do not believe that they would all acquire the same habits as the result of accident. A heavier is said to be even more wary and suspicious than an old hind, and heaviers do not join in the rut, and often do not leave the hinds at all. " Heavier ", by the way, has nothing to do with weight. It comes from the French *hiver*, and indicates that the animal can be eaten in winter. I have only once known a heavier, a New Forest stag and rather an undersized one at that, which led a solitary life throughout the year. Only four names are applied to hinds, and only one of these is technical. They are old, damned, bloody and yeld. Only the last needs any explanation. A yeld hind is *not* a barren hind. As a matter of fact (and despite Lord Fortescue's " Aunt Yeld " in his classic *Story of a Red Deer*) hinds are nearly always fertile and will carry a calf at a great age. A yeld hind is a hind who has missed her season or who for some other reason is without a calf.

Red deer are gregarious. But the sexes live apart except for the rut, which is the autumn breeding season. In January, as a rule, the stags are lonely and harbour in the thickest cover they can find. But the hinds are in herds of from ten to fifty with their calves of the year and the year before in their usual territories, except that if these are on high ground the herd drops down to lower levels in hard weather. Incidentally, red deer are not red in winter, but greyish-brown, and as the winter advances this coat becomes greyer until the time comes to roll in the peat hags and cast off the dull garb of winter for the rich coat of summer. This summer coat is red-brown, short and close with a nice bright nap. Underneath it there is a thick lining of greyish down. In the stags the hair along the spine is coarse and long, and on the neck (especially in the rutting season) it becomes a mane that would do credit to many an African lion. Colour variation is uncommon. There are some stags a little lighter than the normal, but black stags are merely stags that have been rolling in peat hags. White stags—outside Whipsnade—are rare indeed. I have never seen one in Scotland, but for years in the Lucy Hill district of the New Forest there was a magnificent pure white animal that I saw on several occasions.

After the new antlers begin to grow the stags usually leave the thick cover—the velvet is very sensitive and the attentions of flies must be intolerable—and make for the high ground. Here they collect in parties of from three to twenty or more, and so they stay till they are clear of the velvet. From then until the rut the red deer enjoys the best month of his year. The big parties tend to split up into threes and fours, but the really big old stags go off with one companion (the squire, generally a young stag not yet fully grown) to the real heights, where they spend the days eating and resting and relying upon their youthful companions to warn them of danger. At this time of the year it is sometimes possible to approach an old stag quite closely, especially if his companion happens to be careless or asleep. A stag asleep curls up, head to tail, in the manner of a dog, and sleeps soundly. A stag lying down to chew the cud is wakeful enough, and always holds its head up. In May the hinds separate from the herds to drop their calves, rejoining their companions as soon as the calves can follow. I say in May, but calves are born in June in large numbers, and I have found a new-born calf on October 10th, which is well into the stalking season. Generally the stag is in rut from the middle of September to the end of October, but should a hind come into season at any time up to the beginning of February she will be covered. With the rut the stags break up. Throughout the rest of the year they live in perfect accord : now they cannot stand the sight of each other. Each stag that is strong enough to do so collects a herd of hinds and defends it against all others, at the same time rounding up any other hinds that he can manage to separate from other herds without endangering his own. He will drive out all other males (except the year's calves and knobbers) and is very zealous in rounding up any of his hinds that lag or straggle. You can judge the power of a stag by the size of his harem. I once counted ninety-two (and I may well have missed a few) in the harem of a big hummel. During the rut stags roar—it really is a roar with quite a leonine quality about it—and fight. These fights, though themselves very frequent, rarely result in death. There is much awe-inspiring roaring, and much tremendous coughing (each roar ends in a succession of deep coughs), and a fair amount of clashing of antlers as rivals meet, but there is a good deal more noise than fight. The big stags keep the small at bay by threat and bluster, and the clashing of antlers is usually confined to the smaller stags hovering about on the edge of the herd. All the same, a master-stag must fight to keep his harem, and he must always be on the run to prevent smaller animals nipping in and cutting off a hind or two. After a fight the victor always pursues the defeated a little way, but never far, for the moment his back is turned inferior animals will rush in to cut hinds from the herd, and there follows what General Crealock has aptly called " an amorous scrimmage ". All this fighting and running, as well as the actual mating, tells heavily on the master-stags, who become thin and weary, and sooner or later they generally retire and a second, inferior animal takes over the herd. Sometimes before the end of October this beast may give way to a third. More usually on the retirement of the master-stag (I have, by the way, never heard of a hummel retiring) the herd of the master-stag is parcelled out among several inferiors. The hinds show no partiality for any particular beast, accepting any stag that comes along with perfect equanimity.

Red deer feed at nightfall and at dawn. During the day they lie chewing the cud with the wind at their backs. By so doing they can see danger approaching from in front (though as a matter of fact they have not got very good sight) and scent it coming from behind (and they have got very fine powers of scent), and before they feed they will generally drink. The staple food is grass and young heather tops, but they will eat a good deal else besides. They are not popular in the neighbourhood of farms or young plantations. Deer living by the sea-shore will eat seaweed, and deer living inland will eat cast antlers and any bones they may come across for the sake of the salts they contain. The grouse-moor keeper accuses the deer of eating grouse eggs, but I do not know that this has been proved. It has been proved, however, that they will eat rabbits they come across in traps.

When deer move together it is usually in single file. They have an instinct for dangerous places, and never fall into holes and so on as do mountain sheep. They have also an instinct for weather and will leave the tops before a storm. Red deer are not caught in snow-drifts as are sheep, for they will always face out a heavy storm on bare windswept ground. And they have an uncanny knack of making themselves comfortable in appalling weather. But always they are cautious and suspicious (the hinds especially so) and ready to move at the slightest hint of danger, be it by sight or scent or unfamiliar sound. And one party of deer moving will set all the others within sight or smell moving also. Deer, thus disturbed, move up-wind as a rule, a hind leading and the stag bringing up the rear.

And as to their accomplishments. They can run, walk, canter and gallop with equal facility, and their gallop is fast over a short distance. They can run for miles at a good speed. They can jump—a deer fence must be over six feet high. They can slip through gaps that seem altogether too small. They can swim expertly. A hunted Exmoor deer has swum the Bristol Channel, and a hunted deer will always take to water if it can.

Red deer, once out of the calf stage, have only one enemy, man. They are shot and they are hunted with hounds. Deerstalking is said by its devotees to be the grandest sport on earth. I have not had sufficient experience to know about that. Deerstalking is for the most part a rich man's sport. Personally, I would rather have a day's shore shooting any time. But most emphatically I must disagree with those (most of whom have never tried it) who maintain that there is nothing in it at all and that any fool can kill a stag. There is a great deal in it. It requires great physical fitness, a very steady hand and a good eye, and excellent nerves. It is against it, in my opinion, that it needs a professional stalker (the man who actually shoots is called the "gentleman"), which means that all the really interesting part, the approach to the deer, the judgment of wind, the guess as to what the deer will do, the knowledge of ground and habits, is done for one, and little is left for the " gentleman " to do but shoot. That, of course, is quite a lot. It is very much easier to miss a big stag than to kill one. And again, the work after the stag has been killed—the gralloch and so on—is done by the stalker. I suppose that if the " gentleman " had to do it all few stags would be shot, but to one of my temperament, one much more interested in the approach and the actual battle of wits than in the shot, it is a drawback.

And, of course, there is more in deerstalking than the stalk and the shot. Deer have to be managed. Hinds must be shot in winter, in hard weather there must be some hand-feeding. If there is much heather it must be burnt, as on a grouse moor, and a good rule is one-tenth every year. There is a staff to be managed and cared for and so on, and extra hands will have to be taken on for the actual season. Managing a deer forest, if not quite so exacting as managing a grouse moor, is not a job for fools or idle men. Oh yes, there is more in deerstalking than stalking deer. But the main trouble remains. It is all too true that the average deerstalker need never learn anything of the sport. All he needs to be able to do is to withstand physical weariness and to hold a rifle straight and steady. Of the joys of stalking—of the spy and the approach, of the intricacies of wind and scent—he need know nothing. And generally he does know nothing. I think it is a pity.

Deer are also hunted with hounds. This is a process that every now and again rouses the ignorant to loud protest—especially where the Devon and Somerset Staghounds are concerned. But if the Exmoor stags were not hunted, I believe there would be no deer on Exmoor. And personally, I like the deer on Exmoor. The Devon and Somerset Staghounds hunt wild Exmoor stags : in some parts of the country carted stags are also hunted. I confess that hunting the carted stag leaves me absolutely cold. Not because the animal is not killed, but because it knows quite well that it is not in danger and the hounds know quite well that they must not touch it. Indeed, a carted stag will never run itself out (a hind will sometimes do so), and when it feels that it has had enough it just turns and stands at bay. Moreover, I think it is a fact that a carted stag hunted for, say, three years three times a season (and you cannot hunt it more frequently than that because it just refuses to run) will take the same line every time and generally stop in the same place. Now, I do not pretend to be an expert at this business—I do not pretend to know very much about it—but as far as I can make out there is little or no hound work in it, and the followers, if they need a gallop and some jumping, might just as well organise a paperchase.

Hunting the wild red deer of Exmoor is a very different business. Here hounds hunt to kill and the stag knows it. For the kind-hearted it may be pointed out that the deer would be killed anyhow and in much less humane ways. There was no hunting on Exmoor from 1825 to 1827 and again from 1833 to 1841. Poaching in these years was rife, and others than poachers killed the deer. They were not all good shots and most, if not all of them, used shotguns, and many a good beast crawled miserably away to die of lingering wounds in some thicket. Things would be just the same to-day. The only place where you can keep deer and not hunt or stalk them is a park, and the park deer is a poor apology for the wild beast in many ways. To return to hunting: great local knowledge is required. The Devon and Somerset hunt about 450 square miles of country and difficult country at that. It has huge woodlands and is much cut up with combes and valleys. Furthermore, though I believe Exmoor men deny their existence, there are plenty of bogs. A huntsman of the Devon and Somerset has got to be born on the moor, for if he wants to keep anywhere near his hounds he must know the country like the back of his hand. And Exmoor weather taken by and large is pretty testing—especially in winter—so he has to be as tough as they come. In addition to all this he has got to know all about the red deer, and the red deer of Exmoor are as cunning as red deer anywhere else (it is a great mistake to imagine that the Devon and Somerset always kill); furthermore, one of the favourite tricks of an old Exmoor stag is to put hounds on to a fresh young one. A huntsman not up to his hounds will soon find that he is spending tiring, profitless days chasing (not hunting) a succession of fresh beasts.

And again, stag-hunting is a specialised business. It can best be put thus: that in fox-hunting you hunt *a* fox, in stag-hunting you hunt *the* stag. Not just any stag, but one particular stag—a warrantable stag (in the autumn this means a stag of five years and over), and this stag must be found before the meet. This is done by the harbourer, and it requires knowledge of deer as expert as that of the huntsman or, in Scotland, the stalker. The harbourer is told by farmers and friends in the district where the hunt is to meet that deer have been feeding in such and such a field at nightfall. He may be told that

Plate XXXIX

Aggressive display of HEN LONG-EARED OWL. Norfolk, 1940. ERIC HOSKING

HEN TAWNY OWL carrying water shrew to young. Flashlight. Norfolk, 1943
ERIC HOSKING

Plate XL

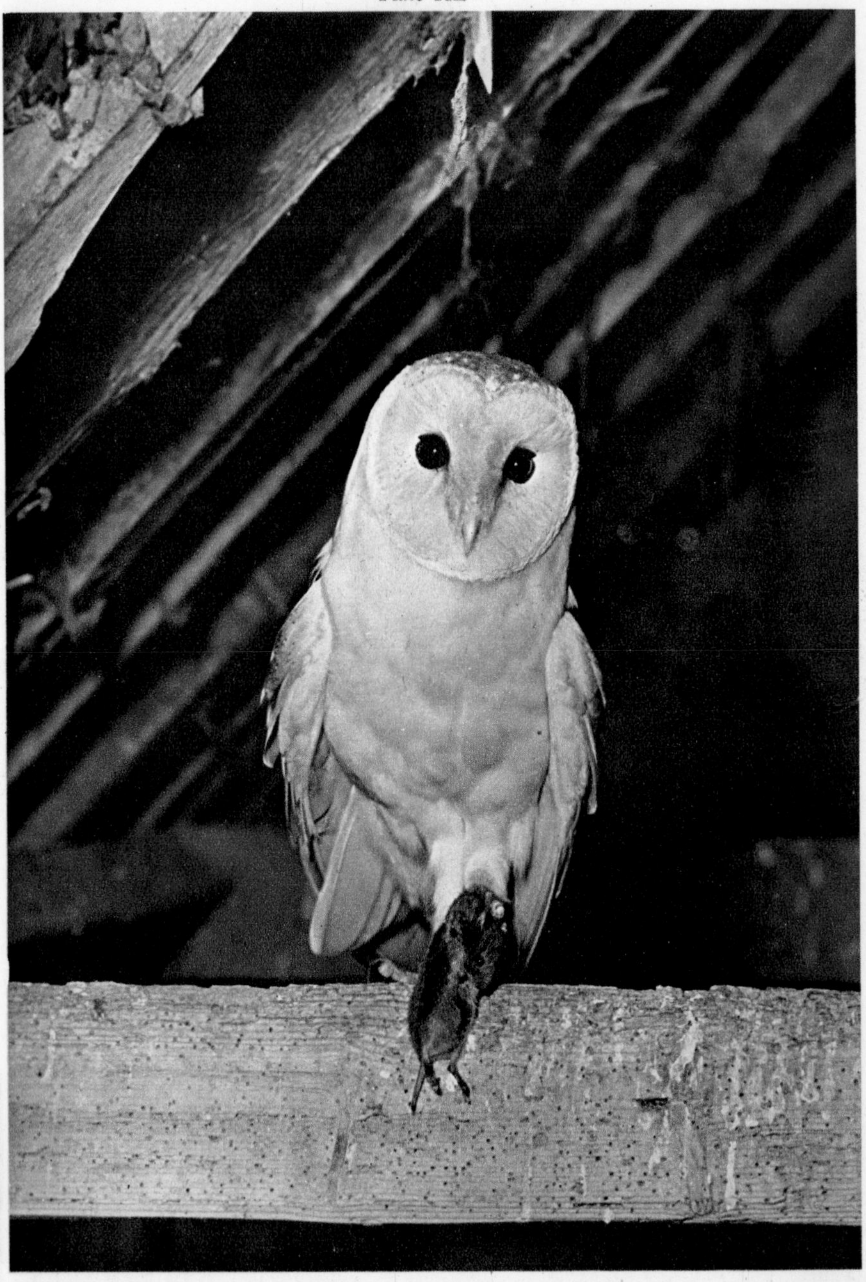

MALE BARN OWL with field-vole. Flashlight. In a Norfolk barn. June 1942
ERIC HOSKING

there is a big stag among them, he may not. He goes down and has a look at the racks (the gaps in the hedges made by the deer). If the ground is damp he will find a slot (the footmark of a deer), and even if it is not he will probably find one, for he knows his business and sees what would escape the eye of lesser mortals. And from this slot he will tell at once what sort of a deer made it, what size he is, and what sort of antlers he carries. He will go out next morning to watch the deer returning from their feed just to make sure that he is right—I believe he always is—and then he must follow the deer up (without disturbing them) to see where they are going to lie up for the day. And having found that he must, if it is a big wood (and as I have said, there are some very big woods in the Devon and Somerset country) he must cast ahead to make sure in which part of the wood the stag is lying. If it is a smallish wood he must cast around it to make sure that the beast has not come out and travelled farther on, as a beast that has been disturbed is sure to do. And, remember, he may well have to do this in fog or in very stormy weather, when deer cannot be seen and can only be tracked, and in the rutting season there is the additional difficulty that stags are very restless and do not stay in one place for long. A harbourer's job is an expert one.

There is another difference also between stag-hunting and fox-hunting—the use of tufters. It is most inadvisable to draw with the whole pack in stag-hunting. (I have seen it done only once, and it resulted in a rare mix-up.) The stag's first idea when put up is to find other deer and to put hounds on to another animal. That animal has the same idea, and so on. It is easy to see what could happen with a full pack and several deer. So tufters are used, and once the stag is away and the line established they are called off—it is easier to stop two hounds than a pack—and the pack put on. After that it is a question of the wiles of the deer versus the wiles of huntsman and hounds. And I think the odds are just about even. Most hunted stags make for water in the end, and the vast majority die, a quick death from the knife, in one of the streams of Exmoor. Hinds are not harboured, and tufters are not used. Hinds are very tough, do not run straight like stags, and are as full of tricks as a house full of monkeys. Hind hunting—an essential proceeding—is very hard work.

THE FALLOW DEER

(*Dama dama*)

FALLOW deer are smaller than red deer. The male (buck *not* stag) stands about 3 feet 2 inches at the withers, and the average weight is about twelve stone. I have seen it stated that New Forest fallow deer are very poor specimens—and it is true that their antlers, as is the case with red deer, will not compare with those of park deer—but some New Forest bucks compare very favourably in weight with the red deer of the Highlands. A good many bucks have been killed in the Forest weighing between fourteen and fifteen stone clean, and the heaviest New Forest buck weighed, I believe, 15 st. 10 lb. clean, which is not a bad weight at all.

The bucks grow flattened antlers on a cylindrical stem, usually (but not always) with no bez point and palmated above the trez. The does (*not* hinds) are smaller, standing 2 feet 10 in. to 3 feet at the withers, and hornless. There appear to be two distinct races of fallow deer in this country—a dark race and a light race. The light race, which is typical of the park deer, has a fawn-coloured coat with large white spots, a white line along the flanks and a line of black hair along the back and tail, and the underparts are greyish white. This coat is not changed in winter, though it is a good deal duller in winter than in summer. The dark race, which is typical of the wild deer, have the same colouring as the park deer in summer, if anything a little brighter, but in the winter this coat is discarded and replaced by a winter coat of rather dark drab grey-brown unrelieved by any spots. Both races may be seen on the same ground, for instance in Richmond Park and now in many of the woods of southern England, but they keep separate and do not apparently ever interbreed, though they do interbreed at Whipsnade.

As with the red deer there are special names for the various ages of fallow deer. Most of them have now died out and are no longer used, but it may be of interest to record them here. A fallow deer in its first year is called a *fawn* ; a buck in its second year is called a *pricket*, in the third year a *sorel*, in its fourth year a *sore*, in its fifth year a *bare back*, in its sixth year a *buck*, and from its seventh year onwards a *great buck*. Of these ancient names only fawn and pricket are used in the New Forest to-day. Nowadays men talk of a three-year-old, four-year-old and so on, and a buck of seven years old and upwards is no longer called a great buck but a full-headed buck or full buck. It is, I think, a pity. As in Scotland all hinds are " old hinds ", so in the New Forest all does are " old does ", but the adjectives commonly applied to the female red deer of the Highlands are rarely applied to the female fallow deer of the New Forest. The term " yeld " is not used at all. Fallow does are every whit as fertile as red deer hinds, and have their first fawn at two years old as against the red deer at three years old. Furthermore, though one fawn in a year is usual, twins are not at all uncommon, and triplets have been recorded. A doe does not appear to have twins until she is at least four years old, and it seems to be a fact that only old hinds have triplets. There is a considerable amount of colour variation. Cinnamon-coloured deer are not uncommon, completely black examples have been recorded from the New Forest, a cinnamon buck with a black head frequented the woods around Singleton in Sussex for some years, a brown type with chestnut underparts appears in the New Forest fairly frequently, and white deer also occur more frequently than among red deer. At the present moment in the New Forest I know of four white deer, three does and a great buck, and I believe that these are all the children of one normal coloured doe. A white buck never seems to get a white fawn, and white does never produce white fawns at the first generation so far as I know, but fairly commonly in the second generation.

When kept in parks fallow deer are noticeably gregarious. In the wild they are less so than red deer, and you will rarely find a large herd. Small parties are the rule, and the sexes keep together from the beginning of the rut until the early spring. The rut commences about the third week in October, and lasts only a short while, but if for any reason a doe should come into season in January she will be covered. The bucks call, but they do not roar in the impressive manner of red stags. The head is held down to the ground and then jerked upwards, and the sound is a mixture of grunt and bark that does not carry a long distance. There is no coughing. Does are silent as a rule, but have a whining bleat of warning to their fawns which is not unlike that of the red deer hind though less nasal. During the rut the bucks fight, but it is a bloodless affair and mostly made up of threat. The " master " buck does not occur, at any rate among New Forest fallow deer, and there is none of the ceaseless chivvying of females to prevent their being cut out by inferior males that is so common a feature of red deer in rut. Fallow bucks have caused the deaths of human beings before now, but they are far the safest of our deer, and even park deer are much less dangerous than other park deer.

The fawns are born in May and June (usually in the latter half of June) after eight months' gestation, but I have twice seen new fawns in October. They are dropped while the doe is standing and have coats dappled just the same as the adults. Unlike the red deer calves they are not helpless. They can run within an hour or so of birth and jump well when only a few hours old. The fallow deer is a magnificent jumper, far better than the red deer. A seven-foot fence is cleared easily, and I have seen a fallow buck clear some incredibly long distances when hunted. The horns are dropped in May—prickets do not drop theirs until late June—and are regrown from May until August, being clean by the end of that month. Fallow deer do not wallow, and when the coat is being changed it is bitten off, the coat on the back of the neck and shoulders being rubbed off against a tree. There seem to be favourite trees for this, which are used by generation after generation.

The food is purely vegetarian. Grass, young shoots, the leaves and bark of trees, chestnuts, acorns, crops, roots, green vegetables and flowers are all taken, and, like red deer, fallow deer generally drink before they feed. The day, in summer, is spent lying up in the thickest cover available, feeding being confined to nightfall and dawn. They are, however, much more restless than red deer and are always getting up and lying down, and they feed on the move, continually raising their heads and always on the alert. They have just as good powers of scent and hearing as red deer and their sight is infinitely better. So far as stalking is concerned, they are much more difficult because, when disturbed, they do not pause to look back. In the winter they move continuously and spend little or none of the day lying up, but rest and move on all through the hours of daylight.

Fallow deer are very widely distributed in this country. Most people regard deer as rare outside the parks because they hardly ever

Plate XLI

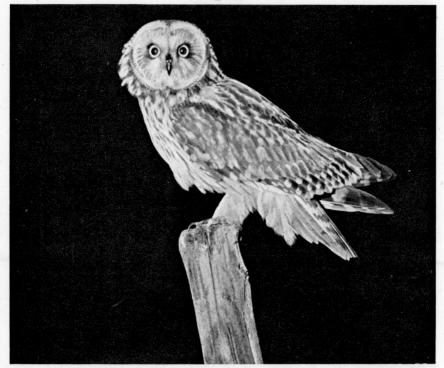

SHORT-EARED OWL. Flashlight. Norfolk, 1942. ERIC HOSKING

HEN SHORT-EARED OWL brooding small young. Norfolk, 1942. ERIC HOSKING

Plate XLII

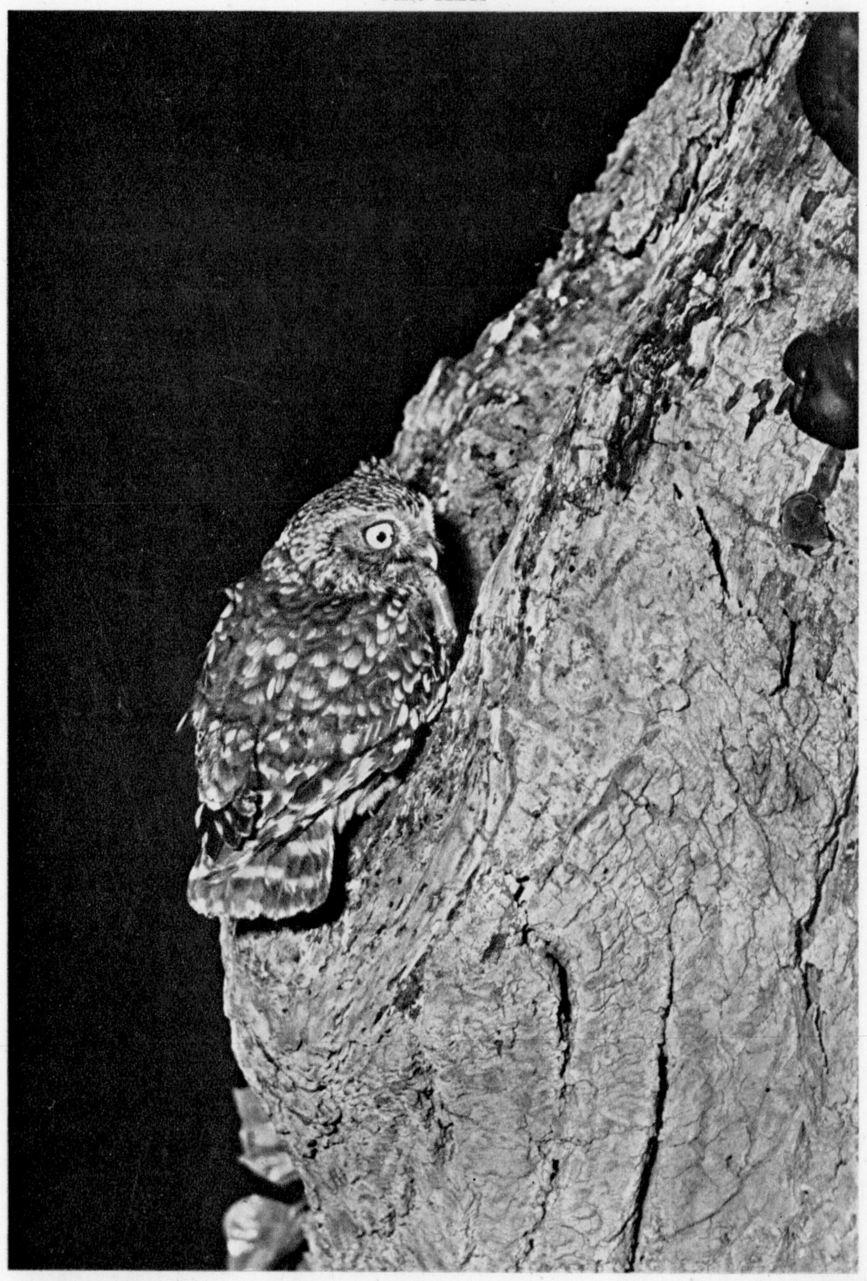

LITTLE OWL brings a caterpillar to its nest in the hole of an ash tree. Flashlight at night
Norfolk 1943. ERIC HOSKING

see them, but fallow deer are most certainly not rare. There are plenty in the New Forest, and they occur in many parts of Scotland and Ireland and throughout most of the wooded country of southern England, particularly in Surrey, Sussex, Hampshire, Dorset and Wilts. For the most part I think these are escapes from parks, but in Hampshire and west Sussex there are undoubtedly a good many genuine wild deer, I mean deer of the dark race. And even those that have escaped from parks have been genuinely wild now for many years, perhaps hundreds of years. I have had fallow deer in the garden in Hampshire many times, and I have seen them in the woods on the outskirts of Farnham—even within a few yards of houses—on several occasions. But in these woods (many are being cut down but there is still plenty of thick timber) you do not see the deer nearly so frequently as their numbers would warrant. You see their tracks. Few people bother to look for their tracks and so have no idea that they are in the woods around them.

There is rather more shooting of fallow deer than is generally realised. In some of the southern counties the farmers every now and then combine in deer drives, and these sometimes result in considerable casualties. A deer drive is not, in my opinion, a pleasant thing, and I fear that a good many deer go away wounded, but the fallow deer can wreak immense damage among crops and something has got to be done. Fallow deer are also hunted—notably by the New Forest Buckhounds (they are also regularly shot by the keepers in the Forest, the only way in which numbers can really be kept down)—and this hunting is on much the same lines as those followed by the Devon and Somerset Staghounds, harbouring, tufters, and so on. Harbouring in the New Forest is more difficult than harbouring on Exmoor, for the area is much more wooded, and in some of the big enclosures it is not possible to make sure that the deer have not moved on after being harboured. Much more attention has to be paid to slots than I believe is necessary on Exmoor, and some of the Forest keepers are uncannily accurate in their reading of slots. And there is also the further difficulty that the New Forest fallow deer, or a large proportion of them, are migratory. Another difference between the two hunts is that the New Forest tufters do not run with the pack after it is laid on.

A hunted fallow buck is full of wiles. Like the red deer stag he will make for other deer and try to get hounds on to a fresh line. He will run into the water, but he will never stop in water for the hounds to come up to him as a stag will do. He can swim well (many have swum the Avon), and he will swim for some distance up- or downstream, but he will not stay in the water. He will also " soil "—that is, jump into water or a pool, roll and jump out with scarcely a pause. Unless beaten a fallow buck will never pass under a bridge. A buck put up and bayed by a few hounds will fight fiercely, and many a New Forest hound has been killed and many more severely injured. But once under way a buck will run until he can go no farther. He moves with a lolloping gallop that appears slow. New Forest hounds are really fast but they cannot catch a buck; they can only wear him down. And if you try to gallop your horse alongside a buck you will at once realise that slow-seeming gallop is really a tremendous pace. A buck at the start of his run has his mouth open and his tongue hanging out. And his mouth stays open until he is beaten and the end is drawing near.

THE ROE DEER

(*Capreolus capraea*)

THE RED deer is the largest and most noble of our deer : the roe deer is the smallest and by far the most beautiful. It is, in fact, by far the most beautiful of all our animals. The sexes, as in our other deer, differ. The male (buck *not* stag) stands between 2 feet 1 inch and 2 feet 5 inches at the withers and weighs between 35 and 60 lb. The average weight of Scottish roebuck is between 40 and 45 lb. The heaviest Scottish roebuck, I believe, weighed 60 lb. clean, which means about 72 lb. on the hoof, which is a very big weight indeed, but there have been several records of animals of over 50 lb. on the hoof. English roebuck are rather heavier on the average, say 50–55 lb. on the hoof. The females (does *not* hinds) are smaller. Scottish does average between 30 and 40 lb., and English does between 40 and 45 lb. The bucks have antlers, which are of yearly growth as in our other deer. They are rough and cylindrical, with one upright shaft and with one forward tine and above it one backward. Mature bucks usually carry six points, but more have been recorded, even, I understand, fourteen from a Continental animal. I have shot a roebuck with three antlers, and I believe that three antlers are not really so uncommon, though I have only seen them once. The normal length of antlers is about 9 inches, and the circumference above the coronet $4\frac{1}{2}$ inches. And roe deer are remarkable among deer in that their antlers do not appear to have deteriorated since prehistoric times, which is a good deal more than can be said for the red deer and the fallow deer.

In colour the roe deer's summer coat is red, a good bright red on the back and a little paler on the flanks and the belly. The summer coat is short and firm. In winter the coat is mouse-coloured and the hair is soft and long. There is an undercoat of chestnut which in some individuals shows up on the flanks. Scottish roe have much more grizzled faces than English roe, and they also have a white patch on the gullet which is absent from the roe of the south country.

Young roe deer (fawns or kids but *not* calves : kid is correct, but you may call them fawns without offending good taste) are dropped about the first week in June. At one time it was thought that the gestation period was eighteen months, but it is now known to be about ten months. Twins are normal, usually one of each sex, and triplets have been recorded. The kids are born with red coats spotted with white and can follow their mother in about a fortnight. As soon as the kids can follow the does return to the bucks. The rut is in June and July. Generally the first barking is not heard before Midsummer Day, and pairing does not take place until about a month later. I have seen red deer and fallow deer couple, but I have never watched the mating of roe, and it is, I imagine, a sight that is rarely seen. After the rut—some time in August—the bucks wander off alone, generally making for the high ground, and they stay there until the beginning of October. Then they rejoin the does and a second, but infertile, pairing takes place. At any rate it is said to be infertile, but I am not sure upon what grounds. After this the sexes stay together until May, when the does drive away their kids in preparation for a new family. Roebuck are often said to be monogamous. Some may be, but many certainly are not. The antlers are shed at any time between September and December, most usually in November, and are clean again by the end of April or early in May.

During the rut the bucks fight fiercely, and they also chase the deer in circular rings. These are not, as a rule, the well-defined circular tracks that have been the subject of so much controversy in the past. The brothers John and Charles Stuart maintained that these were formed around a tree by the deer in their efforts to rid themselves of flies (roe do not wallow) and not by the kids chasing their mothers during the weaning period. William Scrope was of the opinion that they were formed during the weaning period. Probably there is some foundation for both opinions.

Roe are woodland deer. They are mainly nocturnal and so are rarely seen, except when driven by beaters. They live for the most part in parties of up to half a dozen, but I have seen a troop of twenty-five on the move in Hampshire. During the day they lie up in the thickest cover they can find and are very secretive and timid. They feed at nightfall and dawn, and usually drink before doing so. At night several parties may gather at the same feeding ground, but they will separate when returning to rest. During high summer they are more often to be seen in the open, or in open glades and rides in the woods, and this is because they are very bothered by flies, which attack them unmercifully and especially around the eyes, lips and nostrils. Roe suffer a good deal, especially in wet winters, from fluke. They are also hosts to the bot-fly, the parasitical larva of which they pick up while grazing. In winter, in Scotland at any rate, they remain in the thickest woods. Their powers of scent do not seem to be nearly so highly developed as in the red deer, but their sight is good, and they have remarkable hearing. When scared in cover they will bound backwards and forwards every now and again, making a high leap and looking backwards. As jumpers they excel, and can easily clear a six-foot wall, no mean achievement having regard to their size. They swim well, with the head only showing, and in Hampshire sometimes appear to bathe for pleasure. The food is entirely vegetable with an especial fondness for berries. I have also watched roe in the early morning eating mushrooms, ignoring the grass around and making from mushroom to mushroom.

Roe are not hunted. In former times they used to be " baited ". This practice bore no resemblance to bear, bull or badger baiting, but consisted of one man armed with a rifle hunting one particular buck with one dog, usually an old foxhound. It needed great knowledge of the roe and great physical strength on the part of the man, and it must have been a grand sport. It has long since died out. More and more nowadays we like our game driven on to our guns, and the really energetic sports in which brain and strength are fully tested are, unfortunately, becoming less and less popular. Roe are still shot and roe are still stalked. Stalking is excellent sport, and the little red deer when pursued with a rook-and-rabbit rifle (which means a range of not more than 50 yards, even if your rifle is sighted to 150 yards) is a difficult quarry to get close to. Roe are also, unfortunately, driven. They may be shot on a day that includes pheasants and so on—usually a snap shot at excessive range and rarely a successful shot. But they are also driven to a waiting horde of farmers and friends armed with shotguns and No. 5 shot. This is not sport. Bucks, does and kids are fired on indiscriminately, and many are wounded and die lingering and horrible deaths. If one must use a 12-bore one must not fire at more than 20 yards range. But preferably do not use a shotgun, unless it is an eight-bore and you have buck shot.

Roe drives are horrible things. But the roe has unfortunately fallen from its former high estate. The Forestry Commission, a body very unpopular with the majority of sportsmen, endeavours to exterminate it, and to most shooting men it is now merely an item in the "various" column. The grand little roe deserves better than that.

Roes are, happily, still quite common. The stock in southern England are, I think, mainly descendants of animals introduced about 200 years ago. They are fairly common in the New Forest, more common in Dorset and South Wiltshire, and quite common through all the woods of Hampshire, south-west Surrey and Sussex. Probably they are more common than one thinks. I have frequently come across their tracks, and I have frequently had them in my garden, but I do not see them as frequently as I would like. There seems to be some movement northwards from the New Forest and Dorset in the summer after the kids are born, and southwards again as the leaves begin to fall. At any rate, there always seem to be more roe, and more signs of roe, in north-west Hampshire and south-west Surrey in high summer than in winter, and undoubtedly there is a movement southwards and westwards from Alice Holt and through the woods between the Meon and Itchen valleys in autumn.

Note.—In addition to red, fallow and roe deer, Japanese deer and the variety known as Manchurian deer are at large in several parts of the country, especially in the Surrey and Hampshire woodlands, the New Forest and the Midlands. Bucks stand about 2 ft. 8 in. at the withers and weigh about 135 lb. They are said to breed with Red deer, which is, I think, most improbable. Indeed I have also been told that in the New Forest and Dorset they breed with roe deer. There are also in some of the mountainous parts of Scotland, Ireland and Wales wild goats. They are very wild indeed, and offer most exciting stalking. Some of the heads are exceptionally good : horns of 45 inches being recorded.

THE PRESERVATION OF GAME

CHAPTER I

THE ENEMIES OF GAME

THE ENEMIES of game—I have chosen the title deliberately. Most people just call them "vermin", and for that word I have a rooted dislike. It implies in us, and the game we preserve to kill, a superiority we do not in fact possess. We call these creatures vermin for no other reason than that they interfere with our pleasures, a poor enough excuse for bestowing upon them so degrading a title, and one which becomes even less valid when we realise that these pleasures of ours have, almost without exception, been born within the last 150 years, while the Almighty created the creatures we so describe quite a while before that. Furthermore, if you are going to use the word "vermin" as descriptive of the enemies of game, you must be consistent and apply it equally to all the enemies—to the fox and the peregrine no less than to the rat and the crow. The peregrine is one of the noblest birds that fly, and the fox (which does a great deal more damage to game than the peregrine) is the beloved of the hunting man, very few of whom would hear it described as vermin and remain unmoved. If you must use the word vermin confine it to the rat and the rabbit, creatures that are not only enemies of game but of game-preservers.

And which are the enemies of game? Without going so far as the gamekeeper of old who regarded everything that was not game as vermin, we can safely say that they are legion, and to describe them adequately would require a book as large as this one. To begin with, there are thirty-three birds in Britain that can properly be described as predatory birds, and all of them are shot—some frequently, some whenever they are seen, some every now and then—by gamekeepers and game-preservers. Let me list them briefly and give, at the same time, a short résumé of their foods and so on.

The Golden Eagle. A large dark brown bird with some lighter feathers about the head and neck. Breeds in the Scottish Highlands and is for the most part confined to them, but does occasionally appear in southern England, when it is almost invariably shot at once. Feeds on grouse and ptarmigan, hares and rabbits and occasionally young lambs, will also attack and kill roe kids and red deer calves. The last golden eagle that I know of was shot in southern England ; had been feeding on rabbits. Will eat carrion.

The White-tailed Eagle. A large brown bird with a pale head and a white tail. Now only a very rare visitor to these islands (it used to breed), and almost invariably shot as soon as it does appear. Feeds on small birds, including game birds, hares and rabbits, and fishes in the manner of an osprey.

The Osprey. A dark brown bird with a white flecked back and a whitish head with a tuft. Quite unmistakable. Used to breed in these islands, now only a rare visitor. Does not attack game birds, but will sometimes take a rabbit. Is shot when it does appear. I had two sent to me for identification in 1942, both shot in Hampshire by men who should have known better.

The Peregrine Falcon. Slate-grey barred with dark grey above, with white breast spotted and streaked with black. Not uncommon in mountainous districts and along the cliffs all round our shores, and manages to hold its own in the face of incessant persecution from egg-collectors, gamekeepers and shooting men. The fastest and most active of our hawks. Takes grouse, partridges, duck, rooks, gulls, an occasional pheasant, many pigeons and also rabbits. I have seen one stoop at a heron, but sheer off, and also one stoop at and strike (but obviously in play) a farmyard goose. The goose was more surprised than hurt.

The Kite. A reddish-brown bird with a long forked tail, formerly common all over Britain, now reduced to a sorry, inbred remnant in Wales, where under strict protection it manages to breed every year despite the attentions of the egg-collectors. Feeds on small birds, including game birds, will raid poultry yards, takes many rabbits and is fond of snakes. Should be protected throughout the year in the British Isles, but unfortunately is not.

The Sparrow Hawk. Blue-grey back and breast cross-barred with brown. A fierce dashing little bird for whom I have an immense admiration. Takes small birds and woodpigeons, will take young game birds, and so is mercilessly harried, but manages to survive in some numbers in woodland; probably does quite as much good as harm.

The Kestrel. Male reddish-brown with grey head and tail; female a deeper brown. The familiar "windhover" should never be shot. It is true that it will sometimes take pheasant chicks, but it feeds chiefly on mice and voles, and is one of the best friends the farmer has.

The Common Buzzard. A rich brown bird with paler underparts, but there is a good deal of variation in individuals. Fairly common and increasing in numbers in Wales, Scotland, the Lake District, and in our south-western counties. Has recently been introduced and has bred in Surrey. Bred in 1942 in Hampshire. Increasing in numbers in winter in our southern counties. Flies slowly, soaring in great circles, and is beautiful to watch. Looks fierce but is weak. Too slow on the wing to harm game birds. Takes many mice, moles and young rabbits, and also insects. Altogether beneficial and should never be shot.

The Rough-legged Buzzard. Like the common buzzard but larger, with a white patch on the tail and feathered legs. A rare winter visitor. In Britain lives almost entirely on rabbits.

The Honey-Buzzard. A brown bird with a grey head. The underparts of the male are white barred with brown, and of the female white barred with brown and chestnut. A summer visitor arriving in May. Has bred recently in southern England but is steadily decreasing in numbers. Will occasionally take small birds and young rabbits, but feeds mainly on wasps and humble bees and their larvae. Is protected by law throughout the country, but is still shot and is subject to much persecution by egg-collectors. Should never be shot, and egg-collectors should be prosecuted and heavily fined.

The Merlin. The smallest of our hawks. Male slate-blue above narrowly barred with black, and the tip of the tail, beyond a black bar, white. Female brownish-grey above. Is a bird of the open moorland, most common from Derbyshire and North Wales northwards. Does occur in the south, along the South Downs and in the heather of Hampshire, every now and then, and more frequently of recent years. Feeds on small birds and mice, is practically harmless to grouse, and I have never known one to take a partridge, but no doubt has done so on occasions.

The Hobby. A small hawk but little bigger than the merlin. Dark grey with a still darker grey head. The sides of the neck are white, and the breast is flecked vertically with black on a cream ground. A summer visitor much harried by egg-collectors. Arrives in May. Feeds on small birds occasionally, but in the main on insects, and has been known to take bats. I have watched one in my garden make repeated raids on the large white butterflies. Is harmless to game.

The Hen Harrier. Male grey with white underparts ; female brown with a barred tail. Nests in Orkney. An uncommon hawk. Feeds on small birds, mice, voles, rats, rabbits, frogs, snakes and insects. Will undoubtedly take game chicks occasionally, but is almost wholly beneficial and should not be shot.

The Marsh Harrier. Larger than the hen harrier. Male brown with paler head ; female almost wholly brown. Nests only in Norfolk. Takes small birds, young water hens and young snipe, frogs and snakes. Is not a menace to game.

Montagu's Harrier. Very similar to the hen harrier (indeed difficult to tell apart in the field unless one is familiar with both species), but is a little smaller and slighter and has relatively longer wings and tail. Nests in marshes in Norfolk and Cambridgeshire, occasionally elsewhere in England. Very rare in Scotland. Food much the same as that of the marsh harrier. Is not a menace to game.

The Brown Owl. Also called the tawny owl and the wood owl. A large brown and grey owl with some small white spots on the wings. This is the owl with the long musical hoot. Is common and widely distributed in England and Wales, less common in Scotland. Feeds very largely on mice and rats, will sometimes take a young pheasant. Is one of the very best friends the gamekeeper (and the farmer) has and should *never* be shot.

The Barn Owl. A large light buff owl with back faintly marked with grey and brown. Appears white in flight. This is the owl that screeches. Is widely distributed but is, unfortunately, becoming less common. Is absolutely harmless to game, and destroys large numbers of mice, voles and rats. Should *never* be shot.

The Long-eared Owl. Colouring and size much the same as the brown owl, but appears larger because of the tufts on its head and the long tail. Generally distributed and becoming more numerous, but is by no means common. Does take small birds and occasionally a young pheasant. Destroys large numbers of mice, rats and voles. Should *never* be shot.

The Short-eared Owl. A mottled grey and brown bird with short tufts on its head. In the main a winter visitor, but nesting in increasing numbers in Scotland and eastern England. In winter occurs throughout the country. Lives almost entirely on voles, mice and rats. Should *never* be shot.

The Little Owl. Much smaller than other owls. Hunts by day as well as night. An introduced species widely distributed and fairly common. Much controversy has raged over its food. Undoubtedly takes small birds, takes many insects and kills mice and rats. Birds chiefly preyed upon are starlings, sparrows, blackbirds and thrushes in that order. These are taken from May until mid-July. The British Trust for Ornithology examined 2,460 pellets and 51 gizzards, and found that birds formed but a negligible fraction of the animal food taken : 5% of 94% animal matter. Undoubtedly does take game chicks, but the proportion is very small, though individuals may do harm. Gamekeepers maintain that it does enormous damage, but rarely produce positive evidence. Excluding rogues who may during nesting season do some damage, the evidence is strongly in favour of the little owl. Stomach examination, pellet examination, observation by thoroughly competent naturalists is all against the evidence of the gamekeeper. A great deal too much is also made of the damage caused to song birds. The little owl has been at large in this country for some sixty years, during which in the nesting season it has preyed on starlings, sparrows, blackbirds and thrushes. During these sixty years it has steadily increased in numbers, and there has been no corresponding decrease in starlings, sparrows, blackbirds and thrushes. Nor have I heard, nor have I been shown any evidence to suggest that during those sixty years or at any time since the little owl became really numerous has any game-preserver suffered heavily or that the numbers of game birds have decreased. I think that a great deal of the outcry against the little owl is based upon insufficient evidence and hearsay, and that isolated incidents and occasional rogues are (unconsciously) given magnified importance. *But* the little owl is the only owl that I would not give immunity to. It is increasing too rapidly for that.

The Raven. A large black bird with a sheen of blue on upperparts. Highly intelligent. Nests on cliffs, also occasionally in trees. Appears to be increasing. Food is chiefly carrion, but will eat anything (including game-bird chicks), and is a great robber of eggs if it gets the chance.

The Carrion Crow. A black bird just like a rook but without the bare patch at the base of the bill. Widely distributed. Solitary, not gregarious. A savage robber that will eat carrion and anything else. Robs eggs and will kill game-bird chicks, also weakly lambs and sheep. Should most certainly be shot by game-preservers, but is protected in most districts during the nesting season.

The Hooded Crow. Easily recognisable by grey body, black head, wings and tail. Resident in the north, but winter visitor in the south. The remarks made about the carrion crow apply equally to this species.

The Rook. Needs no description. Common and widely distributed. In the main a most useful bird, but a robber of eggs and young birds.

The Jackdaw. Again needs no description. Widely distributed and common. Food mainly insects and worms. Is fond of snails. Will take eggs and young birds, particularly in nesting season.

The Jay. A very handsome bird with a bright blue hackle in the wing and a white tail spot seen in flight. Is a nuisance to the gardener. Kills young birds and sucks eggs. But I am not sure that it actually does much harm to game, though undoubtedly it will kill game-bird chicks occasionally.

The Magpie. One of the most handsome of our birds, black and white, with a long tail shot with green and purple. Sucks the eggs and kills the young of other birds, but does great good in destroying enormous numbers of slugs, snails, insects, and will kill any young mouse it comes across. Again I am by no means convinced that it does much harm to game, though it does undoubtedly kill some game chicks. Has apparently increased of recent years, but I think the truth of the matter is that it has been driven into more restricted localities by changed rural conditions, and so is seen more frequently and in greater numbers.

The Kittiwake. Bill pale yellow ; legs dark green (appearing black), back and wings dove grey and primaries tipped with black. A sea-going gull that is *entirely harmless* to game.

The Black-headed Gull. The common gull of our waterfronts, towns and countryside. In the breeding season has a chocolate-brown head. For the rest of the year a pale grey bird with a white breast ; legs deep red. Eats (officially) fish, worms, slugs and insects : commonly follows the plough. This sounds harmless enough, but it undoubtedly sucks eggs and is acquiring other bad habits. I would be inclined to regard this bird as an enemy, or at least a potentially dangerous enemy, of game.

The Herring-Gull. A large gull with yellow bill and flesh-coloured legs. Grey wings with ends black and white tips, and white tail. Generally the commonest gull on the coast, but occurs far inland and will roost inland in certain places in large numbers. Feeds regularly on arable land and on grass. Eats everything including carrion. Kills and eats anything that is small enough or weak enough. Robs eggs.

The Common Gull. Generally distributed but by no means so common as name suggests. Easily mistaken for herring-gull by the uninitiated, but legs dull green-grey. More frequently inland than the herring-gull, feeding on grass and arable. Omnivorous; eats carrion. Food inland said to be chiefly insects, earthworms and seeds. Will perch in bushes to take berries. Is a great robber of eggs, kills small mammals and birds.

The Great Black-backed Gull. A very large gull with flesh-coloured to white legs and a black back. Large and powerful yellow bill with red patch on the sides. Common in the north, generally distributed but not common in the south. Ranges inland for a distance of about 20 miles from the coast. Eats carrion. A savage killer, powerful enough to kill weak sheep. A great nest robber, and kills many species of birds and the young of many more.

The Lesser Black-backed Gull. A smaller edition of the above but with back dark grey rather than black, and yellow legs. Frequently inland. Widely distributed and plentiful if not common. Eats carrion. Kills many species of birds and the young of many more. A confirmed and ruthless egg robber.

Well, there are the birds. All of them receive some measure of protection by law. Some are protected throughout the year in some counties, some only in the breeding season, a few in a few counties receive no protection. In some cases this protection extends also to the eggs. All this is very muddling to the ordinary man, but then our bird protection laws are completely farcical. As the law stands at present it means that some birds may be shot on one side of a hedge and not on the other, which in practice means that the birds are protected only in name. For all that the law should be observed. Gamekeepers should make themselves familiar with it as it applies to their own districts, and should observe it. Their employers should see that they do. The gamekeeper shooting a protected hawk sometimes has some excuse; the landowner or the tenant of shooting rights has none at all. He is a law-breaker and should know better. A copy of the Wild Birds' Protection Act as it applies to the district can be seen at any police station, but everyone owning or renting shooting rights would be well advised to get the booklet on predatory birds issued by the British Field Sports Society. Almost all the scientific names in this publication are wrong, but the information as to protection is accurate and clearly and concisely put forward. To return to the list given above. It is evident that with very few exceptions, e.g. the barn owl, all the birds mentioned lay themselves open by their habits to being shot in the interests of game preservation. But the game-preserver who did shoot all these birds whenever he came across them would himself deserve to be shot, and would in any case earn the contempt and dislike of his fellows. I will go further into this question of the destruction of predatory birds in a moment: for the present it will be sufficient to point out that there are certain birds which should *never* be shot. They are the kestrel, the brown owl, the barn owl, the long-eared owl and the short-eared owl, the buzzard, the rough-legged buzzard and the honey-buzzard, the hobby and the osprey.

So much for the birds: what of the mammals? Here again the list is a very long one. It might easily be stretched to include every wild mammal and many domestic ones, including the domestic pussy (a very dangerous enemy to game on occasions) and the domestic cow (for I once knew a cow that would eat the eggs of any ground nesting bird she came across), but if we went so far as that we would have to give up game-preserving forthwith. I will therefore confine myself to wild mammals, a long enough list in themselves.

The Wild Cat. Confined to the wilder parts of the Highlands of Scotland. Hunts chiefly at dawn and dusk, stalks by sight, and finishes with a bounding charge at tremendous speed. Is untamable. Mates readily with the domestic cat. Purely carnivorous, and will attack anything living including lambs, roe kids and red deer calves, but feeds mainly on hares and grouse. Was almost extinct in 1900. Now afforded protection by many landowners and has begun to increase. Must not be confused with the domestic pussy gone feral. There are plenty of these about in English woods, and they are a menace to all wildlife and deserve no mercy.

The Otter. Widely distributed and occurs on most streams throughout the British Isles. Very variable in size, length anything from 40 to 54 inches. The dogs are larger than the bitches, weighing between 20 and 26 lb., while bitches run between 16 and 20 lb. Breeds only once a year but in any month, two or three being the usual number in a litter. Does not hibernate and does not store food. Is nocturnal and very shy, being seen as a rule only when hunted. Is a most proficient swimmer, and can pursue, tire and kill a salmon of much greater weight than itself. Has extremely good sight and hearing, and is keen of scent, but not in the same class as, say, red deer. Will also hunt on land and occasionally raids poultry yards, for I once caught one raiding my poultry after sitting up for him on three nights. Main diet fish, but kills also rabbits, ducks, water-hens, snakes, grouse, and has been known to take partridges, and also to attack and kill sheep. Is not the menace on a salmon river that it used to be thought. Kills a great many eels, and certainly does more good than harm. Does not merit the serious consideration of the game-preserver. There are occasional rogues, but the number is small, and the otter, anyway, is a delightful animal.

The Marten. Confined to a few districts of Scotland, Wales and Ireland, and to the Lake District. Is waging a losing battle with extinction, and the numbers are very small. Looks like a large stoat, but has no smell or, if any, pleasant. A full-grown male should measure 34 inches of which 12 inches is tail, and weigh up to 3½ lb. Frequents only very thick woods or rocky hillsides, and is the wildest and shyest of all our animals. Takes rabbits, squirrels, moles, snakes, birds (including poultry), robs eggs, and has been known to kill lambs. Also eats berries and wasps. Is very easy to trap. Much too rare to merit the consideration of the game-preserver. In any case, should be protected by law.

The Polecat. Extinct over most of the country. Occurs in small numbers in Scotland and in Wales, where in some districts there has been a marked local increase in the last few years. A large black stoat with a foul smell. Males about 30 inches long (of which 8 inches is tail) and about 2¾ lb. in weight. Females about 26 inches long (of which 6 inches is tail) and weighing about 1¾ lb. Frequents woods, especially those on hillsides. Mainly nocturnal, and takes rabbits and poultry in preference to anything else, but also game birds, geese, turkeys, hares, and has been known to kill very young lambs. Is very brave and will attack a man if cornered. Is exceptionally easy to trap. An expert swimmer and fisherman and useful in catching large numbers of eels. Is much too uncommon to worry the game-preserver. In any case, it would be a pity if it became extinct.

The Badger. Widespread and common. Boars usually weigh about 25 lb., but 40 lb. occur fairly frequently, and 60 lb. has been recorded. Sows weigh 22–26 lb. Young are not born every year. A partial hibernator, lives in " setts ", which usually have several entrances and tunnels at different levels. Is extremely cleanly and makes a delightful pet. Nocturnal, but not shy. Very intelligent and resourceful and very difficult to trap. Has got good sight, but altogether exceptional powers of scent and hearing. Omnivorous : eats fruit, honey, wasps and many insects, rabbits, snakes, moles, young birds and mice. Old badgers will take to raiding poultry yards. Is frequently accused of killing sheep, but no sound evidence, and this is probably always the work of foxes. Individual badgers undoubtedly do take game birds and their eggs, but in the main they are good friends of the gamekeeper, and I should want very good evidence indeed before I destroyed a badger.

The Fox. Common throughout Great Britain and Ireland, but not in Scottish islands except Skye. Sexes live apart except during the breeding season, when several dogs will follow one vixen. Is mainly nocturnal and extremely cunning. Will eat carrion. Kills and eats hares, rabbits, rats, poultry, geese, swans, turkeys, all game birds, ducks, lambs (and full-grown sheep if weakly), pony foals (in New Forest), and has even been known to kill a young calf : also insects, frogs, snakes and fish. Kills wantonly and for pure love of killing. Despite the fact that it takes rats is a very dangerous enemy (I would place it second on the list of dangerous enemies) of the game-preserver. Owes its survival entirely to hunting, and has become a major rural industry. Offers the gamekeeper many problems and causes him many headaches, but is valuable to the countryside.

The Stoat. Common and widespread. Males usually about 15 inches long (of which 4 is tail) and weighing about 10 oz. (I have shot a male of 1¾ oz.), females about 13 inches long and weighing about 8 oz. Black tip of tail distinguishes the stoat at all seasons. The change to a white winter coat is rare in this country (though stoats on the top of Ben Nevis are white throughout the year) and does not seem to be entirely related to temperature. I have seen white stoats in Hampshire in very ordinary winters and ordinary ones in very cold and snowy weather, as in early 1940. In agricultural country stoats live in hollow tree-trunks, walls, banks, mole-hills, old rabbit buries,

Plate XLIII

OTTER. London Zoo, 1930. A. R. THOMPSON

OTTER. London Zoo, 1930. A. R. THOMPSON

Plate XLIV

BADGER. Flashlight. Cheshire June 1938. 11 p.m. H. PLATT

BADGERS. Flashlight. C. Down. July 1938. T. O. RUTLEDGE

and so on. They are not nocturnal, but do hunt at night: hunt by sight and smell, seizing victim by the throat or the artery behind the ear. They do not suck blood. Stoats pair very early, and young—five to ten in a litter—are born in April or May. I have seen young stoats in September. The young are blind for the first nine days, but soon become active and follow the mother on her expeditions. Almost untamable. Very clever and cunning, but very easy to trap. Cleanly and excrete outside home. Very clever at rolling eggs under chin, sometimes taking them a long way without harm. Can run fast, climb excellently, jump both high and far, swim excellently, and get through crevices apparently much too small for it without trouble. Kills wantonly, but will live with and play with rabbits. Eats rats, voles, mices, rabbits, hares, birds (including game birds), eggs, fish (is a good fisherman), and also carrion. Is preyed on by foxes, cats, owls, pike and man. Above all, man: every man's hand is against the stoat, and it is a miracle how it manages to keep up its numbers. This is, in my view, a very short-sighted policy on the part of man. For though the stoat does take poultry and game it destroys very large numbers of rats and mice.

The Weasel. A smaller edition of the stoat, but without a black tip to the tail. Males about 11 inches long (of which 2½ is tail) and about 3½ oz. in weight; females about 9 inches long (of which 2 inches is tail) and about 3 oz. in weight. Lives in much the same sort of places as the stoat and has much the same habits, but does not climb or swim so much as the stoat, though it can do both well enough. Young—four to six in a litter—born in April or May. Two or three litters a year. Will take game birds occasionally, but feeds mainly on mice, voles and rats, and also young rabbits. Is very definitely the farmer's and the gamekeeper's friend. Comparatively easy to tame, but very difficult to keep in captivity.

The Hedgehog. Common and widely distributed except on high ground, where it does not occur. Male and female are about the same size (males very slightly larger) and weigh from 1½ to 2½ lb. Two litters a year—four to seven in a litter—born in May or June and August or September. Mainly nocturnal, spending most of the day hidden in very thick cover or in holes. When asleep snores loudly. In the autumn is much more frequently seen by day. Sight is very poor, but scent and hearing are good, and the hedgehog is very sensitive to vibrations. When attacked or thoroughly alarmed rolls into a tight ball presenting a forest of spikes to the attacker. All foxes and badgers know how to open a hedgehog, and some dogs also know, in particular bull-terriers of the Staffordshire breed. Eats beetles and other insects, slugs, worms, mice, rats, young rabbits, frogs, young birds and eggs. Is undoubtedly the gardener's friend. Does not attack poultry, but eats carrion, which may account for the poultry stories. Is very fond of eggs and will eat any partridge or pheasant eggs it comes across, but I do not think it deliberately sets out to find them. Certainly, so far as the gamekeeper is concerned, it does more good than harm. Hedgehogs are fearless of man and easily tamed, and are very fond of milk.

The Grey Squirrel. An introduced species that is becoming a pest. The sexes are alike and about the same size. The normal weight is about 1½ lb., but I have shot many grey squirrels weighing over 2 lb. and one that weighed 2 lb. 9 oz. There does seem to be a general tendency towards increased weight and size in our grey squirrel during the last ten years or so. Has three to five young in a litter and two, often three, litters a year. Breeds at a year old. Does not hibernate. Migrates in winter, sometimes in large bodies, to areas with better food supply. I have seen as many as 80 in a body in Hampshire moving steadily south-west and followed them for more than a mile, during which time they scarcely paused. Makes large domed nests (called dreys) in trees, but will also use hollow trees, old ricks and thatched roofs of barns for nesting sites and winter quarters. Feeds out in the open, well away from trees or hedgerows in the autumn, and will also live underground in rabbit buries. Very destructive in gardens, destroying much more than it eats. Omnivorous and will eat carrion. Eats buds and shoots of young trees, fruit, nuts, seeds, vegetables and root crops, also stored grain, kills and eats young birds (including game birds), rabbits, mice, and is very fond of eggs, searching for and destroying nests, including those of game birds. Will kill a rat in a fight, but does not kill rats normally. I have also known grey squirrels to kill a big tom cat. Is not easy to shoot and very hard to trap. Swims well and easily. I regard the grey squirrel as a very dangerous enemy to game, and would place it high on the list, perhaps as high as No. 3. Fortunately it is very good to eat.

The Brown Rat. Excessively common. Sexes are alike, but size is very variable, varying from 12½ inches to 25 inches (including tail), and in weight from 3 oz. to 1½ lb. (very rarely more). The heaviest brown rat I have personally killed weighed 2 lb. exactly, but I am assured by many countrymen that they have known them considerably heavier. Normally $1\frac{1}{2}$ lb. is a big rat. This animal is beyond any question public enemy No. 1 both of the nation and of the game-preserver. It lives everywhere and anywhere except actually on the tops of mountains, is very cunning, very savage, very filthy, very adaptable and appallingly prolific. Has from 1–20 young in a litter (usually about ten), and has a litter every six weeks throughout the year. Breeds when only six months old, and the gestation period is only three weeks. Is gregarious and promiscuous. Sometimes migrates in large numbers. After the bombing of Southampton the countryside for some twelve miles round was infested with rats. Will gnaw through a 2-inch lead pipe to get at water, of which it needs very large quantities. Is very hard to trap, will fight fiercely if cornered, and will attack anything if in numbers. A terrible menace to man, his products, and his sport. Destroys much stored grain and also standing crops, kills and eats game birds and poultry, destroys eggs (and searches for them deliberately), and in addition carries deadly diseases—bubonic plague, trichinosis, perhaps foot and mouth and equine influenza. It is quite impossible to say one good word for the brown rat, which should be destroyed whenever it is seen. Every week in the year should be a rat week. The black rat, an equally unpleasant brute, does not occur in the countryside (all the same I shot two after the bombing of Southampton in a field nine miles from the town), and is not therefore an enemy of the gamekeeper.

Further consideration of these creatures, both birds and mammals, must await another chapter. It is high time we considered the man responsible for the preservation of game, the man who must wage war upon the predators.

CHAPTER 2

THE GAMEKEEPER

THE OLD TIME gamekeeper—the man who flourished in the 'eighties and the 'nineties and into the opening years of this century—was from all accounts a rather terrible person, quite uneducated, tough, frequently brutal and very rarely (taking the country as a whole) a good keeper. The only knowledge of natural history he was expected to possess was the ability to distinguish a hooked beak from any other sort of beak, and his work was usually judged by the number of corpses he could display upon his gibbet. That type, fortunately, has disappeared, or almost so. What has taken its place?

Sir Peter Jeffrey Mackie, writing in the sixteenth edition of *The Keeper's Book*, which was published as recently as 1929, divides gamekeepers into three classes—good, bad and indifferent (by which he means inefficient). He goes on : " It must be admitted that there are many keepers whose chief occupation up till the 12th August, or even till the 1st September or the 1st October, seems to consist in going about with a dog and a gun, and in virtually doing nothing—that is, nothing of real value to the shooting under their control. In no other class of men do we find such extremes : on the one hand of skill, energy and efficiency, and on the other of stupidity, laziness and incapability. Taking the occupation as a whole, and regarding it as a department of skilled labour, we must admit, though the admission may give offence, that it does not reach the average level of efficiency of other skilled labour.

" The fact that an outstanding minority of keepers are more than efficient, and combine the qualities of patient and intelligent keepers of ground with all the interests and capacities of thorough sportsmen, does not get rid of the truth of the general criticism. Of course, no one would insult the profession of gamekeeping by placing it in the same category with any branch of unskilled labour in the industrial community. It is because we believe the duties of a keeper demand a high

Plate XLV

FOX CUB. Flashlight. Radnorshire. May 1935. ARTHUR BROOK

TAME DOG FOX. Essex, 1936. A. R. THOMPSON

Plate XLVI

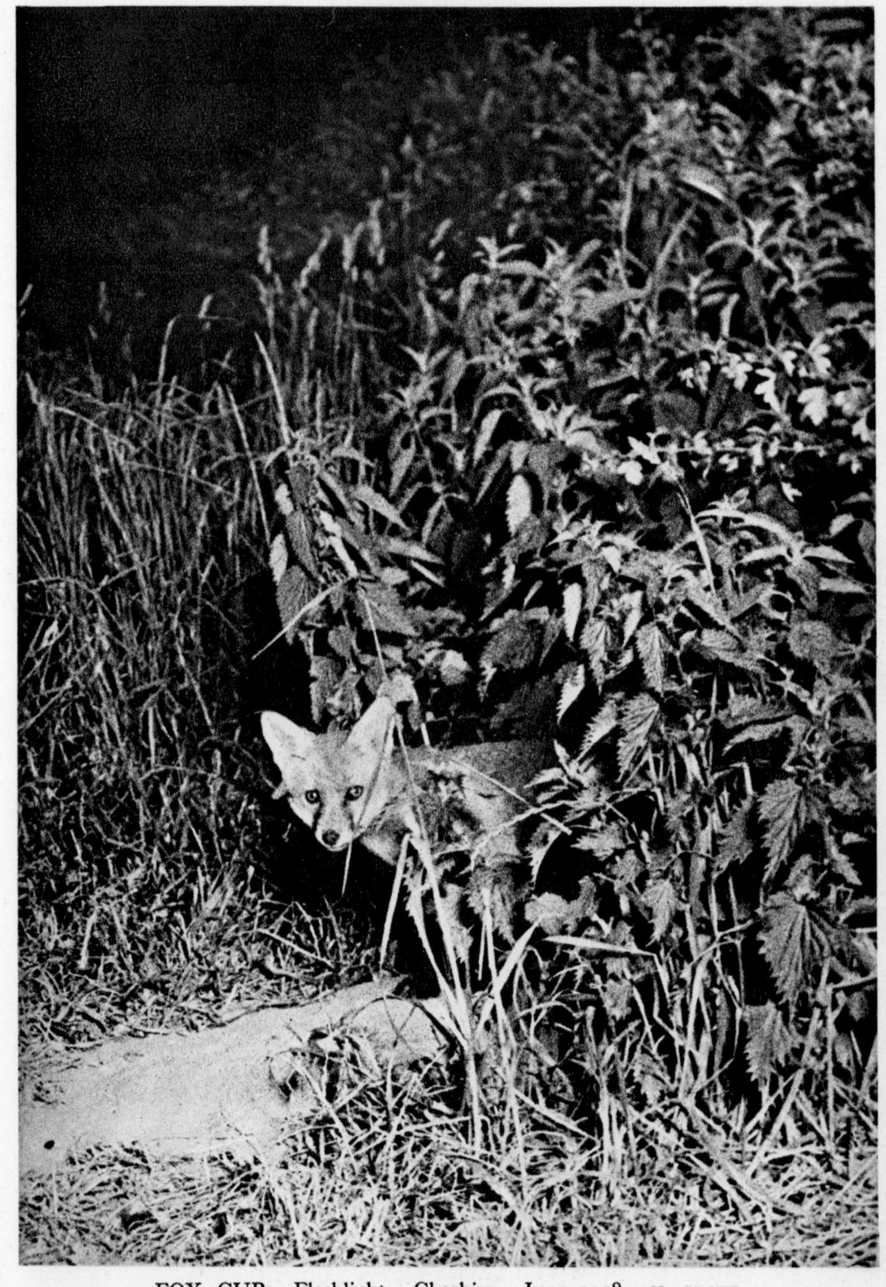

FOX CUB. Flashlight. Cheshire. June 1938. H. PLATT

standard of observation, skill, patience and energy, that we have to admit the failure in the common run of the calling to reach that standard. Viewing them on the side of moral character alone we readily realise that for probity and general temperance gamekeepers compare favourably with any other section of society, In fifty per cent of cases they are sober, honest, good-tempered and naturally generous, and to these qualities they add, as a rule, an exceptionally keen sense of humour. But considering the responsibilities of their work the percentage of efficient and trustworthy workmen is very much smaller than the figure quoted above."

That, in the considered opinion of a man who knew more about gamekeepers than anybody else, was the position in 1929. Has it altered in the last sixteen years ? I think there can be no doubt that it has, and on the whole for the better.

In assessing the present level of the profession it would be unwise in the extreme to take account of public opinion. Gamekeepers undoubtedly are often unpopular. In general they seem to have the reputation of being surly and morose, even of being downright rude and tough. It is in the nature of their work that they should be unpopular. For example, no one—honestly believing that he is doing no harm—likes being turned off ground. So gamekeepers are, as a rule, unpopular with rambling and hiking clubs. I do not intend here to go into the difficult question of access : it is sufficient to point out that they are unpopular because they are performing one of the duties for which they are paid. You will not find a *good* gamekeeper to be unpopular with the country folk of his neighbourhood. He may not be popular—usually he leads too isolated a life for that—but he will not be unpopular and he will be respected. Country people know full well what sort of a job he has and judge him on how he does it.) Discounted, too, must be the cry, which has of recent years become somewhat shrill, that gamekeepers are not good naturalists : the corollary being, presumably, that to be a good gamekeeper it is essential to be a good naturalist. Originally raised by the bird-lover community (very few of whom have any idea at all what gamekeeping means), it has been taken up by the anti-blood sport societies, and now forms one of the main planks in their propaganda against shooting. Inevitably it has produced the counter-cry from shooting men that gamekeepers are good naturalists. If by the word naturalist is meant someone with a keen interest in and some knowledge of butterflies, beetles, birds, beasts, wild flowers and so on, then I agree entirely that very few gamekeepers are good naturalists. Judged from that standpoint very few bird-lovers, very few ornithologists, very few anti-blood sport enthusiasts, very few shooting men, are good naturalists. In any case, such argument is quite beside the point. I have no patience at all with the bird-lover or the ornithologist who expects every gamekeeper to have a comprehensive knowledge of small birds, to know as much about the habits of a grasshopper warbler as about the habits of a sparrowhawk. He is not paid to have an expert knowledge of the ways of warblers. He is paid to keep game. He must be judged by his ability to do so. So judged, I am of the opinion that there has been a considerable change since 1929. I should doubt if there has been any increase in the numbers of good gamekeepers. On the other hand, there has been a very considerable increase in the numbers of indifferent keepers, and a very considerable decrease in the numbers of bad keepers. And that, taken as a whole, can only be accounted a change for the better.

Excluding the odd-job men and the farm labourers who do a bit of what they are pleased to call keepering (usually for small syndicate shoots) in their spare time, there were probably not more than 10,000 wholetime gamekeepers in Britain in 1939, and of these some 7,000 odd were head keepers or single-handed men. Taking 1939 again (to-day prices are doubled), the *average* wage of a head keeper was £2 10*s*., and that of a single-handed keeper was £2, with in each case a cottage free of rent and rates, free firing, at least one free suit of clothes a year, and various other perquisites. Even allowing for the perquisites, these average wages were too low. From the point of view of numbers gamekeeping is not a large profession, and it is certainly not a highly organised one. There is a Gamekeeper's Association—the Gamekeeper's Association of the United Kingdom which was founded in 1900—and there is a Keeper's Benevolent Society. The title of the latter speaks for itself. The former is not in any sense a Union. It was founded to maintain a register to enable men of good character to secure posts and to help members in adversity, and it has never gone beyond its original aims. It publishes a bi-monthly paper, *The Gamekeeper's Gazette*, and this, with the really excellent monthly magazine *The Gamekeeper and Countryside*, makes the sum total of periodical literature published in this country devoted solely to the interests of gamekeepers. But if gamekeeping is a small, not overwell paid and loosely organised profession, it is also an immensely important and extremely varied one. It is this extreme variation that makes it so difficult of comprehension for the layman.

Gamekeeping varies from county to county, and even from district to district within a single county. The work of a gamekeeper on a Scottish grouse moor is quite different from that of a gamekeeper on a Yorkshire grouse moor, indeed it would be true to say that no two Scottish grouse moors are alike in the work they provide. The work of a keeper on an East Anglian partridge manor will, in all probability, be quite different from that of a keeper on a Hampshire manor, and again it would be safe to say that no two Norfolk keepers have just the same work, while the work of two keepers in Hampshire will differ considerably. Again, work on an estate mainly concerned with the rearing and shooting of pheasants will differ from that of an estate on which the partridge has pride of place, and both will be as different as can be from the work of the man whose chief concern is the grouse. Furthermore, no two consecutive days in the life of a good gamekeeper provide just the same succession of jobs. It would be quite impossible to describe a day in the life of an active gamekeeper that could be regarded as typical for the professsion as a whole. There are, of course, certain duties common to gamekeepers everywhere, and it is possible to judge the work of a man by the manner in which these duties are performed. But even more important are the qualities essential to a good gamekeeper.

A gamekeeper is, or should be, very much more than a destroyer of vermin or a rearer of game. A gamekeeper is a servant placed in a peculiarly responsible and peculiarly isolated position. His is a position of trust that demands the sort of qualities you might expect to find only in the "Situations Required" column in *The Times*, but which you do, in fact, find quite surprisingly frequently among gamekeepers.

Let us consider a first-class head keeper, or a first-class single-handed man. Supposing that you wished to appoint such a man, for what qualities would you look? Personally, having satisfied myself so far as possible as to technical ability—rearing of game, management of coverts, destruction of vermin, suppression of poachers—I should require at least ten years' experience as under keeper on an estate of not less than 2,000 acres in country very similar to my own in the case of head keeper.

I should expect :

(1) Absolute integrity.

(2) Managerial and organising ability. Shoots need managing just as an office needs managing. The planning of actual shooting days is not the haphazard business that so many people think it is, nor is the proper control and deployment of beaters an art that can be picked up in a day or two.

(3) A sound understanding of farm and estate interests. A head keeper or a single-handed keeper should be the liaison between the shoot owner and the farmer and farm workers. He must, therefore, be a good (but never a free) mixer, and he must understand the point of view of the agricultural workers, both farmers and employees. The land is the farmer's living and the livelihood also of his men : the shoot is the owner's amusement. The proper relation between the two must never be forgotten. Provided that it is not—and it is part of the job of a good keeper to see that it is not—shooting and farming are complementary and mutually beneficial.

(4) A very sound knowledge of guns, their care, handling and use.

(5) A sound knowledge of dogs, their training and handling.

All these things in addition to sound technical ability is asking rather a lot for £2 10*s.* a week, you may think, and you will be right. You will not get such a man for £2 10*s.* a week (that, remember, was the *average* wage) or for anything like so small a sum. But there are such men in the profession, and there would be many more, I am sure, if the wages were not so low. Gamekeeping is a hard life, and the work is hard, very hard. I wonder how many shooting men realise what it means, in terms of physical labour, to bring a good bag of pheasants to the guns ? I know a successful man of business who was a gamekeeper on a good estate. He left when he considered one evening what it had cost him to bring to the guns 927 pheasants before noon, and he did not include the pick-up. There is many another good man who has left his gamekeeping profession for just the same reason. It is a very hard life physically, and the rewards, as a rule, are very much too small. A good gamekeeper is a jewel beyond price. And—this is an invariable rule—you will only find such men employed by good employers.

I know many gamekeepers, almost as many perhaps as any other man in the country. And I know them from both sides of the fence, an advantage possessed perhaps by no other man in the country. I know them on the right, the respectable side of the fence as an employer and a guest. I know them from the more exciting side of the fence because I have travelled a good deal with gypsies—and when I do so I do not look altogether unlike a gypsy—because I am incurably curious, and because I am very keenly interested in animals. I must in my time have trespassed on a very considerable acreage of private property in England, Wales and Scotland, and in doing so I have met and had an opportunity of summing up a large number of keepers.

The good gamekeeper, as I have already said, is a jewel beyond price. He is a splendid servant, sturdy and independent, and with opinions which he is not afraid to express when asked for them. He is absolutely loyal, putting his employer's interest before everything else, and he is always a first-rate sportsman. He is keenly observant, and knows about all there is to know about the habits of game on his land, and the steps that should be taken to improve both stock and ground. He is always anxious to keep abreast of developments and is not ashamed to learn. He is sober, quiet, friendly, humorous and usually well read. His employer, if he be anything of a man at all, will soon discover this, but he will not, unless he is altogether an exceptional employer, realise how immensely valuable his gamekeeper is in all sorts of ways that cannot easily be defined. Take poaching, for example—and I may as well admit that I know a good deal about poaching. You cannot stop poaching, and the gamekeeper who sets out to stamp it out on his ground is merely asking for more trouble than he can handle. Yet on ground controlled by a good gamekeeper there is very little poaching. The odd rabbit is taken, of course, and winked at—but the poaching gang will not visit the land of a good gamekeeper if they can possibly go elsewhere. A good gamekeeper enlists (though he does so unconsciously and the response is also unconscious) the neighbourhood on his side so far as strangers are concerned, and that in itself is almost the whole of the battle against organised poaching.

Then what is a bad gamekeeper? Technically, a man who does not rear as large or as healthy a stock of game as he should, who does not destroy vermin as he should, who sets pole traps in well-hidden places, who sets gin traps but does not visit them regularly. In my own experience he is usually a man who drinks rather more than he should, but is not a drunkard ; a man who is ignorant, boastful and cocksure ; a man who is rude to those to whom he considers it safe to be rude—and especially to trespassers—and servile to others. He may—he probably will—sell some of his master's game on his own account. Occasionally, very occasionally, I think (but I have known two instances), he may receive a regular payment from a poaching gang for information and so forth. He may, in fact, be a real bad lot or he may be just a bad gamekeeper. The former is very uncommon, the latter, though less common than, say, fifteen years ago, is still much too common. Bad gamekeepers are employed only by bad, that is to say ignorant, employers—it is an invariable rule—and so long as there are ignorant employers for so long will there be bad gamekeepers. It would not matter very much if the effect of a bad keeper was confined to his employer, his employer's purse, game and land. Unfortunately it is not. The game and the purse of his master suffer through organised poaching, through the deliberately careless boot of the farm labourer, through plain carelessness and inefficiency—and all this affects his neighbours, for a gamekeeper's influence does not cease at the boundary fence. Again, the bad keeper's ground will be overstocked with vermin, especially rats, and this, too, will affect his neighbours. A bad keeper may affect the whole tone of a neighbourhood, but, worse, he will affect the fair name of his profession, for one bad gamekeeper obscures the merits of a dozen good men in the eyes of the public.

While the numbers of bad gamekeepers have decreased of recent years the numbers of indifferent keepers have increased considerably. It is not at all easy to define an indifferent keeper. He is often a good shot and a good trapper. He is often a good handler of game. He is respectful to guests no matter what the size of their tips (an employer should always note the attitude of his keeper towards his poorer guests). He is often a charming man with a fund of good anecdote. He has, in fact, many of the attributes of a good gamekeeper, and just is not one. Not infrequently he is a lazy man, and gamekeeping is a strenuous job involving much more than shooting, trapping and getting over the guns. But it would be most unwise to suggest that the increase in indifferent keepers is due solely to an increase in the number of lazy men. There are a number of reasons for the increase, of which undoubtedly the increase in the syndicate shoot is the chief. No man can serve two masters, much less five or six. And still less when those five or six are continually changing.

Is there any way in which the general level of proficiency in the profession can be changed? I have said that were I appointing a head keeper I should require at least ten years' experience as under keeper on an estate of not less than 2,000 acres in country very similar to my own before I would consider an applicant. At present there is no other form of training than this—the serving of an apprenticeship under a head keeper. And that it is not a very satisfactory system is shown by the general level of the profession, by the small number of really good gamekeepers. So much depends upon the head keeper and his methods. It does not take very long to learn something, sufficient for ordinary purposes, about the rearing of pheasants. It does not take very long to learn quite a lot about the trapping of rabbits and vermin. It takes a good deal longer to learn anything worth while about partridges, but this is forgotten or not realised by the young keeper, who having learnt something of the rest considers himself to be an efficient keeper. Actually all he has learned are the rudiments of his calling, enough to carry him along provided that no great demand is made upon him. Comparatively few head keepers allow their assistants to take responsibility. It is understandable but unfortunate. The young men will be fit enough, good enough trappers, will know enough of the ground work, but when it comes to planning a shoot, directing their own assistants, controlling beaters, outwitting poachers and so forth on their own, the full weight of responsibility is often crushing. The present system is by no means perfect. Is there anything to take its place?

There is not. But it has been suggested that keeper's colleges might be set up, and it has also been suggested keepers might go for a "refresher" course to some institute or other at one of the universities. The latter suggestion may be dismissed forthwith. The idea behind it is not that keepers should be made better keepers, but that they should be trained to be better naturalists—a good idea—but better naturalists for whose benefit? The idea ignores the fact that the gamekeeper is a private servant. Who is to pay for this refresher course, who is to look after the game and the vermin and so forth during the keeper's absence? But these are mere details, beneath the attention of academic minds. Only if the gamekeeper were a public servant, and then only if his chief duty were not to keep game, might this idea be seriously considered.

The keeper's college does merit consideration. The days when the landowner took a keen personal interest in his shoot and in game preservation and kept a close personal touch with his head keeper throughout the year are unfortunately past, or as nearly as does not matter. On the larger shoot the syndicate has come to stay, and the head keeper, who, except for the few days of actual shooting, will probably not see his employer or even his employer's bailiff, agent or factor, is to all intents and purposes his own master, and carries a very heavy responsibility. Almost certainly the syndicate system will be greatly extended, with the result that more and more gamekeepers will be working on their own without supervision. The young men are at war now : the old men are getting no younger : there were not so many good gamekeepers before the war, certainly not nearly as many as would be required to train under the old system all the head and single-handed keepers that will be necessary when things have settled down again. It seems evident that a new system will have to be instituted, and the keeper's college is certainly the soundest that has been put forward. The idea originated with Mr. Colin Maclean, a sportsman of great experience. He visualised a college at which suitable men could attend for a short course of instruction, and after an examination, which would include practical work, be granted a form of certificate. The training syllabus visualised is a varied one and would include, among other things, vermin, partridges, grouse and blackgame, pheasants, wildfowl, ground game, care and training of dogs, care of guns, loading, the use of maps and the keeping of records. No man whose personal character would not bear the closest investigation would be admitted to the college, and the holder of a certificate would obviously—once the scheme was known—have preference over other candidates for a post. The idea is an excellent one. It would not be difficult to secure the right sort of building at a reasonable rent, and it would not be very difficult to find the money to run it. But there are some very sharp snags.

The biggest snag, to my mind, is the extreme variation of game-keeping, variation of conditions, of climate and so on. It would not be possible, should the college be situated in Hampshire, to teach much that would be of use to the man who was to work in Argyll, or for that matter in Montgomery, or Yorkshire. There would have to be a number of colleges in different parts of the country. Nor would it be possible to teach much of value in a short course. I have already said that my minimum requirement for a head keeper would be ten years' experience as an under keeper. I am certain that a lengthy apprenticeship is essential to the making of a first-class keeper. And finally, who would instruct at this college or these colleges? There would be innumerable applications from wartime Pests Officers of

Plate XLVII

STOAT, captive. Bedfordshire, 1938. OLIVER G. PIKE

WEASEL. Essex, 1933. A. R. THOMPSON

Plate XLVIII

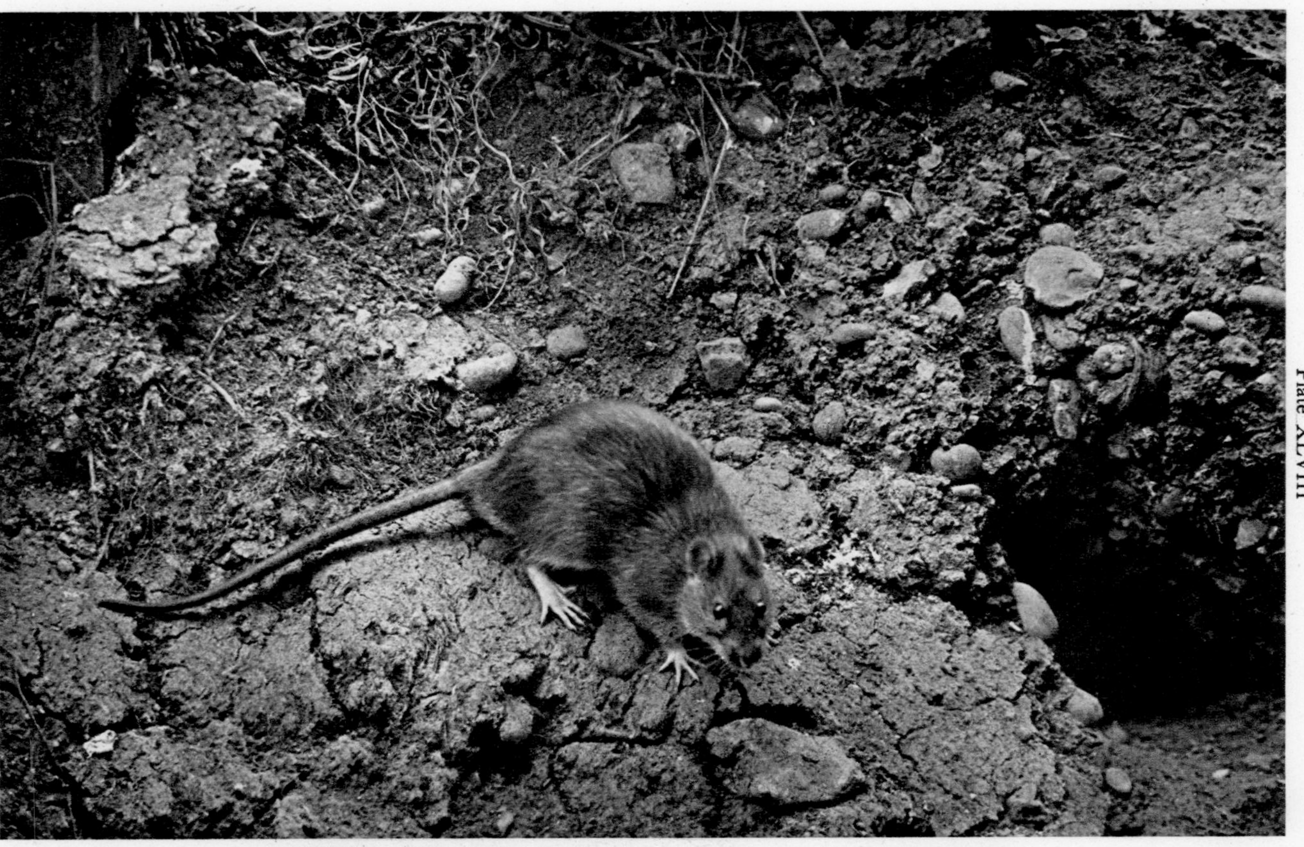

BROWN RAT. Under Hertfordshire hedgerow, 1936. JOHN MARKHAM

course, but good instructors would be wanted. They could only be found in the ranks of keepers themselves, with possibly here and there a sportsman or an estate bailiff to teach those points that are essential to the keeper working free from supervision. All in all, I think that the old way—the long apprenticeship—must remain, but I do think that, having served the apprenticeship, a short course at a "finishing school" would be an excellent thing. Two finishing schools—one in Scotland and one in, say, Hampshire—would be sufficient, and a very large staff would not be necessary. Here an examination on the practical side and also tests in diplomacy, estate management and so forth would be held, and those who passed would receive a certificate. And, in addition to shooting, trapping, rearing and so on, I would suggest that every would-be holder of a certificate is required to run (the gamekeeper tends to fall into a slow policeman's trudge which can be a great handicap), to jump, to swim, and to climb trees with and without irons. But no short course and no examination can take the place of the apprenticeship under a good man.

And no course and no examination, nor for that matter apprenticeship, can altogether overcome the delicate question of relationship, the variable human quality. For the keeper left on his own to run a shoot for a syndicate temptation to slack, to do no more than is necessary to keep the job, must be very strong. It is a thousand to one that the members of the syndicate will not know—they will be different next year anyway—and the wages paid are usually so small (they are the wages that bring the average down to the ridiculous level of £2 10*s.* or £2 a week) that temptation is increased proportionately. And for the keeper—head or single-handed—working under his employer, relations with the employer are of supreme importance. A very great deal depends upon the employer. I do not mean that an employer should be as expert in the art of keepering as his keeper. That should be impossible. The most gifted employer, as Mackie pointed out, can never be more than a gifted amateur; the keeper should be an expert. But I do suggest that the employer should be interested in more than the size of the bag, that he should make himself familiar with the humdrum of the keeper's life, that he should realise that game-preservation is no more than a by-product (albeit a very important one) of country life, and that the major industry of the countryside—and incidentally of the nation—is farming, has always been farming, and must, if we are to survive, always be farming, that he should aid the keeper in his relations with the farmers over whose land he must work and with the farm labourers with whom he must come in contact daily. Such an employer will have a good as opposed to an indifferent gamekeeper. And there are other factors which do not operate in the case of a good owner, for he is aware of them instinctively. A gamekeeper is a man with a most responsible job. He is in a position to do his master great service or great harm. A responsible job deserves good pay *and* the confidence of the employer. Far too many keepers are underpaid and have no prospect of advancement. And far too many keepers do not receive the confidence of their employers. The old relationship of master and man is being broken up, and we have not yet found anything very good to put in its place. I doubt if we ever shall. And, finally, loyalty deserves to be rewarded. Far too often it is taken for granted and ignored. Personal loyalty is a very precious thing. It is also a very tender plant and withers easily if slowly. I have seen it wither in many a gamekeeper in the last twenty years. I have seen many a potentially first-class gamekeeper sink to indifference through lack of encouragement and interest, sink to doing just enough to hold his job and no more, which is comparatively easy to do because few employers know enough to spot the difference between really good work and just adequate work.

Though it is possible to teach the technical details of gamekeeping, though it would be an excellent thing to have a passing-out school and a certificate of proficiency in the practical side, there is yet and there always will be much in gamekeeping that is intangible, that cannot be defined, that is quite beyond the reach of any college or any certificate. And it is this intangible quality that is so important, that makes gamekeepers as a whole as fine a body of men as any in the country. If the level of efficiency is not as high as it might be, and that, you will remember, was Sir Peter Jeffrey Mackie's opinion with which I found myself in agreement, I am also in agreement with another dictum of Sir Peter's. I would rather it than mere efficiency. "There are three occupations which contain a specially large proportion of men of great charm and gentleness, and a superiority of tone and character to the general run of mankind, and they are all open-air pursuits—those of gamekeeper, shepherds and gardeners. They are men who live in close touch with Nature, and are students of natural history: and, as someone has said, the closer to Nature the closer to God."

THE PRESERVATION OF GAME

"THE FIRST essential condition, in order to increase a stock of game on an estate, is the destruction of vermin," writes Tom Speedy in *The Keeper's Book*. Like so many generalisations it is an exaggeration. But Speedy when he wrote his chapter in *The Keeper's Book* obviously meant just what he said, and as a result he wrote the most depressing, and in some ways the most short-sighted, essay on "vermin" that I have ever read. Had he substituted the word "reduction" for "destruction", I would find myself in complete agreement with him.

A great deal of first-rate nonsense has been written, both by game-preservers and naturalists, about the killing of predators. There are —and there used to be many more—game-preservers who honestly believe that if every predator (except the rat which most of them forget) were exterminated, then all would be well in the game-preserving world. (It would not : but I will come to that in a minute.) In particular most of these men have a rooted objection to hawks. I have seen it stated in print that if a pair of peregrines were allowed to quarter a moor for a season then there would be no grouse on that moor. Did the grouse then spring into being, a miraculous conception out of air, with the commencement of game-preservation in Scotland ? And if not, was the grouse a very rare bird on the moors in former days ? And what did the peregrines, having destroyed all the grouse, live on ? You will find plenty of other thoughtless, and ignorant, assertions in the literature of game-preservation.

But all the thoughtless and ignorant assertions are not on one side by any means. The present attack upon the killing of predators had its origin in reaction to the ruthless and wholesale manner in which the old-time gamekeeper, often employing means of extreme cruelty, destroyed everything that was not game and might in any way affect the interests of game. That type of gamekeeper has disappeared or almost disappeared. But the attack continues. For the most part it springs now from two sources, the " bird-crank " and the collector. Naturalists, and ornithologists especially, vary immensely; the work of the really sound scientific ornithologist is one thing, the work of many talented amateurs too often another. Then there is the " bird-crank ", a breed that has increased enormously of recent years. And finally there is the collector, whether of skins or eggs. The " bird-crank " is an ultra-humanitarian and perhaps the worst enemy of bird-life in this country, because he or she is always sentimental and almost always ignorant. The collector is as great or almost as great a menace. He is usually a man of education, frequently a man of some position and attainments: he is very rarely a naturalist himself. He often pays some less fortunate person to do his work for him. If you really want to get at facts do not go to the collector or to the " bird-crank ". You will do much better to go to a good gamekeeper or to a good gunner (I do not include as gunners those gentlemen who have " days " at driven partridges or pheasants and care for nothing save the number of birds they shoot themselves), or preferably to the scientific ornithologist, for he, by the very nature of his work and his training, has a much broader view than anyone else and a much more accurate knowledge of and insight into the interplay of conditions.

There is a good deal of loose talk about the " balance of nature " in relation to this question of game-preservation. There are those who regard the "balance of nature" as something that has been lost and who demand its immediate restoration: there are others who deny that there is such a thing. Neither class knows what it is talking about. There is some balance in nature in my opinion. But it is not the slightest use talking about restoring " a previous balance of nature ". Man, in this country at any rate, has altered it whatever it was. It is not the gamekeeper and the game-preserver alone who have changed it, as many people spend a good deal of time trying to prove. The farmer, the builder, the surveyor, the engineer, the humanitarian have each played a large part. It is the advance of " civilisation ", " the march of progress " that has changed the balance of nature. Incidentally, it is not only the gamekeeper who is responsible for the present rarity of many of our once common species. One of the most amusing things about this controversy is the violence with which shooting men attack collectors, and collectors attack shooting men. There can be no doubt that in the past the gamekeeper has reduced materially the number of hawks, and that this has affected the present situation. One of the few points about which there can be no argument is this:

that a dead bird cannot breed. But equally there can be no doubt whatever that collectors have done as much harm, and no doubt whatever that once a bird is uncommon the collectors drive it to the point of extinction or beyond. There are gamekeepers and gamekeepers, shooting men and shooting men, and equally there are collectors and collectors. A few, those who can justly claim the title öologist, do a very considerable service to science, and we owe to them much of our present ornithological knowledge. The remainder, a very large number, suffer from a peculiarly virulent form of acquisitiveness and should be restrained. But the chief reasons for the rarity of some species are those that do not easily meet the eye (a gun is a noticeable instrument and makes a noise, and a dead bird is good concrete evidence) : the spread of houses, the draining of fenlands, the building of roads and railways, the increase of travel. These are the things that chiefly cause rarity. And these are the things that have chiefly changed our animal communities.

I think it is beyond dispute that there has been a great increase in the number of sportsmen with a leaning towards the nature lover's point of view—a great increase in the number of shooting men who do not want to kill every hawk just because it is a hawk. True, you still come across men who will shoot buzzards because their observation leads them to think that the buzzard harms game—I met one only the other day who shot buzzards in Devonshire (where they are protected by law throughout the year)—but these are men who do not know how to observe and jump to conclusions, living examples of the truth of the old saying that " a little knowledge is a dangerous thing ". There are, happily, few of them. It is, too, beyond dispute that the gamekeeper's attitude towards predators is changing. As a result there has been much less wanton destruction recently (the British Field Sports Society deserves much praise for its educative work in this direction), and this position will, I have no doubt, improve. But that does not mean that predators will not be destroyed. They will and they must. The question is, which predators and how many?

When we come to this we come to the complicated part of the problem. Predators do not only prey upon game. They prey also upon one another, and they also compete with one another. And further to this there are many different forms of sport in this country, and some of them have interests that are diametrically opposed. For example, the golden eagle is undoubtedly a menace to grouse. One appearing over the skyline is sufficient to ruin a grouse drive. The Scottish gamekeeper does not therefore look upon the golden eagle with favour, though he may do so at times with pleasure. On the other hand, grouse are unquestionably a nuisance on a deer forest, so the deer stalker regards the golden eagle with immense favour. Similarly with the fox : the fox is beyond question a very deadly enemy of game, and no gamekeeper likes the fox. But the fox in England is a valuable animal from the hunting point of view, and so the gamekeeper (as a rule) puts up with it. In Scotland there is little or no hunting, and the fox is regarded in a very different light.

But the fox, though very dangerous to game and poultry (I was a poultry farmer once and I know), is also a very dangerous enemy to the rat, and the rat is itself a still more dangerous enemy of game. It is the same with the stoat and the weasel. The latter is a good friend to the farmer and a great destroyer of rats, but it is no use pretending that it is a friendly and innocent creature on a rearing field. Still less is the stoat. But the stoat is also a great destroyer of rats and rabbits. If you destroy all the foxes, all the stoats and all the weasels (happily it is not easy to destroy them all), even if you destroy most of them, you do not do your game any great service. You only give to the rat a greater freedom from danger. And the rat, let me stress again, is a more deadly enemy to game than the fox, the stoat and the weasel combined—and also, of course, to man himself.

Let me reconstruct Tom Speedy's sentence (quoted at the head of this chapter) as it should read :

The first essential condition, in order to increase a stock of game on an estate, is the *reduction* of vermin.

The second essential condition is that, with the exception of the rat, the *reduced population of vermin should be maintained.*

The third essential condition is that the ground should not carry a greater head of game than it can support in good health.

The first is obvious. If your place swarms with vermin you will not have sufficient game to make game-preserving worth while, and your shooting will have no value in the market.

The second will be revolutionary to many gamekeepers and shooting men. The idea that in addition to preserving game one should preserve a stock of stoats, weasels, and hawks will strike them as ridiculous in the extreme. It is not : it is sound sense. And it is not any more difficult to preserve a certain minimum stock of predators than it is to preserve a head of game. It means a bit more work, but it is worth it every time, and I have proved that from personal experience.

I did not destroy hawks, owls or jays. I was overrun with magpies originally, and I did destroy them until I was left with the very reduced population of four pairs which I maintained without difficulty. I did not destroy hawks because I like hawks, and I did not find that they did any great damage. They did not increase. The hawk requires a large territory and maintains it fiercely against its own species, and it drives away its young once they are fully fledged. The jay, in reasonable numbers, is a friend. It will tell you the moment anyone enters your woods, and is an excellent guardian of your property against the attentions of poachers. I employed my keeper's time in trapping rats and reducing the enormous rabbit population, and I left him stoats and weasels to aid him. It paid me hand over fist. And so far as stoats and weasels are concerned, you have only got to keep your eyes open, know your ground really well, and get to work when the litters are about six weeks old. Stoats and weasels are excellent rat catchers, very much more deadly and skilful (with all due respects to the profession) than any gamekeeper I know. When I was running some thousands of head of poultry I did not interfere with the stoats or the weasels. I had some losses—I also had losses from foxes, gulls, and an otter—but it paid me. With the aid of the stoats and weasels and some consistent trapping I really did get control of my rat population. The first essential qualification in my eyes in a gamekeeper is that he should be a hard, good and consistent destroyer of rats, and the second, that he should regard rabbits as doubtful blessings on the ground. If he has these two qualifications in good measure the others follow more or less naturally.

Owls—with the possible exception of the little owl—I regard as sacrosanct. They are enormously beneficial, and if one now and again makes a mistake and takes a chick of mine, why, it is welcome to it. Buzzards are also sacrosanct : I believe that a buzzard will occasionally take a grouse chick, more occasionally a pheasant chick (I have never seen one do so, and I do not know of anyone who has : the evidence of bones at the eyrie is no evidence at all as the buzzard will take carrion), but they do enormous good in keeping down the numbers of young rabbits and voles, and if they do take an odd chick occasionally, why, they may be excused. The kestrel is in exactly the same position, and the hobby should never be shot. The rook is sometimes doubtful. It can be a nuisance if not controlled : in normal numbers it is nothing but beneficial.

The rare mammals and hawks should not be shot under any circumstances. Marten and polecat (so far as England is concerned), osprey and white-tailed eagle, kite and hen harrier, marsh harrier and Montagu's harrier—the only problem here is one of preservation, not reduction. Man can destroy a species : he cannot make one. An extinct animal is lost for ever. I have nothing but contempt for the man who shoots or traps any rare bird or animal. He is nothing more than an ignorant and murderous lout.

Of the others : carrion crow and hoodie are no good to the game-preserver and need their numbers drastically reduced. The raven, too, is a menace in game-preserving areas, but on a lesser scale. And I regard all gulls, when away from the coast, with the gravest suspicion. It is noticeable (though it may be no more than coincidence) that they have only taken to coming inland in great numbers since game-preservation has attained a high level of development, and they are ruthless robbers. I have known common gulls attack my poultry, and I always do what I can to drive a gull back to the coast or at any rate to convince its friends that other neighbourhoods are healthier. And the grey squirrel is another menace that has so far not received the attention it deserves from gamekeepers. The peregrine and the golden eagle and the sparrow hawk undoubtedly do do damage. But how much damage do they do ? I have never seen any convincing figures, and I have no evidence of my own sufficient to justify me in robbing myself of the pleasure of watching them.

Rabbits come into another category. They do not prey upon game, but undoubtedly they do game much damage indirectly, and I, personally, wage war upon them. I can find no good word to say of the rabbit—even its pretty white scut does not soften my heart—and as it is good to eat, if not especially nourishing, there seems to me a doubly good reason for killing it.

Disease, not the predator, is the gamekeeper's chief enemy. In Scotland this is especially so, and in England it is so at any rate on the partridge manors. Nine times out of ten disease is the direct result of overcrowding. In the wild if any animal attains too great a population remedial factors (predators as well as parasites) instantly get to work. There is an increase in predators, there is an outbreak of disease. A great increase in voles produces short-eared owls almost magically, a great increase in woodpigeons produces disease, a great increase in lemmings not only an increase in predators, but also disease. So, too, with grouse. And disease, it seems to me, must always be spread through the weak members, those that have not done so well in the fierce struggle for a restricted food supply. It is often said that predators strike down only the weakly, and as often denied. I do not know. It is true that a peregrine will strike down any bird in a covey or a flock, that it does not always pick the last bird or the first; but as one has no opportunity of determining the condition of the bird struck down, one cannot say for certain that it is not a weakly bird. Be that as it may, there can be no doubt that predators do help in some measure to retain a balanced stock. The craze for large bags has brought its own evils in its train, and these far outweigh the benefits. If shooting men would be content with smaller bags and more difficult sport game, and the countryside generally would benefit.

One should always regard the question of game-preservation with its attendant problem of predator control against the background of country life as a whole. It is always as well to try to preserve a sense of proportion as well as game.

THE following is a list of some of the books in my own library, many of which I have consulted in writing this book, and makes no pretence at being a complete guide to the literature on the many aspects of British Game. But it is, I think, a fairly representative collection and should prove of use to those who wish to read further. Some of the books listed below are scarce and can be obtained only with difficulty (and at a price) from good booksellers. Many others are now out of print, but turn up regularly on the second-hand market.

ADAMS, ENA (AND OTHERS).—*Deer, Hare and Otterhunting* (London, N.D.).
ALINGTON, CHARLES.—*Partridge Driving* (London, 1904).
ALPHERAKY, SERGIUS.—*The Geese of Europe and Asia* (London, 1905).
ANONYMOUS.—*A Perfecte Booke for Kepinge Sparhawks or Goshawks* (London, 1886).

BACON, ALBAN F. L.—*Enchanted Days with Rod and Gun* (London, 1926).
BANKS, A. G.—*The Book of the Rifle* (London, 1940).
BARTON, F. T.—*Pheasants in Covert and Aviary* (London, 1912).
BEEBE, W.—*A Monograph of the Pheasant* (London, 1919-22) ; *Pheasants, Their Lives and Homes* (London, 1935).
BELL, THOMAS.—*A History of British Quadrupeds* (London, 1874).
BLAINE, GILBERT.—*Falconry* (London, 1936).
BLOME, RICHARD (ed. E. D. CUMMING).—*Hawking or Faulconry* (London, 1929).
BOLAM, GEORGE.—*The Birds of Northumberland and the Eastern Borders* (Alnwick, 1912).
BONNETT, FRANK.—*Mixed and Rough Shooting* (London, 1914).
BRATBY, MICHAEL.—*Grey Goose* (London, 1939).
BREADALBANE, MARCHIONESS OF.—*The High Tops of Black Mount* (Edinburgh, 1895).
BROMLEY DAVENPORT, W.—*Sport* (London, 1885).
BUND, J. WILLIS.—*Oke's Game Laws* (London, N.D.).
BURRARD, SIR GERALD.—*The Modern Shotgun* (London, 1931-32).
BUXTON, EARL.—*Fishing and Shooting* (London, 1902).

CAMERON, ALAN GORDON.—*The Wild Red Deer of Scotland* (Edinburgh, 1923).
CHALMERS, PATRICK.—*Green Days and Blue Days* (Dublin, 1912) ; *A Peck o' Maut* (Dublin, 1914) ; *The Frequent Gun* (London, 1928) ; *At the Sign of the Dog and Gun* (London, 1930) ; *Mine Eyes to the Hills* (London, 1932) ; *Gun Dogs* (London, 1935) ; *Deer-stalking* (London, 1935) ; *Field Sports of Scotland* (London, 1936) ; *The Shooting Man's England* (London, N.D.).
CHAPMAN, ABEL.—*Bird-life of the Border* (London, 1889) ; *The Art of Wildfowling* (London, 1896) ; *The Borders and Beyond* (London, 1924) ; *Retrospect* (London, 1928) ; *Memories* (London, 1930).
CLAPHAM, RICHARD.—*The A.B.C. of Shooting* (London, 1930).
COCHRANE, ALFRED.—*Collected Verses* (London, 1903) ; *Later Verses* (London, 1918).
COLQUHOUN, JOHN.—*The Moor and the Loch* (London, 1840).
CORNISH, C. J.—*Wild England of To-day* (London, 1895) ; *Nights with an old Gunner* (London, 1897).
COWARD, T. A.—*The Birds of the British Isles* (3 vols.) (London, N.D.) [1920].

COX, HARDING AND LASCELLES, HON. GERALD.—*Coursing and Falconry* (London, 1892).
COX, NICHOLAS.—*The Gentleman's Recreation* (London, 1686).
CREALOCK, H. H.—*Deer-stalking* (London, 1880).
CUMMING, E. D.—*British Sports, Past and Present* (London, 1909).

DALGETY, C. T.—*Wildfowling* (London, 1937).
DANIEL, REV. W. B.—*Rural Sports* (London, 1801-02-13).
DARLING, F. FRASER.—*A Herd of Red Deer* (Oxford, 1937) ; *A Naturalist on Rona* (Oxford, 1939).
DAWSON, KENNETH.—*Son of a Gun* (London, 1929) ; *Just an Ordinary Shoot* (London, 1935) ; *Marsh and Mud Flat* (London, 1931).
DEWAR, DOUGLAS.—*Game Birds* (London, 1928).
DEWAR, G. A. B.—*The Faery Year* (London, 1906) ; *Wild Life in Hampshire Highlands* (London, 1899) ; *Life and Sport in Hampshire* (London, 1908).
DOBIE, W. G. M.—*Winter and Rough Weather* (London, 1938).
DORCHESTER, LORD.—*Sport, Foxhunting and Shooting* (London, 1935).
DUNCAN, STANLEY AND THORNE, GUY.—*The Complete Wildfowler* (London, 1911).

FALLON, W. J.—*Practical Wildfowling* (London, 1907).
FISHER, CHARLES HAWKINS.—*Reminiscences of a Falconer* (Gloucester, 1901).
FITZGERALD, EDWARD.—*Rough Shooting* (Dublin, 1900).
FITZGERALD, GERALD.—*Pot Luck* (London, 1938).
FOLKHARD, HENRY COLEMAN.—*The Wildfowler* (London, 1859).
FORTESCUE, JOHN WILLIAM.—*The Story of a Red Deer* (London, 1897) ; *My Native Devon* (London, 1924).
FRASER, SIR HUGH.—*Amid the High Hills* (London, 1934).

GATHORNE HARDY, A. E.—*Autumns in Argyllshire with Rod and Gun* (London, 1900).
GLADSTONE, SIR HUGH.—*Record Bags and Shooting Records* (London, 1922) ; *Shooting with Surtees* (London, 1927).
GOODWIN, SIR JOHN G.—*Making a Shoot* (London, 1935).
GORDON, DOUGLAS.—*Field Philosophy* (London, 1934).
GORDON, SETON.—*Hill Birds of Scotland* (London, 1915) ; *The Land of the Hills and Glens* (London, 1920) ; *The Charm of the Hills ; Wanderings of a Naturalist ; Afoot in Wild Places ; Thirty Years of Nature Photography ; In Search of Northern Birds.*
GRIMBLE, AUGUSTUS.—*Deer-stalking* (London, 1886).

HAIG BROWN, ALAN.—*My Game Book* (London, 1913).
HANGAR, COLONEL GEORGE.—*To All Sportsmen* (London, 1814).
HARE, C. E.—*The Language of Sport* (London, 1939).
HARTING, J. E.—*Essays on Sport and Natural History* (London, 1883) ; *Recreations of a Naturalist* (London, 1906) ; *The Rabbit* (London, 1898) ; *Hints on the Management of Hawks* (London, 1898) ; *Bibliotheca Accipitaria* (London, 1891) ; *The Ornithology of Shakespeare* (London, 1901).
HARTLEY, GIFFORD W.—*Wild Sport and Some Stories* (London, 1912).
HAWKER, LT.-COL. PETER.—*Instructions to Young Sportsmen* (London, 1864) ; *Diary* (2 vols.) (London, 1893).
HEATHERBY, FRANCIS.—*The Peregrine Falcon at the Eyrie* (London, 1913).
HENDY, E. W.—*Wild Exmoor through the Year* (London, 1930).
HIPGRAVE, WALTER.—*The Management of a Partridge Beat* (London, 1922).
HUTCHINSON, HORACE.—*Shooting* (2 vols.) (London, 1903).

JEFFERIES, RICHARD.—*The Gamekeeper at Home ; Wild Life in a Southern County ; The Amateur Poacher ; Round About a Great Estate ; The Life of the Fields ; The Open Air ; Field and Hedgerow.*
JONES, OWEN.—*The Sport of Shooting* (London, 1910).
JONES, OWEN AND WOODWARD, MARCUS.—*A Gamekeeper's Notebook* (London, 1911) ; *Wood-craft* (London, 1910).

KEITH, E. C.—*Gun for Company ; A Countryman's Creed.*
KIRKMAN, F. B. AND HUTCHINSON, HORACE.—*British Sporting Birds* (London, 1936).
" KLAXON."—*Heather Mixture* (London, 1922).
KNOX, A. E.—*Autumns on the Spey* (London, 1872).

LACY, RICHARD.—*The Modern Shooter* (London, 1842).
LANCASTER, CHARLES.—*The Art of Shooting* (London, 1924).
LASCELLES, HON. GERALD.—*Thirty-five Years in the New Forest* (London, 1915).
LEGGATT, ASHLEY.—*Stalking Reminiscences* (London, N.D.).
LESLIE, A. S. AND SHIPLEY, A. E.—*The Grouse in Health and Disease* (London, 1911).
LEWIS, ERNEST.—*In Search of the Gyr-Falcon* (London, 1935).
LYNN-ALLEN, E. H.—*Rough Shoot* (London, 1942).

MCCONNOCHIE, ALEXANDER.—*Deer-Stalking in the Highlands* (London, 1924).
MACINTYRE, DUGALD.—*Round the Seasons on a Grouse Moor* (London, N.D.) ; *Wild Life in the Highlands* (London, 1936) ; *Highland Gamekeeper* (London, N.D.).
MACKENZIE, E. G.—*Guns and Game* (London, 1906).
MACKENZIE, EVAN.—*Grouse Shooting and Deer Stalking* (Edinburgh, 1907).
MACKENZIE, OSGOOD.—*A Hundred Years in the Highlands* (London, 1922).
MACKIE, SIR PETER.—*The Keeper's Book* (London, 1907).
MACPHERSON, REV. H. A. (AND OTHERS).—*The Pheasant* (London, 1896) ; *The Partridge* (London, 1893) ; *The Grouse* (London, 1896) ; *The Hare* (London, 1896) ; *The Red Deer* (London, 1896) ; (All in the Fur and Feather Series).
MACRAE, SIR ALEXANDER.—*A Handbook of Deer Stalking* (Edinburgh, 1880).
MALMESBURY, LORD (ed. F. G. AFLALO).—*Shooting Journals* (London, 1905).
MAXWELL, CAPTAIN AYMER.—*Grouse and Grouse Moors* (London, 1910) ; *Partridge and Partridge Manors* (London, 1911) ; *Pheasants and Covert Shooting* (London, 1913).
MEYSEY THOMPSON, COL. R. F.—*A Shooter's Catechism* (London, 1907).
MILLAIS, J. G.—*Game Birds and Shooting Sketches* (London, 1897) ; *British Deer and their Horns* (London, 1897) ; *The Wildfowler in Scotland* (London, 1901) ; *The Natural History of British Surface-feeding Ducks* (London, 1902) ; *The Natural History of British Game Birds* (London, 1909) ; *British Diving Ducks* (London, 1913) ; *Deer and Deer Stalking* (London, 1913).
MILLARD, F. W.—*Game and Foxes* (London, N.D.).
MITCHELL, E. B.—*The Art and Practice of Hawking* (London, 1900).

NICHOLAS, W. W.—*A Sparrow Hawk's Eyrie* (London, 1937).
NICHOLLS, J. C. M.—*Birds of Marsh and Mere* (London, 1926).

OGILVIE, F. M.—*Field Observations on British Birds* (London, 1920).
OGILVIE GRANT, W. R.—*Game Birds* (London, 1912).
" OLD STALKER, AN."—*Days on the Hill* (London).

PAGE, RICHARD.—*New Ways with Partridges* (London, 1925).
PARKER, ERIC.—*Shooting Days* (London, 1915) ; *Elements of Shooting* (London, N.D.) ; *Partridges Yesterday and To-day* (London, 1927) ; *Field, River and Hill* (London, 1927) ; *English Wild Life : Game Birds, Beasts and Fishes* (London, N.D.) ; *The Shooting Week-end Book* (London, N.D.) ; *Predatory Birds of Great Britain* (London, N.D.).
PARKER, ERIC (AND OTHERS).—*Shooting by Moor, Marsh and Field* (London, N.D.) ; *The Keeper's Book* (London, N.D.).
PATTEN, CHARLES J.—*The Aquatic Birds of Great Britain and Ireland* (London, 1906).
PATTERSON, A. H.—*A Norfolk Naturalist* (London, 1930) ; *Notes of an East Coast Naturalist* (London, 1905) ; *Man and Nature on Tidal Waters* (London, 1907) ; *Wild Life on a Norfolk Estuary* (London, 1909) ; *Wildfowlers and Poachers* (London, 1929).
PAYNE, GALLWEY, SIR R. F.—*The Fowler in Ireland* (London, 1892) ; *Letters to Young Shooters* (3 vols.) (London, 1891-96) ; *High Pheasants in Theory and Practice* (London, 1913) ; *Shooting, Field and Covert* (London, 1886).
PERRY, RICHARD.—*At the turn of the Tide* (London, 1938).
POLLARD, HUGH B. C.—*Wildfowl and Waders* (London, 1928).
PORTAL, MAURICE AND COLLINGE, W. E.—*Partridge Disease and its Causes* (London, 1932).

PORTER, ALEXANDER.—*The Gamekeeper's Manual* (London, 1907).
PRICHARD, H. HESKETH.—*Sport in Wildest Britain* (London, N.D.).

RADCLYFFE, C. E.—*Round the Smoking Room Fire* (London, 1933).
RAWSTORNE, LAWRENCE.—*Gamonia* (London, 1929).
ROSS, JOHN.—*The Book of the Red Deer* (Edinburgh, 1925).

ST. ALBANS, BOOK OF.
ST. JOHN, CHARLES.—*Wild Sport and Natural History of the Highlands* (London, 1846) ; *A Tour in Sutherland* (London, 1849).
" SCOLOPAX."—*A Book of the Snipe* (London, 1904).
SCOTT, LT.-COL. LORD GEORGE.—*Grouse Land and the Fringe of the Moor* (London, 1937).
SCOTT, PETER.—*Morning Flight* (London, 1935) ; *Wild Chorus* (London, 1931).
SCROPE, WILLIAM.—*The Art of Deer Stalking* (London, 1838).
SEDGWICK, N. M.—*The Young Shot* (London, 1940).
SEIGNE, J. W.—*Irish Bogs* (London, 1929) ; *A Bird Watcher's Norebook* (London, 1932).
SEIGNE, J. W. AND KEITH, E. C.—*Woodcock and Snipe* (London, 1936).
SELOUS, E.—*Bird Life Glimpses* (London, 1905) ; *Realities of Bird Life* (London, 1927) ; *Bird Watching* (London, 1901) ; *The Bird Watcher in the Shetlands* (London, 1905).
SHARP, HENRY.—*The Gun Afield and Afloat* (London, 1904).
" SIXTY-ONE."—*Twenty Years' Reminiscences of the Lews* (Edinburgh, 1871).
SMITH, SYDNEY W.—*Snowden Slights, Wildfowler* (London, 1912).
SOBIESKI, JOHN AND STUART, CHARLES EDWARD.—*Lays of the Deer Forest* (Edinburgh, 1848).
SPEEDY, TOM.—*A Shooting Man's Calendar* (London, 1927) ; *The Art of Shooting and Rough Shoot Management* (London, 1930) ; *Pheasant Shooting* (London, 1935).
STEPHENS, MARTIN.—*Grouse Shooting* (London, 1939).
STRUTT, JOESPH.—*The Sports and Pastimes of the People of England.*

TEASDALE-BUCKELL, G. T.—*The Complete Shot* (London, 1907).
TEGETMEIER, W. B.—*Pheasants, their Natural History and Practical Management* (London. N.D.).
TENNYSON, JULIAN.—*Rough Shooting* (London, 1938).
THORNTON, COL. THOMAS.—*A Sporting Tour through the Northern Parts of England and Great Part of the Highlands of Scotland* (London, 1804).
TURBERVILLE, GEORGE.—*Booke of Faulconrie or Hawking.* (My copy, dated 1575, is bound with the *Booke of Hunting.*)

" UNCLE RALPH."—*Letters to Young Shooters* (London, N.D.).

VESEY-FITZGERALD, BRIAN.—*A Book of British Waders* (London, 1938) ; *A Country Chronicle* (London, 1942).

WALLACE, FRANK.—*British Deer Heads* (London, 1913) ; *A Highland Gathering* (London, 1932).
WALLACE, FRANK AND EDWARDS, LIONEL.—*Hunting and Stalking the Deer* (London, 1927).
WALSINGHAM, LORD.—*Shooting, Moor and Marsh* (Badminton Library) (London, 1886).
WATKINS-PITCHFORD, DENYS.—*The Sportsman's Bedside Book* (London, 1937) ; *Manka* (London, 1939) ; *The Countryman's Bedside Book* (London, 1941).
WATSON, A. E. T.—*The Young Sportsman* (London, 1900).
WHITE, GILBERT.—*The Natural History of Selborne* (London, 1789).
WITHERBY, H. F., JOURDAIN, F. C. R., TICEHURST, C. B., TUCKER, B. W.—*The Handbook of British Birds* (5 vols.) (London, 1938-1941).
WOOD, CASEY A., AND FYFE, MARJORIE.—*The Art of Falconry* by Frederick II of Hohanstaufen. Stanford University, California, U.S.A., 1943.
WORMALD, J.—*How to Increase a Stock of Partridges* (London, 1912).

YEATES, G. K. AND WINNALL, R. N.—*Rough Shooting* (London, 1935).
YORK, EDWARD, DUKE OF.—*The Master of Game.*

INDEX